About the Author

Sharon Kendrick once won a national writing competition by describing her ideal date: being flown to an exotic island by a gorgeous and powerful man. Little did she realise that she'd just wandered into her dream job! Today she writes for Mills & Boon, featuring often stubborn but always *to die for* heroes and the women who bring them to their knees. She believes that the best books are those you never want to end. Just like life…

£27,539.87

Mills & Boon Stars

COLLECTIONS

Lynne Graham
RUTHLESS DEMANDS

January 2019

Sharon Kendrick
CONVENIENT VOWS

February 2019

Cathy Williams
SINFUL PROPOSALS

March 2019

Michelle Smart
PASSIONATE BARGAINS

April 2019

Maya Blake
SEDUCTIVE NIGHTS

May 2019

Caitlin Crews
SHOCKING SCANDALS

June 2019

Mills & Boon Stars Collection: Convenient Vows

SHARON KENDRICK

MILLS & BOON

First Published in Great Britain 2019
By Mills & Boon, an imprint of HarperCollins*Publishers*
1 London Bridge Street, London, SE1 9GF

MILLS & BOON STARS: CONVENIENT VOWS © 2019
Harlequin Books S.A.

A Royal Vow of Convenience © 2016 Sharon Kendrick
The Paternity Claim © 2000 Sharon Kendrick
The Housekeeper's Awakening © 2014 Sharon Kendrick

ISBN: 978-0-263-27543-8

0219

MIX
Paper from
responsible sources
FSC™ C007454

This book is produced from independently certified FSC™ paper to ensure responsible forest management.

For more information visit: www.harpercollins.co.uk/green

Printed and bound in Spain
by CPI, Barcelona

A ROYAL VOW OF CONVENIENCE

This book is dedicated to my two greatest achievements—Celia Campbell & Patrick Kendrick, who are talented, hard-working and funny.

I'm very proud to be your mum

CHAPTER ONE

THE CLATTER WAS deafening as the helicopter descended from a cloudless blue sky, and a nervous bead of sweat trickled down between Sophie's breasts.

'He's here,' said Andy abruptly as the blades stopped turning. 'Don't look so worried, Sophie. Rafe Carter might be the big boss but he doesn't bite. He just doesn't suffer fools gladly and as long as you remember that, you'll be okay. Okay?'

'Okay,' Sophie echoed dutifully. But her throat was still tight with tension as Andy left the veranda and ran towards the helicopter where a powerfully built man had just appeared at the open door, raking his fingers through dark and wind-ruffled hair. Pausing briefly to scan the horizon, he shook his head as a busty blonde in a tight blue uniform tried to get his attention, before jumping to the dusty ground, leaving the woman staring after him—her shoulders hunched with dejection.

Another feeling of panic prickled over Sophie's skin but now it was underpinned with something else. Something which made her pulse start racing as the man stood very still, just staring at the land—his frozen stance drawing attention to his proud profile and the shadowed jut of his jaw.

Even from this distance she could see the hard definition of his body. In an immaculate suit, which hugged his muscular physique, he looked sophisticated and urbane—as out of place in the dusty Outback setting as his expensive helicopter. Everything about him proclaimed the fact that this was the billionaire owner of one of the world's biggest telecommunications companies, whose enormous cattle station was simply one of his 'hobbies'. Rafe Carter. Even the name sounded sexy. She'd overheard the other staff talking about him—tantalising snatches of gossip which had made her ears prick up—though she'd been careful not to pry or show her curiosity.

Because Sophie had learnt very quickly that if she wanted to keep her identity secret, it was better to be seen and not heard. To dress demurely and fade into the background. To not ask questions about the man who owned this property and all the land as far as the eye could see. All she knew was that he was rich. Very rich. That he liked planes and art and beautiful women—in addition to a rural Australian life he dipped in and out of as he pleased. Her breasts prickled with an unfamiliar beat of anticipation. She just hadn't expected him to be quite so...*mesmerising*.

She watched as Andy moved forward and the two men exchanged a few words of greeting before walking towards the homestead as the helicopter rose back up into the sky. It was hot on the veranda. Even at this early hour the mercury was shooting up the scale. Summer had arrived and sometimes it felt as if she were living in a giant sauna. Her palms were covered in a fine layer of sweat and she rubbed them over her cotton shorts, willing her heart to stop pounding—because surely that would make her unease seem somehow *obvious*.

She wondered what it was about the arrival of Rafe Carter which made her feel as if her world were about to come tumbling down around her. Fear she would be found out? That he might succeed where everyone else on this cattle station had failed—and work out who she really was? That he would discover the crazy lengths she'd gone to in order to secure herself a place here in the wild peace of the Australian Outback, because she'd wanted to escape from her gilded life and forge a more worthwhile existence? She'd never met him, but it wasn't beyond the realms of possibility that he'd seen her photograph in a newspaper—because didn't their gilded worlds have distant connections? Her mind began to race even faster. And what if he *did* find out—then what?

A series of disturbing scenarios flashed before her and she clenched her fists as a wave of determination swept over her. Because that wasn't going to happen. She wouldn't let it. For the first time in her life she'd been enjoying the simple pleasures of anonymity and the rewards of honest hard work and was feeling cautiously optimistic about the future. Nobody knew who she was and nobody cared. There were no eyes following her every move. She was on her own—properly on her own—and it was both daunting and exciting. It couldn't last. She knew that. Her brother had given her an ultimatum and time was fast running out. He wanted her back in Isolaverde—preferably by Christmas, but certainly by the time of her little sister's nineteenth birthday at the end of February. In a couple of months it would all be over and she was going to miss the sense of peace and freedom she'd known in this out-of-the-way place. She was going to have to return to the world she'd run away from and face up to the future, but she wanted to do it on her own terms. To leave here in the same way she'd arrived—without fuss or fanfare.

Leaving the heat which hung over the veranda like a heavy blanket, Sophie hurried into the kitchen where the air-conditioning did little to cool her heated skin. She fanned her face with her hand as she heard the heavy tread of masculine footfall and tried not to let her nerves get the better of her.

'Sophie? Come and meet the boss.'

Andy's broad Australian accent shattered her thoughts and suddenly it was too late for any more reflection because the station manager was walking into the kitchen, a smile wreathing his face—in stark contrast to the expression of the man who followed him. And try as she might, Sophie still couldn't tear her eyes away from the newcomer, even though her upbringing had taught her it was rude to stare.

Close up, he was even more spectacular. His hard-boned face was shockingly beautiful and so was his body. But his physical perfection was underpinned by a dark quality which shimmered around him like an aura—an edge of danger which was making her feel self-conscious. Did he know the effect he had on women? she wondered. Did he realise that her mouth was as dry as the dust in the yard outside and that her breasts had started to swell, so that they were pushing against the suddenly constricting material of her cheap underwear? She wondered how he managed to look so cool in a suit and, as if reading her thoughts, he slid the jacket from his broad shoulders so she was confronted by the hint of hard, honed torso—shadowy beneath the pristine silk of his white shirt.

Another bead of sweat trickled down her cleavage and soaked into her T-shirt as she met the steely grey eyes which were trained in her direction. He narrowed them in contemplation as he looked her up and down and Sophie's apprehension gave way to indignation because she wasn't used to men looking at her that way. Nobody *ever* stared at her so openly. As if he had every right to do so. She swallowed. As if he knew exactly what she was thinking about him and his beautiful face and body...

'Rafe.' Andy's voice was relaxed as he gestured in her direction. 'This is Sophie—the woman I was telling you about. She's been cooking for us for nearly six months now.'

'Sophie...?'

It was the first word he'd spoken—a lash of dark silk which whipped through the air towards her. Rafe Carter raised his eyebrows in question and Sophie gave a nervous smile in response. She knew she shouldn't hesitate because hesitation was dangerous. Just as she knew she should have had this answer all pat and ready—and she would have done if she hadn't been so distracted by the lure of his deep, mellifluous voice and the effect that paralysing stare was having on her.

'It's Doukas. Sophie Doukas,' she said, using the surname of her Greek grandmother, knowing that nobody would be able to contradict her, because she hadn't shown anyone her papers. A wave of guilt washed over her. She'd managed to distract them for long enough to forget they'd never seen them.

The steely gaze became even more piercing. 'Unusual name,' he observed.

'Yes.' Desperate to change the subject, she cleared her throat, mustering up a smile from somewhere. 'You must be thirsty after your flight. Would you like some tea, Mr Carter?'

'I thought you'd never ask,' he drawled. 'And it's Rafe.'

'Rafe,' she repeated, aware that his cool tone contained the hint of a reprimand. *So pull yourself together. Start remembering that he's the boss and you're supposed to be pleasant and obedient.* 'Right.' She forced a smile. 'I'll make some right away. Andy, how about you?'

'Not for me, thanks.' The station manager shook his head. 'I'll wait for the morning smoko. See you outside when you've had a brew, Rafe. Take you on a quick tour.'

Sophie's self-consciousness spiralled as Andy walked out, leaving her alone with Rafe Carter in a room whose walls seemed to be closing in on her. And even though making tea was a task she performed countless times every day, she felt like a coiled spring as she busied herself around the kitchen, aware of his eyes following her every movement. His grey gaze seemed to laser through her as she lifted a kettle which suddenly felt ridiculously heavy. *Why was he even here?* she thought as she poured boiling water into the teapot. Andy had said he wasn't expected until springtime—by which time she would be gone and nothing but a distant memory. He certainly wasn't expected this close to Christmas—which was now only weeks away.

She took a cup down from the dresser. It had been easy to forget Christmas in this exotic and tropical area of Australia, with its lush foliage and steamy heat, and the kind of birds and mammals which she'd only ever seen in nature documentaries. Yet because the men had demanded it, she'd made a stab at decorating the homestead with paper chains and plastic holly and a cheap tree made out of tinsel which she'd bought from the local store. The effect had been garish but it was so *different* that it had allowed her to forget all the things she was used to.

But now the familiar images of what she'd left behind came crowding into her mind, as she thought about Christmas on her island home of Isolaverde. She pictured mulled wine and golden platters piled high with sugary treats. She thought about the enormous tree which took pride of place in the palace throne room, which was decorated with real candles and diligently lit by the legions of faithful staff who served her. And beneath it the huge pile of presents, which she and her brother would hand out every year to the children of the city. She remembered the eager looks lighting up their little faces and, without warning, a wave of loneliness came washing over her. Suddenly she felt *vulnerable*. She knew how easy it would be to just throw the towel in and go home, but she didn't want to do that. Not yet. Not until she'd worked out what she wanted her new future to be...

Giving the teapot a quick stir, she hoped Rafe would take his tea outside, or go to his own lavish quarters, which were in a separate part of this giant homestead. But her heart sank as he rested his narrow hips against the window sill with the look of a man who wasn't going anywhere. And, unlike most people, he seemed content to let the silence grow. Didn't he realise she was getting more flustered by the moment despite the fact that she'd spent her whole life being stared at? It just didn't usually affect her like this. It didn't make her breasts tingle, or a slug of disconcerting heat begin to gather low in her belly...

So say something. Pretend he's one of those countless strangers you've spent your life meeting and exchanging polite words with.

'Have you flown in from England today?' she questioned, pouring milk into a china jug.

He didn't smile back. 'No. I've been on an extended trip to the Far East and I arrived in Brisbane yesterday. I was so close that it seemed crazy not to visit.' His grey eyes gleamed. 'And just for the record, I don't live in England.'

She met the steely gaze. 'But I thought—'

'That my accent was English?'

She gave a weak smile. 'Well, yes.'

'They say you never really lose the accent you were born with, but I haven't lived there in a long time. Years, in fact.' He frowned. 'And speaking of accents—I can't quite work yours out. I don't think I've ever heard anything like it before. Are you Greek?'

Sophie distracted him by holding up the jug, her bright tone matching her smile. 'Milk? Sugar?'

'Neither, thanks. I'll take it how it comes.'

She handed him the tea, wishing he wouldn't stretch out his legs like that—a movement which was making the dark material of his trousers spread tautly over his powerful thighs. Was it his intention to get her gaze to linger there, like some reluctant voyeur? Yet ogling men was something she didn't do. It wasn't in her nature to be predatory. Any such behaviour would have been picked up and frowned on by the cameras which had followed her every move since birth. Even the man to whom she'd been betrothed— a man popularly known as one of the world's sexiest men—had never aroused this kind of heart-pumping interest, which was making her fingers start to tremble.

In an attempt to hide her nerves, she brushed some imaginary crumbs from the table. 'So where *do* you live?' she questioned.

'Mainly in New York, although I lived here full-time when I first bought the station. But I move around a lot between cities—constantly on the move. I'm what you might call an urban gypsy, Sophie.' He took a sip of his tea, mocking eyes studying her over the rim of his cup. 'And you still haven't answered my question.'

'I'm sorry?' She batted him a confused look, hoping he might have forgotten. 'What question was that?'

'I asked if you were Greek.'

Sophie didn't want to lie but if she told him the truth it would be like hurling a bomb into the room. Her anonymity would be over and her sanctuary would end. There would be questions. Lots of them. Because what could she say?

I'm a princess who doesn't want to be a princess any more. I'm a woman who's been brought up in a palace who has never had to cope with real life before. A woman who has been hurt and humiliated. Who has struck out to discover if she can cope with life without the protection she's known all her life.

She met the cold gleam of his gaze. 'My grandmother was Greek,' she said. 'And Greek is my mother tongue.'

He was even more watchful now. 'Any other languages?'

'English. Obviously.'

'Obviously.' His eyes glinted. 'And that's the lot?'

She licked her bottom lip. 'I can get by in Italian. French, too.'

'Well now, aren't you the clever one?' he questioned softly. 'You certainly have a lot of qualifications for someone who's spent the last few months frying steak and buttering bread for a bunch of station workers.'

'I didn't realise linguistic ability was a bar to being a cook on a cattle station, Mr Carter.'

Their gazes clashed and Rafe tried not to be affected by the sudden challenge sparking from her eyes, which was easily as distracting as the pert thrust of her breasts. On one level he was aware she was playing games with him by avoiding his questions and he wasn't sure why. He frowned. But there was a lot he wasn't sure about right now. Plenty of young women came from abroad to work in remote parts of this country—but he'd never come across anyone like Sophie Doukas before. He wondered just what she was doing here, when she looked as out of place as a diamond you might find in the rough. Andy had told him that when she'd first arrived she'd been green and naïve, but had been eager to learn. Rafe had wondered why his gruff Australian station manager had employed someone without even the most basic of skills, but now he'd seen her—he had a pretty good idea why.

His throat grew dry.

Because she was beautiful.

Really beautiful.

Not the kind of beauty which came from spending hours in front of the mirror or having a plastic surgeon on speed-dial. Something told him she looked that way without even trying. Her cheekbones were high, her eyes as blue as a Queensland sky and her dark hair was tied back in a shiny ponytail. She wore no make-up—but with lashes that long, he guessed she didn't need to. And her lips. Oh, man. Those lips. His groin hardened. Just one glance at them and he could think of a million different X-rated ways he'd like her to use them—starting with that cute pink tongue working a very fundamental kind of magic.

But her appeal didn't stop at her face. She had one of those bodies which looked amazing in clothes but probably better out of them. Even her cheap white T-shirt and unremarkable cotton shorts failed to disguise her long legs and curvy bottom, and she moved with the natural grace of a dancer. She was one very desirable female, that was for sure—and Rafe imagined Andy's reaction when he had first seen her. What man could have resisted a woman who looked like this, turning up out of the blue as if in answer to every hot-blooded man's dreams?

But Andy had also told him that she'd kept her distance. She wasn't one of those foreign backpackers keen to enjoy anything new—including sex. Apparently she hadn't flirted with the men or indicated that she might be up for some late-night hook-up. His manager had told him she seemed *wary* and could turn the ice on without really trying, which was why nobody had dared to make a pass at her. Rafe frowned. Yes. Wary was right. She was regarding him now in a way which reminded him of a bowerbird which had once flown into the homestead by mistake—its beautiful wings battering uselessly against the window pane as it tried to escape from its domestic confinement.

He took another sip of his tea, his interest stirred in more ways than one because he could sense she was trying to distance herself from him, and that never usually happened. He was used to instant compliance from the opposite sex whenever he wanted it. A gushing desire to tell him everything he ever wanted to know—and then more.

But not from Sophie Doukas it seemed. He wondered why she was being so cagey. And whether her reluctance to talk was responsible for the powerful beat of desire which was pooling even harder in his groin.

'No,' he conceded dryly. 'Your linguistic ability is to be commended, even if you haven't had much chance to practise your language skills out here in the bush.' He shifted his weight a little. 'I understand you and I are going to be sharing accommodation.'

She looked uncomfortable. 'We don't have to. I've been living in the far end of the main house since I arrived. Andy said it seemed crazy for it to stay empty and that it was much cooler in here. But now you're back...'

She looked him straight in the eyes without any hint of the flirtation he would have expected from any other woman in the circumstances.

'I can easily move into one of the smaller properties,' she continued stiffly. 'I'd hate to feel I was in your way.'

Rafe almost smiled. No. She definitely *wasn't* flirting. Hell. When had been the last time that had happened? 'That won't be necessary,' he said. 'It's plenty big enough for two people. I'm sure we won't have any problem keeping out of each other's way. And I'm only passing through—one night max. Which reminds me.' He leaned back against the window and looked at her speculatively. 'I don't remember Andy mentioning how long you're planning on staying?'

He watched as her body language changed. And how. She picked up a teaspoon she'd left lying on the table and carried it over to the sink as if it would explode if she didn't quickly plunge it into a bowl of water.

'I...hadn't really decided,' she said, still with her tensed back to him. 'Soon. Just after Christmas, probably.'

'But won't your family miss you at Christmas?' he probed. 'Or maybe you don't celebrate Christmas?'

She turned to face him then and Rafe saw that her face had grown pale. Her blue eyes had darkened so that suddenly she looked almost *fragile* and he felt an unexpected kick of guilt—as if he'd done something wrong. Until he reminded himself that all he'd done was ask her a straightforward question and, as the man who was paying her wages, he had every right to do that.

'Yes, I celebrate it,' she said quietly. 'But my parents are dead.'

'I'm sorry.'

She inclined her head. 'Thank you.'

'You don't have brothers, or sisters?'

Sophie thought how persistent he was—and how she wasn't used to being interrogated like this. Because nobody would usually *dare*. She wondered why he was so interested. Did he realise that his station manager had been less than meticulous when he'd interviewed her—or was there something else? She stared at the teapot and watched it blur in and out of focus. She was innocent, yes—but she wasn't completely stupid. She'd seen the look he'd given her when he walked into the kitchen—a look of surprise which had swiftly turned to one of appreciation. She had been subjected to a brief but very thorough evaluation of her face and her body—one she doubted he would have done if he'd known who she really was. But he didn't know, did he? And he wasn't going to find out.

Because her first instincts had been the right ones, as instincts so often were. She'd felt apprehension when she'd first seen him and she hadn't known why. But now she did. As he'd looked at her, she'd felt something alien. A feeling which had nothing to do with the fear of being found out, but which was just as disturbing. A sudden heaviness in her breasts and a melting sensation low in her belly. Her skin suddenly felt as if it were too tight for her body and her cheap underwear seemed to be digging into her flesh.

And just as she would have recognised sunburn if

she'd never experienced it before, she knew that what she was feeling for Rafe Carter was desire. Hot and very real desire, which was making her heart pound so erratically. Making her wonder what it would be like to be held by Rafe Carter and have him touch her. For him to run those long olive fingers over her newly sensitised skin and take away some of this terrible aching. And she'd never felt that before, not with anyone.

Guilt rippled over her.

Not even with Luciano.

She realised he was still waiting for an answer and she struggled to extract some coherent answers from the unfamiliar erotic fog of her thoughts. 'I have a younger sister and a brother.'

'And won't they be expecting you home?'

Sophie shook her head. After she'd left Isolaverde, she had phoned to let her brother, Myron, know she was safe and well—and begged him not to send out any search parties. She'd told him she needed to escape the pressure of what had happened, and so far he had heeded her request. On the few occasions she'd managed to get online and search the news outlets, there had been no public acknowledgements regarding her sudden disappearance and her younger sister, Mary-Belle, had stepped in to take over all her official engagements. Maybe Myron understood that her pride had been hurt and she'd needed to get away to lick her wounds after her very public rejection by the man she'd been meant to marry. That she was more than happy to resume all the responsibilities of her role as princess, she just wanted a little time to get her head together. Or maybe he was just too busy ruling their island kingdom to pay her much attention. He took his position as King of Isolaverde very seriously and for too long now had been coming under pressure to find himself a suitable bride.

'You've got exactly six months to have your little stab at rebellion,' he had clipped out, over the crackly phone line. 'And if you're not back by February, then I will send out search parties to bring you home again. Make no mistake about that, Sophie.'

Remembering her brother's sense of control—and the way that people had always tried to control her all her life—Sophie turned round to meet Rafe Carter's inquisitive stare, knowing she had to stop him doing the same. So be strong. Ask *him* something, she thought. Put *him* on the spot.

'And how about *your* Christmas? You'll be sitting around the Christmas tree with your own family, will you?' she questioned. 'Pulling crackers and singing carols in the old traditional way?'

His face hardened and Sophie saw something in the depths of his eyes which looked almost like pain. She blinked. Surely not. She couldn't imagine a powerful man like this ever *hurting*.

'That kind of Christmas only exists in fairy tales,' he said and suddenly his voice grew harsh with cynicism. 'And I never did believe in fairy tales.'

Abruptly he stood up and moved away from the window and suddenly he was close enough for Sophie to touch. Close enough for her to notice that his jaw was dark with the hint of new growth, even though he could barely have been out of bed for more than a few hours. As a symbol of virility, he couldn't have sent out a more potent message and another rush of unfamiliar desire pulsed through her.

'Why look,' he observed, his steely eyes glittering before they were shaded by his ebony lashes as he glanced down at her fingers. 'Your hands are trembling. What's the matter, Sophie? Is something bothering you?'

She suspected he knew exactly what was bothering her but she concealed her embarrassment behind a shake of her head.

'Actually, there is,' she said. 'I get nervous if someone stands around watching while I work—especially if that someone happens to be the boss. I'm about to start making the men their mid-morning smoko and you know how hungry they get.' She gave a quick smile, hoping it hid the way she was feeling. Hoping he wouldn't notice the fact that her nipples were pushing like little hard stones against her T-shirt or that her cheeks were getting hotter by the second. 'So if you'll excuse me?'

'I get the distinct feeling I'm being dismissed,' he said silkily. 'Which is something of a first. Still, since dedication to work is a quality I've always admired, you won't find me objecting.'

But before he reached the door he paused, and suddenly he was no longer the mildly curious boss asking idle questions about her background or pointing out that her fingers were trembling. Suddenly he was the billionaire station owner with the shiny helicopter, who was regarding her with a certain sense of entitlement.

'I have no objection to sharing the homestead with you, just as long as you realise that I like my own company. So please don't feel you have to seek me out or engage me in conversation, especially if I'm working. If it happens to be a beautiful day, we'll take that as a given, shall we?' His voice hardened. 'I certainly don't need to hear your views on the sunshine levels or having you brightly enquire how I'm planning to spend my day. Understand?'

Sophie met his piercing grey gaze, thinking that was possibly the rudest thing anyone had ever said to her. Engage him in conversation? Why, she'd rather talk to one of the large bugs which regularly scuttled across the veranda each morning! But her face betrayed nothing as she nodded, even if her voice was stiff. 'Of course.'

She was glad when the door swung shut behind him. He was the most arrogant man she'd ever met—even more arrogant than her brother—but he was also the most attractive. By a mile. Briefly she closed her eyes as she reminded herself of the effect he'd had on her. She'd been stumbling and uptight in his company and that wasn't her. Just as trembling fingers and aching breasts weren't her either. She'd let him *get* to her just because he looked like some fallen Greek god who'd been given more than his fair share of sex appeal and she mustn't allow that to happen again. He was her boss—nothing more. A man who was just passing through.

But despite her best intentions, something made her go to the window as he crossed the yard and something kept her there, watching him.

The morning sun was touching his ebony hair with splashes of dark red and she could see the powerful thrust of his thighs as he walked. A pulse started beating deep in her groin and Sophie felt a yearning so powerful that she had to grip onto the window sill for support.

It was just unfortunate that Rafe Carter chose that very moment to turn around and catch her staring.

And she couldn't mistake the lazy arrogance of his smile.

CHAPTER TWO

IT WAS TORTURE having your boss hanging around for longer than he was supposed to. Sophie gave the bowl of cake mix a vicious stir as he began to walk across the yard towards her. Sheer torture. Why was he still here four days after telling her he was just 'passing through'? Wasn't he supposed to be some important international CEO with loads of calls on his time? Not someone who helped his men repair fences and muster cattle before standing in the evening sunlight with a bottle of cold beer held to his lips. Sophie swallowed. And why the hell did he have to walk around the place looking like...*that*?

Her heart pounded as she watched him approach the homestead, the expensive grey suit he'd worn on his arrival now just a memory. He was wearing faded denim jeans, which might as well have been *sprayed* onto his muscular legs, and a clinging black T-shirt, which emphasised his washboard abs and the powerful lines of his arms and shoulders.

It was getting uncomfortable. Embarrassing, even. Every time he came into her eye-line, a load of unsettling things started to happen to her body. Things which centred around her aching breasts and a newly sensitive spot between her thighs. Things which had never happened to her before. She'd tried telling herself that it was because she was in this very elemental place instead of the rarefied atmosphere of her palatial home which was making her so aware of her own physicality. She'd tried keeping out of his way as much as possible—scuttling out of sight whenever she spotted him in the distance—but nothing seemed to help. Whatever qualities Rafe Carter had, he had them in abundance and she just couldn't stop thinking about him...

He pushed open the door and walked into the air-conditioned cool of the kitchen. His black hair was curling in damp tendrils around his hard-boned face and a single line of sweat arrowed down the front of his T-shirt before disappearing beneath the soft leather of his belt. She put down the bowl of cake mix as she forced her gaze upwards to his face, but that wasn't much better. Why couldn't she just look at those sensual lips without wondering what it would be like to be kissed by them?

'Anything I can do for you, Rafe?'

'You mean, apart from looking as though you'd rather I was anywhere else but here?'

'I told you,' she said stiffly. 'I get uncomfortable if people watch me while I'm working.'

'So you did,' he said softly. 'Well, you won't have to endure my company for much longer because I'm leaving first thing tomorrow.'

'Oh.' Sophie tried to keep her stupid wash of disappointment at bay. 'You are?'

'I am. So I'll be out of your hair once and for all.' He paused. 'I thought you could cook the men a special meal tonight. An early Christmas celebration, if you like. A kind of thank you from me to them for all their hard work over the year. We could open some decent wine—and afterwards go into Corksville for a drink.' His eyes gleamed. 'Think you could manage that, Sophie?'

When he looked at her that way she felt incapable of managing anything except dissolving in a puddle, but somehow Sophie produced an efficient nod of her head. 'Of course!'

She spent the rest of the day rushing around, consulting online recipes as she attempted to make a traditional Christmas dinner for the men, but her thoughts were mostly occupied with what to wear. Because even though she was only there to cook and serve, her cheap dresses and shapeless shorts didn't seem appropriate for a celebration dinner and besides—wasn't there a stupid part of her which *wanted* to dress up? Who wanted Rafe Carter to see her as a real woman for a change, rather than just the fading-into-the-background person she had tried her best to be?

She looked longingly at the one dress which was hanging in her wardrobe and the only outfit she'd brought with her from Isolaverde. It was made to measure by her favourite designer and deceptively simple; she loved the soft blue cotton material, which brought out the colour of her eyes. Just as she loved the fitted bodice and short swinging skirt which brushed her bare thighs as she moved. She slipped it on, along with a pair of strappy sandals, then applied a little mascara and lip gloss. She even left her hair loose for once, clipping it lightly back from her face in case bossy Rafe Carter started giving her a lecture on health and safety regulations while she was cooking.

With barely an hour to spare and the realisation that there were no after-dinner chocolates, she made a last-minute dash into the nearby town of Corksville where Eileen Donahue, the woman who ran the local store, gave her a very curious look.

'I hear the boss man is back,' she said as Sophie put a box of dark chocolate mints on the counter.

Sophie nodded. 'That's right. But he's leaving to-morrow.'

'Shame. The town could do with a little more eye candy.' Eileen gave a sly smile. 'Good-looking man, Rafe Carter.'

Sophie kept her voice neutral. 'So they say.'

'Got himself a permanent woman yet?'

'I really have no idea, Mrs Donahue.'

'Yeah. Heard he plays the field and all.' The store-keeper's eyes narrowed perceptively. 'Still, nice to see you in a dress for a change. Makes you look kind of...*different*.'

It felt like reality slapping her hard across the face and Sophie's fingers stiffened as she pulled a note from her purse.

What did she think she was playing at—risking months of careful anonymity just because she wanted to make some pathetic impression on the boss?

Quickly, she picked up the chocolates and left, but her throat felt dry with anxiety as she drove out of Corksville in a cloud of dust. Had Eileen been look-ing at her suspiciously as she'd picked up her change, or was she just getting paranoid?

She was putting the finishing touches to the dining-room table when she looked up to find Rafe standing framed in the doorway and she wondered how long he'd been standing there, watching her. He was dressed in a pair of dark trousers and a silk shirt, which was unbuttoned at the neck, all traces of the day's dust and sweat gone. He had the slightly glowing appearance of a man who'd just stepped out of the shower and the sheer intimacy of that fact didn't escape her. And he was looking at her in a way which was making her heart crash painfully against her ribcage.

'Well, well, well.' He blew a soft whistle from between his lips as she placed a folded napkin on one of the placemats. 'It's the Sophie Doukas transformation scene.'

She pretended not to know what he was talking about. 'I'm sorry?'

'The pretty dress. The loose hair. The make-up.'

'You don't like it?'

His lips curved into a smile, which suddenly looked wolfish. Dangerously and attractively so.

'Don't fish for compliments, Sophie. You look very beautiful as I'm sure you're perfectly aware. And the dress is...' he seemed to be having difficulty completing the sentence '...quite something.'

She grabbed another napkin and turned away. 'Thank you.'

Rafe frowned, wondering why her abrupt reaction to a simple compliment was so perplexing—as if she wasn't used to a man telling her she looked beautiful. But then, everything about her was perplexing and he couldn't work out why. He glanced around, taking in the flowers and candles and a starched white tablecloth she must have got from heaven only knew where. Paper chains were looped from one side of the ceiling to the other and, on the plastic Christmas tree, fairy lights gleamed. The overall effect was tacky and yet it was also homely. It was unmistakeably a woman's touch—as if she'd been trying very hard to make the place look comfortable. Something inexplicable twisted at his heart, because Poonbarra was supposed to be about basics. About hard work and getting back to nature. It wasn't supposed to be about *comfort*.

He'd ended up staying longer than planned because he was dreading going back to England for the christening of his half-brother's son. Given his reputation for being the family's habitual no-show—for reasons which were painfully private—nobody could believe he'd agreed to attend in the first place. And in truth, neither could he. He swallowed down the acrid taste which had risen in his throat. He knew that dark and bitter memories were going to be unavoidable, but he told himself he couldn't keep avoiding them for ever. That maybe he needed to ride out the pain once and for all. That maybe you never properly healed unless you faced the reality of what you had done.

But one day had bled into two and then three and delaying his trip had become more…*complex*. He'd underestimated the effect of Poonbarra. Of the peace and calm which always descended on him there— a feeling which had been magnified by the decorative presence of Sophie Doukas…the woman who didn't flirt. The woman who spent her time avoiding him—something which was both novel but ultimately frustrating.

He tried to concentrate on the bottle of wine he was opening, but couldn't seem to stop his gaze from straying to her, no matter how hard he tried. Because she was…a *challenge*? Was that why he couldn't stop thinking about her? Why his hot and erotic dreams had featured plenty of X-rated images of his aloof cook? She must be as aware as he of the sizzling attraction which had sparked between them from the get-go, yet she hadn't acted on it as most women in her position would have done. There had been no unexpected sightings of her around the homestead wearing just a skimpy bath towel. No unexplained 'nightmares' intended to bring him running into her room late at night. She'd done what he'd asked her to do. She'd kept out of his way as much as possible— leaving him frustrating and restless, with a painful ache between his legs.

Yet human nature was a conundrum, that was for sure. When you were used to women flinging themselves at you, it was curiously exciting to discover one who was actively fighting that attraction. In fact, it was the biggest turn-on he knew and it had never happened to him before. He wondered if it was necessary for her to fuss around the bubbling pans quite so much and found himself almost *resenting* Andy and the other workers as they trooped in and sat round the table. All through dinner the overpowering scent of liberally applied aftershave hung cloyingly in the air. Suddenly, the room seemed overcrowded.

Were they in complete thrall to her? Rafe wondered—caught midway between amusement and irritation—as he watched the men lavish praise on her food. Was that why they were acting like tongue-tied adolescents whenever she spoke to them, or appeared with yet another steaming dish held enticingly in front of those magnificent breasts?

He ate and drank very little and when the meal was finished, the men all got up to leave and Andy turned to her.

'You coming to the pub with us, Soph? Let us buy you a beer as a thank you for all your delicious cooking?'

With a smile, she shook her head. 'Not for me, thanks. I'm going to clear up in here and get an early night.'

But Rafe could see her unmistakeable look of... was that *alarm*?...as the men trooped out and he remained seated. He saw the uneasy flicker of her tongue as it edged rather nervously along her bottom lip.

'You're not going to the pub with the others?' she questioned, a touch too brightly.

He shook his head. 'Not me. I've got a long day ahead of me tomorrow.' He gave the ghost of a smile. 'And besides, I might cramp their style.'

'Oh. Right. Well, you'll excuse me if I get on.' She clattered a pile of plates together and carried them out to the kitchen.

Rafe stretched his arms above his head and knew he ought to move. To go to bed and sleep and figure out how the hell he was going to get through Oliver's christening, especially now that Sharla's presence had been confirmed. The trouble was he didn't want to go anywhere. Not when it was so comfortable sitting here, watching Sophie clear away the dishes. Watching as she busied herself around the table and studiously tried to avoid his gaze. The only trouble was that meant he could stare at her without censure. His eyes lingered on the gleam of her shapely calves and the way the blue cotton dress swished about her bottom as she moved. He found himself thinking longingly about sex and how it might blot out the darkness of his thoughts—and the idea of having sex with Sophie was becoming something of an obsession.

Yet these days he avoided one-night stands—even if he hadn't always made it a rule never to get intimate with employees. Women were tricky enough as lovers without the added complication of them being on the payroll. He'd seen friends and peers get their fingers burned by over-familiarity with staff. Seen how a formerly cool colleague could morph into a bunny-boiling maniac once she'd slipped between the sheets and discovered there wasn't going to be a big rock on her finger as a result. Even if you were honest with a woman from the start and told her you just wanted a no-strings fling, they never believed you. They always thought they'd be the one to change your mind. And how could you escape a rejected lover's wrath if you had to stare at her vengeful face across the other side of the boardroom, or when her manicured fingers were flying across the keyboard?

Or when she was leaning across the table to grab an unused serving spoon and you could smell a trace of her perfume?

Nope. That was an area he had always steered clear of.

So stop looking at her breasts. Stop imagining what it would be like to part those delicious thighs

*and slip your fingers inside her panties and see how
long it would take to make her wet.*

'Would you like some coffee, Rafe?'

Her unfathomable accent punctured his thoughts
and Rafe met the question in her eyes as he shifted
uncomfortably in his seat.

'No,' he said, more curtly than he'd intended. 'I
don't want any more to drink. Come and sit down.
You've been working all evening. Have you eaten
anything?'

'Honestly—I'm fine. I had something before I
started serving.'

'Have some chocolate, then. Surely there isn't a
woman alive who can resist chocolate?'

'I've still got some clearing up to do.'

'You've done most of it. Leave the rest for now.
And that's an order. For heaven's sake, *relax*, Sophie—or is that such an outrageous suggestion?'

Sophie edged towards the chair he was indicating,
her heart crashing against her ribcage. *Relax?* He had
to be joking. She felt about as relaxed as a mouse
which had just glanced up to see a metal trap hovering overhead. Which was slightly ironic for someone who'd spent her whole life being introduced to
strangers and putting them at their ease. But for once
she was the one feeling nervous in the company of
a man who was currently pouring her some wine—
though she noticed he'd barely touched his own glass
all evening.

'Here,' he said, pushing it across the table towards
her.

She took the drink and sipped it, grateful for the

sudden warmth which flooded through her veins. 'Mmm. This is excellent.'

'Of course it is. Australia produces some of the best wine in the world.' His eyes glittered. 'As well as having the kind of wild beauty which takes the breath away.'

Sophie swirled the wine around and watched it stain the sides of the glass. 'You sound as if you love it. The country, I mean.'

'That's because I do.' He shrugged. 'I always have.'

She looked up from the glass to stare directly into his eyes. 'Was that why you bought a cattle station here, so far away from England?'

Rafe didn't answer her question straight away because it was a long time since he'd thought about it. What had started out as a bolt-hole from the unbearable had become one of his favourite places. He'd always revelled in the extreme conditions of the Outback and whenever he returned—less and less these days—he settled in right away. He'd come here first for sanctuary, far away from the brutal world he'd left behind. He'd *needed* the hard work and sweat and toil which had helped heal his shattered heart and broken soul. It had been his first stop in a series of places to lay his head without ever really considering any of them home. But then, he'd never had a real home during his childhood, so why should adulthood be any different? His description of himself as a modern-day gypsy had been truthful, though he knew from experience it was an image which turned women on.

Had it turned Sophie on? he wondered. Was that why she was staring at him now, her blue eyes shadowed in the candlelight and those amazing lips slightly parted, as if she wanted him to kiss her? And wasn't the desire to do so almost overwhelming? 'Aren't I supposed to be interviewing *you*,' he said acidly, 'rather than the other way round?'

'Is this an interview, then?' She put her glass down. 'I thought I'd already got the job.'

'Yes, you've got the job. Yet it's interesting,' he mused as he leaned back in his chair, 'that when I asked Andy about your background, he knew nothing about you. And that after several days in your company, I find myself in exactly the same boat. You're a bit of a mystery, Sophie.'

'I thought my role here was to feed the men, not entertain them with my life story?'

'True.' Rafe frowned, thinking that her casual tone was failing to disguise her sudden air of defensiveness. 'Yet apparently, when you arrived, you didn't know one end of a frying pan from the other.'

'I soon learned.'

'Or have a clue how to load the dishwasher.'

She shrugged. 'It's an industrial-sized dishwasher.'

'And you looked at the tin-opener as if it had just landed from outer space.'

'Gosh,' she said sarcastically. 'Just how long did you and Andy spend discussing me?'

'Long enough.'

'And did you come to any conclusions?'

'I did.'

'Which were?'

He stretched out his legs. 'I came to the conclusion that you're someone who's never had to get her hands dirty before,' he observed softly. 'And that maybe you've led a very privileged life up until now.'

Sophie stiffened. How perceptive he was, she thought—her unwilling admiration swept away by a sudden whisper of fear. Because wasn't this what she had dreaded all along—that the cool and clever Englishman would guess she wasn't what she seemed? That he would blow her cover before she was ready to have it blown, and force her into making decisions she still wasn't sure about.

So brazen it out. Challenge him—just as he is challenging you.

She raised her eyebrows. 'But none of the men—or you—have any complaints about my work, do you?'

His eyes glittered. 'Are my questions bothering you, Sophie?'

'Not bothering me so much as boring me, if I may be frank.' She lifted her eyebrows. 'Didn't you tell me when you first arrived that you'd prefer it if I left you alone? That you didn't want me to engage you in conversation just for the sake of it.'

'Did I say that?'

'You know you did,' she said, in a low voice. 'Yet now you're doing exactly that to me!'

'Well, maybe I've changed my mind. Maybe I'm wondering why a young and beautiful woman is hiding herself in the middle of the Outback without making a single phone call or getting any emails.'

She froze. 'What are you talking about?'

'Andy says you don't use a cell-phone. That you haven't received a single letter or card since you've been here—and that you only ever use the Internet very occasionally.'

'I didn't realise I was being constantly monitored,' she said crossly. 'Surely my life is my business.'

'It is, of course. But I'm always intrigued by people who are reluctant to talk about themselves.'

And Sophie suddenly realised why that might be. Because a man like Rafe Carter would have people falling over themselves to tell him everything he wanted to know, wouldn't he? She wondered how he would react if she blurted out the truth. If she told him who she really was. Something told her he wouldn't fawn all over her, the way most people did when they came into close contact with a royal. Something told her he would stay exactly the same—and that was a very tantalising prospect.

Yet she couldn't risk it. No matter how normal he might be in those circumstances, things would inevitably change. He might be angry she hadn't mentioned it before. And what if he inadvertently mentioned it to one of his friends, who mentioned it to someone else—and the wretched press got hold of it? That would be a disaster.

But it was more than his reaction which made Sophie want to keep her secret. She just didn't want to pop this bubble of feeling so *normal*. Of feeling just like anyone else. Why *shouldn't* she talk about herself without mentioning her status? Unless being a princess was the only thing which defined her.

'What exactly do you want to know?' she questioned.

Pushing his wine glass away, Rafe sat back in his chair as he considered her question, but in his heart he knew the answer. He didn't want facts. He wanted her. He'd wanted her from the first moment she'd turned round and looked at him with those big blue eyes. He wanted to crush those amazing lips with his own. To peel that cotton dress from her body and see what delicious treasures lay beneath. To hear her gasping his name as he pushed deep inside her...

He shifted his weight to try to ease his discomfort, realising he was sitting there like some frustrated teenager with a hard-on—and suddenly common sense overrode the primitive needs of his body. What the hell was he thinking of? He forced himself to stand, reminding himself he was leaving tomorrow and that in a week he would scarcely remember her name. 'It's okay, Sophie. You're right. Your life is none of my business.' Suddenly, he smiled. 'But for what it's worth—you're doing a pretty good job.'

It was the praise as much as the smile which got to her and Sophie blinked at him, stupidly moved by his words. She was naturally suspicious of praise because usually it was delivered with some sort of agenda, usually because people were trying to ingratiate themselves with her. But Rafe's words were genuine. He didn't *know* she was a princess. He was saying those things because he meant them. His praise was *real*.

And suddenly she knew she had to get away from him—before another small act of kindness had her rolling over like a puppy wanting its stomach stroked. Her chair scraped loudly against the wooden floor as she also stood up. 'Thanks,' she said. 'I appreciate it. And in order not to blot my brilliant record, I guess I'd better finish clearing up.'

She went into the kitchen and started washing the glasses, feeling stupidly disappointed when he said goodnight and left her to it. The room felt empty without him. *She* felt empty without him. What had she *wanted* to happen? For him to remove her hands from the soapy water and take her into his arms and start to kiss her?

Yes. That was exactly what she wanted.

Frustrated, she went to her room and took a quick shower before climbing into bed. But despite all her hard work and the thought of the early-morning start, she spent countless minutes lying wide awake in the darkness. Every time she shut her eyes, she was haunted by Rafe's image. By his hard-boned face and powerful body. By the way those steely eyes swept over her, making her stomach turn somersaults. She pushed the cotton sheet from her hot body, going through all the relaxation techniques she knew but nothing seemed to work, until eventually she gave up and got out of bed.

Walking over to the window, she peered out at the beautiful night, where the moon had risen high in the clear and unpolluted sky. She could see its milky glimmer on the surface of the pool and suddenly the thought of a swim seemed irresistible. If she was very quiet she would disturb no one. She could cool herself down and wear herself out and, afterwards, crawl back into bed exhausted.

Pulling on her swimsuit, she slipped her feet into a pair of flip flops and padded quietly outside. Switching on the pool's floodlights, she scanned the surroundings for any of the ubiquitous cane toads who sometimes swam there until the chlorinated water poisoned them, but there were none. Everything was silent except for the ghost-like wailing of a curlew in a distant tree.

Slipping into the water, she swam with strong,

regular strokes which were the result of hours spent practising in the palace pool. She swam until she was pleasantly tired. Floating on her back in the water, she was just thinking about getting out when she heard a splash and, glancing down to the other end of the pool, she froze as she saw a powerful male body swimming beneath the surface of the floodlit water towards her. She held her breath as the man emerged beside her, wet dark hair plastered to his head—his muscular torso painted silver by the moonlight.

'Rafe!' Her heart crashed violently against her ribcage. 'You scared the life out of me!'

'Who did you think it was?'

'A cane toad!' she declared furiously.

'Pretty big cane toad,' he said, a smile curving the edges of his lips.

He dived beneath the water again—swimming several lengths of the pool and back again. It was an impressive display, thought Sophie reluctantly. A deliberate and very macho display and she would have needed to be made of wood not to have responded to it. And Sophie was not made of wood. Far from it. Right then she felt like cream which had been whipped up into soft peaks. Suddenly he emerged beside her again, shaking his head so that little droplets of water showered over her skin.

Tilting his head back, he looked up at the bright canopy of stars. 'Amazing, isn't it?'

Sophie forced herself to follow his gaze. To try to concentrate on the glittering constellations overhead when all she wanted to do was to stare at the magnificence of his wet body. He was so near. So very near. The danger which whispered over her skin was followed by a potent sense of excitement. A sense that she was standing on the edge of the unknown. 'Very beautiful,' she said. The shiver she gave wasn't faked, but it had nothing to do with the temperature and suddenly Sophie felt out of her depth in more ways than one. 'It's…getting cold, isn't it? I'd better go in.'

'Please. Don't let me curtail your swim,' he said softly, his hooded eyes gleaming. 'I'd hate to think I was driving you away. Or that my presence was bothering you.'

Of course it was *bothering* her. He must have known that. Even if his voice hadn't suddenly dipped, the tension which had been growing between them for days now seemed to be reaching a climax. Her breathing had grown so shallow that she barely seemed capable of taking any air into her lungs and Sophie was aware of the blood beating hotly through her veins. He was coming onto her and she wasn't doing a thing to stop him and it was crazy. She knew that.

And yet…

She swallowed.

Why *shouldn't* she respond, when it had been nearly killing her to keep out of his way as much as she had been doing? She'd never done this before. Never had an intimate late-night swim—not even with the Prince to whom she'd been promised in marriage. In fact, she'd never been alone with a man like this—half dressed and totally unguarded—because her life on Isolaverde had been like living in the Dark Ages. She wondered what Rafe Carter would say if he knew she was a stranger to seduction and everything which went with it, but right now she didn't care.

Because for the first time in her life she felt unencumbered by protocol and acutely aware that this opportunity wouldn't come her way again. Her time here was limited and she was hurtling towards an unknown future—a bit like one of the cyclones which would soon dominate and threaten this very region. But none of that seemed to matter now. It was as if everything which had happened in her life up until that moment was about to be tossed aside by a powerful force of nature—in the very alpha shape of her half-naked boss.

With a splash she flipped over, bobbing underneath the water so he couldn't see the pointing of her nipples. But he wasn't looking at her breasts. He was looking at her face and suddenly she was looking right back at his. In the moonlight his eyes gleamed with an intense brilliance which made her stomach flip.

'Rafe?' she said uncertainly, but he silenced her with a shake of his head.

'Come here,' he said, his voice a sudden growl.

She knew he was going to kiss her even before he pulled her against him, against the hard wet planes of his muscular body. She could feel her breasts being crushed against his bare chest and the warmth of his breath just before he crushed her lips beneath his. Her eyelids fluttered to a close as he deepened the kiss and his thumb flicked over the wet stud of her hardening nipple through her swimsuit, making her moan with disbelief that something could feel this good. Because nobody had ever touched her before. Not like this. He slid his hand further down, before letting his fingertips skim over her belly and she wriggled impatiently, wanting him to touch her where she was hot and molten. Made weightless by the water, her thighs parted as if her body was programmed to know exactly how to respond and she sucked in another disbelieving breath as he slipped aside the panel of her swimsuit and pushed his finger deep inside her.

'Rafe,' she gasped against his lips, writhing her hips against him. 'Oh, Rafe.'

Her breathless use of his name seemed to break the erotic spell and when he pulled his hand away she immediately found herself wanting his finger right back where it had been. His eyes were unreadable in the moonlight and his features were harder than she'd ever seen them—his cheekbones two taut slashes against the obvious tension in his face.

'I want to have sex with you,' he said unsteadily. 'And clearly you feel exactly the same way. But there are a few things you need to understand.'

Her heart was thundering so loudly she felt as if she might faint. 'What kind of things?'

'You're staff,' he said bluntly. 'And I don't usually sleep with employees.'

'Oh.' There was a pause as she licked some of the chorine off her lips. 'Well, I guess that's honest, at least.'

'I'm nothing if not honest, Sophie,' he said. 'And if we're going to do this, it has to be on my terms.'

She met his gaze. 'What terms are they?'

'One night. That's all,' he told her, his gaze raking over her. 'No more. No dates. No promises. No happy ever after or follow-up emails. No Christmas present or surprise ticket to New York. And you certainly won't be getting love because I don't do love.

I'm out of here tomorrow and it's goodbye. Do you understand what I'm saying?'

Sophie bit her tingling lips as she considered his question. She was caught in the perfect storm of moonlight and desire and opportunity, even though the voice of common sense was urging her to get out while she still could.

But hadn't she always played by the rules and done what was 'right'? And look where it had got her. Deserted by the Prince her people adored and left a laughing stock. She had been placed on a pedestal from the moment of her birth. She was the Princess. People could look but they could never, ever touch. But Rafe had touched. She stared at him. Rafe didn't have a clue who she really was and he didn't care. All she could see was desire in his eyes and a hard, tense body which was calling out to her on the most primitive level of all. He wanted her. Not Princess Sophie. Just Sophie. More than that, she wanted him. Not the billionaire in his shiny helicopter but the elemental man who was making her feel like a real woman for the first time in her life. Him. Rafe Carter.

'I understand,' she said quietly.

His wet brow furrowed into a frown. 'Just like that?'

'Exactly like that.' She shrugged. 'Maybe I want exactly the same thing as you do, Rafe. One night. No strings.'

There was the glint of something predatory in his silvery eyes as he lowered his mouth to kiss her again, only now the kiss was underpinned with a new urgency, which sent the blood beating hotly through her veins. As the water lapped around them he kissed

her hard and deep before raising his head, his eyes
smoky with lust. 'Then what the hell are we waiting
for?' he said roughly, splaying his hand possessively
over one wet buttock.

CHAPTER THREE

SOMEHOW RAFE GOT her out of the pool and set her down onto the dripping tiles, his fingertips brushing wet strands of hair away from her face.

'Let's get you inside,' he said, his voice unsteady.

But Sophie hesitated. It seemed so *perfect* right where they were. She was terrified that moving away from that moonlit spot might break the spell—and she couldn't bear that to happen.

'Why do we have to go inside?' she whispered.

He gave a low and silky laugh. 'Call me old-fashioned, but I'd prefer the first time to be in private. Maybe you're one of those women who gets turned on by the prospect of discovery, but if that's the case, don't worry. I can promise you won't need any added extras to make this a night to remember.' He lowered his head to graze his mouth over hers. 'Plus, I didn't exactly arrive carrying condoms. It might have looked a little presumptuous, don't you think?'

His introduction of such an intimate topic silenced her and Sophie let him take her by the hand through a side entrance to an area of the house which she'd never used before and which took them directly into his private quarters. Her damp feet were cooled by the marble floor as she looked around her, blinking in amazement, feeling as if she'd fallen asleep and woken up in another country. It was an incongruous sight—to find such luxury and opulence on an Outback cattle station—and she tried to take it all in as he led her through the different rooms. A study lined with rare, old books led into an enormous sitting room, the walls covered with beautiful paintings of the country he loved so much.

But her admiration of the fixtures and fittings dissolved once he took her into a bathroom as big and as luxurious as any found in her Isolaverdian palace—although with decidedly more masculine overtones. 'It's huge,' she said dazedly.

He paused in the act of sliding a strap of her swimsuit down over one shoulder, his eyes glittering with devilment as they sent a glance slanting in the direction of his groin. 'I assume that wasn't just a flattering innuendo?'

She prayed he couldn't see the faint rise of colour in her cheeks. She prayed he wouldn't discover that she was new to all this. 'I'm talking about your suite of rooms,' she said primly.

His fingers moved towards the second strap. 'You mean you didn't come peeping, before I arrived?'

'No, I...*oh*...' She bit her lip as he tugged the damp fabric down over her breasts. 'I certainly did not.'

He bent to fasten his lips over one cold nipple and then the other, tantalising the acutely sensitised and puckering skin with the faint graze of his teeth. She looked down to see his dark hair contrasted against her pale skin and spangles of pleasure rippled over her body as she buried her fingers in the damp tendrils.

A sudden fervour seemed to grip him as he finished peeling off her swimsuit before removing his own wet shorts and towelling her dry. And before she really had time to register that they were both naked, he picked her up and carried her into a vast bedroom, putting her down on a king-size bed. Part of her felt like a sacrificial lamb as she lay there, outlined against his sheets in the silvery moonlight—but the heated hunger of her body was powerful enough to make any anxieties melt away. Plus, he was just so beautiful. Powerful and strong, with long, muscular legs and narrow hips, his buttocks a paler colour than the deeper olive glow of his skin.

Sophie licked her lips. She'd never seen a naked man before—not unless you counted the famous statues which brought visitors flocking to the Isolaverdian national museum during the winter months. And those naked men were made of marble, usually with a fig leaf covering their modesty. It occurred to her that Rafe would have needed an entire bunch of fig leaves to cover *his* most intimate part and that maybe she should have been daunted by the stiff, proud column of his erection. But she wasn't. As he moved over her, she just felt...*eager*.

'Well, just look at you,' he said unsteadily, as his fingertip trailed a slow path from her neck to her belly button. 'Aren't you gorgeous?'

She gave a wriggle of pleasure. 'Am I?'

'You know damned well you are. A million men must have told you so.'

His remark brought reality creeping into the room but Sophie didn't want reality. She wanted to *feel*, not to think. She wanted to feel a man's fingers on her skin. To be intimate with a man who desired her, not because of her position or her status—but because they had a powerful chemistry which could not be denied.

So she coiled her arms around his neck and looked up at him, invitation vying with reprimand in her voice.

'I don't want to talk about other men right now,' she said honestly.

His smile was hard as he cupped one breast with possessive arrogance, grinding his hips a little, so that she could feel the hard brush of his erection against her skin.

'Me neither,' he said.

He began to stroke her, the slow graze of his fingers exploring her. She gasped when his thumb first brushed against the tight bud above so much honeyed warmth, but within seconds she was hungrily anticipating more. Each practised stroke of his finger took her deeper—deep into a place of almost unimaginable pleasure and she heard him laugh as she gasped his name out loud. It felt as if her body was opening up to him, sensation flooding through her with relentless, rhythmical beats, and Sophie began to move restlessly, wanting more. And although he must have sensed her impatience, he took his time—eking out the pleasure, second by delicious second. He stroked her until she was writhing beneath him and, although she was eager to explore his body, she was shy about touching him *there*. Because what if she did the wrong thing? What if she destroyed the magic with some clumsy caress? Her lips sought his as she lifted her hips up, so that she could feel the weight of his erection pressing into her belly.

He made some little curse beneath his breath as he drew away and reached inside the drawer of the nightstand and Sophie stiffened as he tore open a little foil packet, scarcely able to believe that it was going to happen. After all the years of waiting, of saving her innocence for a man whose parents had bartered with her parents for her hand in marriage, she was about to lose her virginity in the anonymity of the Australian Outback, with the man who was paying her wages. A man who had promised her no tomorrows and scorned the idea of love. And yet she didn't care. It was as if she'd been living in a dark cave which was about to be flooded by something brilliant and beautiful—and her life would never be the same again.

She watched as he began to stroke on the rubber and lifted his gaze, curving her a complicit smile as if silently acknowledging her enjoyment of the floorshow. Would he be shocked if he knew what she was *really* thinking—that she'd never seen either a condom or an erection before? Was he going to be disappointed once the truth was out and wouldn't it be better to tell him now?

Instinct overrode her brief spike of conscience as she coiled her arms around his neck. Because this was an education, she reminded herself fiercely. A rite of passage. Something she needed to do to shake off the shackles of innocence and join the ranks of real women. Nothing more than that. This was what modern, normal people did. They met, they were attracted to one another—and they had sex. Why spoil it by revealing all her hang-ups and compromise her anonymity in the process?

He was moving over her and it felt slightly scary

as he guided himself towards her—to where she was so hot and sticky. She tried not to tense up as he eased himself inside her, but he was so big she couldn't help herself gasping out. For a moment he stilled, lifting his head to look at her—an expression of incomprehension etched onto his dark features.

His one-word question was incredulous. 'You—?'

'Yes,' she gasped as her hips jerked forwards all of their own accord, so that he went in even deeper. 'But don't stop, Rafe. Please don't stop.'

Rafe gave a strangled groan as he went deeper into her tight heat. How could he possibly have stopped when she was raining urgent kisses all over his shoulder and squeezing her pelvic muscles in a way which instantly made him want to come?

This really *was* just going to be once, he told himself grimly—so he had better make it something she would remember for the rest of her life. The best sex she would ever have. The only sex she would ever have—with him. Holding back his own hunger, he began to tease her clitoris with his finger as he thrust in and out of her, making her moan with pleasure— her cries getting louder with each penetration. He halted and lifted his head to look at her as a cold kind of anger rippled over his skin.

'Keep quiet,' he ordered. 'I don't want you waking the men.'

But she didn't—or couldn't—keep quiet. Least of all when she began to come and he sensed that her gasps of disbelief were going to morph into cries of ecstasy. So he bent his head to kiss her, and the frantic touch of her lips seemed to intensify his own orgasm—and suddenly it was *his* cry being stifled by *her* kiss and the balance of power had shifted and he didn't like that either.

He could feel her contracting around him as his body jerked like a puppet whose strings had been cut, and only when nature had finished with him and emptied him of all his seed did he have the strength to pull out. To roll away from her and close his mind to the rapturous look on her face as her eyelids fluttered to a close. To ignore the ruffled hair and dreamy expression of someone who had just experienced sex for the first time. Because although he wanted to lick her breasts and slide his hand between her thighs again and make her come all over his fingers, he didn't intend touching her until she'd given him some kind of explanation.

A virgin! Dazedly, he shook his head. Whoever would have guessed it, when she'd agreed to have casual sex without any degree of hesitation? She'd been so up for it that they could have done it in the swimming pool. Or in the garden. If he'd laid her out on the kitchen table where she buttered bread each morning, he reckoned she still would have given him the green light. Why, she'd acted like someone completely at ease with her own sexuality—right up to the moment when he'd thrust inside her and she'd made that broken little cry. Why the hell hadn't she told him she was innocent—and at least given him the option of whether or not he wanted to be the first?

And yet it had been amazing, hadn't it? The most amazing sex he could remember?

Pushing away the rogue thought, he didn't speak until he was certain his words would come out as measured and controlled. But even then his throat felt constricted and he could feel another rush of heat to his groin as he remembered easing into her slick tightness.

'You're certainly a woman of surprises,' he said. 'You don't happen to have any more hidden up your sleeve?'

Sophie froze as she realised it was probably the most astute question he could have asked in the circumstances. *What would he say if he realised what else she wasn't telling him*? She kept her eyes shut, not daring to open them, afraid of what they might reveal—when she wasn't even sure herself. She felt... what?

She swallowed.

Complete? Yes. Satisfied? Very. She felt shy yet strangely confident, because she'd done it and it had *worked*. She'd had sex! She'd had an orgasm! Underneath all the glitz and the unusual upbringing, she was no different from any other woman—and that thought gave her hope for the future. It made her feel strong. As if she was capable of pretty much anything she set her mind to. And Rafe had touched her as she'd always dreamed a man might do. Not in a reverential way. Not treating her as if she were made of porcelain or making her acutely aware of her 'blue blood'—but treating her just like a woman. And before he'd made love to her, he'd hugged her, hadn't he? Held her close. He'd picked her up and carried her. Cradled her tight against his wet chest—and that had blown her away nearly as much as the sex, because she wasn't used to physical contact. Even as a child, her parents had never been demonstrative. The Queen used to appear before dinner—all dressed up in her finery—and one of the palace nannies would troop the royal children in for a quick kiss goodnight. Why, she'd been touched more tonight than in her entire life.

Sophie sighed as she wriggled against the rumpled bedsheet, not sure whether she wanted to slide beneath it with her happy, private thoughts, or to dance around the room in celebration. But what she wanted most of all was to tiptoe her fingers over Rafe's silky flesh and have him kiss her again. She wanted him to wipe that curiously judgemental expression from his face—because what did it matter that she'd never had sex before? She wondered what the etiquette for dealing with a situation like this was and how ironic that she, an expert in etiquette, should be at such a loss.

Well, she wasn't going to cower away like someone who was ashamed, because she wasn't. Maybe she should just let him know how *much* she'd enjoyed it and then maybe he would do it to her all over again.

She felt liquid heat pooling low in her stomach as her eyelashes fluttered open and she was unprepared for the punch of emotion she felt as she looked at him—the man who up until a few minutes ago had been deep inside her. He looked the same, and yet he seemed different—but then she'd never seen him naked in the moonlight before, or softened by the intimacy of sex. Her gaze drifted over his powerful dark body, outlined against the rumpled white sheets, because surely what had just happened gave her the right to study him like this. Something melted deep inside her as she felt her heart skip a beat. How was it possible to want him again so quickly—and did he want her, too?

Her tongue slid out to moisten her lips. 'That was—'

'Don't tell me.' His voice was a hard and cynical drawl. 'Amazing? Wonderful? Women usually say it was the best sex they've ever had, although I suppose in your case that would be difficult to gauge since it's the *only* sex you've ever had.'

Sophie went very still, thinking he must be making a joke—and a joke in very poor taste—to discuss his other lovers at such a sensitive time. But as her eyes sought his face she could see no trace of humour there and she realised that he seemed *irritated*. Disenchantment whispered over her but she didn't show it—grateful for years of social training, which meant she was able to return his gaze with a cool impartiality. 'You sound disappointed, Rafe. Do you have a problem with the fact that I was a virgin?'

'Only the same kind of problem I might have if I took a ride in a car with somebody who hadn't bothered to tell me they were a learner driver.'

His cutting words shattered the last few traces of bliss and Sophie stared straight ahead at the unfamiliar wall of the moonlit bedroom. 'Thanks for the comparison,' she said flatly.

'Why the hell have you never had sex before?' he demanded. He shook his head in disbelief. 'You're young. You're beautiful. You were clearly up for it. And this is the twenty-first century.'

Sophie swallowed. Now was the time to come clean. To say what she would need to repeat at least once, because he would think she was making it up.

You might have been living in the twenty-first century, but I certainly wasn't. Because I was born a royal and betrothed to one of the world's most eligible men and part of the deal was that I would go to him as a virgin on my wedding night.

And then what?

A nightmare, that was what. Once she'd convinced him she wasn't a complete fantasist, she would be obliged to dredge up a past she was trying to move on from. She would be forced into a truth she didn't want to have to face—that she was a princess with an unknown future. And even worse—what if he suddenly became very interested? True, he didn't seem the type—but you never *really* knew. Lots of people were turned on by palaces and crowns and a status which couldn't be bought, or earned. And wouldn't it only reinforce her plummeting self-esteem if he decided he wanted her for *what* she was, rather than *who* she was?

Suddenly she was filled with an overwhelming desire to temper his arrogance. To see if she could unsettle *him* for a change. 'Maybe I was just waiting to meet the right man,' she said innocently, watching as he sat up in bed, quickly covering the lower part of his body with the rumpled bedsheet. But not before she'd noticed that he was aroused again and for some reason that gave her a fleeting feeling of triumph.

'I think we'd better get one thing clear, Sophie,' he said as a pulse worked frantically at his temple. 'The sex we just had was amazing. More than amazing—especially as it was your first time. You don't have enough experience to know that, but let me assure you it's true.' He paused, as if picking his words carefully. 'But the fact remains that I'm not in the market for any kind of commitment. I meant every word of what I said to you in the pool. This changes nothing.'

She widened her eyes. 'Oh?'

'I don't want you having any unrealistic expectations, that's all. I'm not the kind of man who is blown away by the fact you were a virgin—I don't have some primitive, chest-thumping desire to shout it from the rooftops. It doesn't mean anything to me and neither do you. Sorry to be so blunt, but it saves any kind of misunderstanding. I'm not looking for a partner and even if I was, that partner wouldn't be you. I told you that I believe in honesty and I'm being honest now. We have very different lives,' he added, almost gently. 'You're a cook on some kind of late-onset gap year and I'm a globetrotting CEO. Think about it.' He gave a shrugging kind of smile. 'It could never work.'

Oh, the arrogant, *arrogant* man! Sophie resisted the urge to pick up the nearest hard object and hurl it at him, before telling herself that behaving rashly wouldn't improve anything and it would compromise any remaining dignity. But at least his attitude made her decision easier. There would be no confidences shared with this particular Englishman. She wasn't going to tell him a single thing about herself—why should she, when he obviously couldn't wait to get away from her?

Some of her inbuilt royal confidence came rushing back as she returned his stare. 'I think you flatter yourself,' she said coolly as she got out of bed and picked up the discarded towel which was lying in a heap on the floor. 'I agree with every word you say.

It was nothing but an initiation to sex and a pretty amazing one. So thanks for that—but rest assured that I'm not looking for commitment either. I told you that in the pool. Maybe I should have let on that I was a virgin but I didn't want to destroy the mood. And since you're such a busy globetrotting CEO who is flying out of here tomorrow, I'd better let you get some peace so you can sleep. Goodnight, Rafe.' She flashed him a smile. 'Sweet dreams.'

And Sophie felt a very different kind of satisfaction as she saw the expression of disbelief on Rafe Carter's face just before she turned and walked out of his bedroom.

CHAPTER FOUR

RAFE WAS WOKEN by the insistent sound of his phone
vibrating and he stifled a groan as he picked it up. It
was one of several he owned but the only one whose
number was given to those closest to him. He glanced
at the flashing screen to see that it was William, one
of his assistants, calling from New York. He frowned.
William was in a completely different time zone and
had strict instructions not to disturb him unless absolutely necessary.

He hit the button and waited.

'Rafe?'

'Of course it's me! Who else did you think it
would be? It's five o'clock in the flaming morning!'
Rafe answered, his mood not enhanced by the sight
of Sophie's discarded swimsuit lying on the floor of
the en-suite bathroom. Or by the fact that an image
of her face had been haunting him for hours, meaning that he'd only fallen into a fitful sleep a restless
hour ago.

A rush of heat flooded through his groin as he
remembered the sex of the night before. Remembered her beautiful body laid out like a feast on top
of his sheets with those big blue eyes looking up

at him and her long legs parted in invitation. And she had been a *virgin*, he reminded himself grimly. She hadn't bothered telling him *that* before she had thrust her wet breasts against him in the swimming pool, had she?

Because women had their secrets, he thought bitterly. Every damned one of them keeping stuff hidden away and not caring about the consequences.

And sometimes their secrets became your secrets and they gnawed away deep inside you until there was nothing but a dark and empty hole.

He sat up, his fingers tightening around the phone. 'I thought I told you I wasn't to be disturbed unless absolutely necessary,' he bit out.

His assistant's voice grew serious. 'This is very necessary, Rafe.'

Rafe stilled, because even though he came from the world's most dysfunctional family, they were still family. Yet if somebody was ill, it wouldn't be his assistant ringing him. It would be Amber, or one of his half-brothers, surely. 'What's the matter?' he demanded. 'Is someone sick?'

'No. Nobody's sick.'

'What, then?' questioned Rafe impatiently.

There was a split-second pause. 'That girl you've got working at the station.'

'Sophie,' said Rafe instantly and then could have cursed himself. Surely he should have taken longer than a nanosecond to recall the name of one of his itinerant workers. 'The cook.'

'She's not a cook.'

'She may have only the most basic of culinary skills, but I can assure you she most certainly is.'

'She's a princess.'

There was a pause. 'William, have you been drinking?'

'She's a princess from Isolaverde,' his assistant continued doggedly. 'One of the world's richest islands. Gold, diamonds, petroleum, natural gas, uranium. They hold some international yacht race every year. They've even—'

'I get the idea, William. And I've heard of it. Get on with it.'

'She's young and beautiful—'

You're telling me. 'The *facts*,' bit out Rafe.

'She was engaged to some prince. Prince Luciano of Mardovia— known as Luc. Bit of a player—lived on another Mediterranean island—known each other since they were kids. Just before the engagement was due to be announced he goes and makes some English dressmaker pregnant. Big scandal. He was forced to marry the dressmaker—so the wedding with Princess Sophie had to be called off. And that's when she disappeared.'

'Disappeared?' repeated Rafe slowly, his mind spinning as he tried to get his head round the relevant facts. Not just the fact that the name Luc rang a distant bell in his memory, but a far more worrying one. He'd just had sex with a virgin *princess*?

'Into thin air. She ran away. Or rather, flew away. Nobody really knew about it because her brother instigated an information lockdown. And no one had any idea where she was. At least, not until now.' Another pause. 'They know she's at Poonbarra, Rafe.'

'And how...?' Rafe drew in a deep breath. 'How the hell do they know that?'

'Seems like Eileen Donahue—that's the woman who runs the general store in Corksville—recognised Sophie yesterday. Said she was, and I quote, "All dolled up for a change" and that she seemed "familiar". So she looked her up on the Internet—and what do you know? Sophie *is* familiar. She's royal, no less. Eileen contacted one of the papers in Brisbane and I'm afraid the rest is exactly how you imagine it would be. The journalists did their research and I'm ringing to say that you can expect a deputation of the world's press on your doorstep before too long.'

Rafe's fingers clasped the phone so tightly that he heard his knuckles crack. 'That can't be allowed to happen, William,' he said in a low voice. 'I don't want a circus invading town. Poonbarra is a place of privacy. The one place in the world where I am guaranteed peace. I want you to kill this story and I want you to kill it now.'

'I don't see how that's going to be possible, boss. It's already got legs.'

'Well, just get me out of here before they arrive.' Rafe's voice was cold.

There was a pause. 'Let me see what I can do.'

Rafe swore as he cut the connection and resisted the desire to crush the phone in the palm of his hand. Pushing back the sheet, he got out of bed, trying to temper his mood and think rationally—even though all he wanted to do was storm through the homestead to find Sophie Doukas and give her a piece of his mind. Another wave of anger enveloped him. Not only had she kept her innocence secret, but she'd omitted to tell him that she was a royal. *A royal on the run!* Deceitful woman. *Scheming* woman.

Anger and resentment washed over him but he could still smell her on his skin and taste her in his mouth and it was tantalising and distracting. Even the thought of her was making his body grow hard, so he forced himself to stand beneath the icy jets of the shower, which did little to cool his heated blood. Dragging a razor across his jaw, he somehow managed to nick his skin in the process and that only increased his frustration.

Pulling on a shirt and a pair of trousers, he went looking for her but, since it wasn't quite six, the house was completely silent and there were no sounds of clatter coming from the kitchen. His rage mounting, he strode along the quiet corridors—forcing himself to knock on her door even though part of him just wanted to kick it open in a primitive way, which was not his usual style at all.

She was already up and dressed and answered the knock immediately but her eyes were hooded and cautious when she saw it was him. She was wearing a pair of shapeless cotton trousers and a T-shirt, yet all he could think about was the magnificence of her naked body and the way she'd cried out when he'd opened her legs and entered her. And once again he was furious with himself for the hot surge of lust which flooded through his bloodstream, knowing that he should be concentrating on her lies and subterfuge, not her undeniable physical appeal.

'Rafe,' she said, her fingers flying to the base of her throat where he could see a small pulse hammering.

'Oh, don't worry,' he said, with a disdainful curl of his lips. 'I haven't come here for sex.'

'Oh? Then why have you come here?'

She tilted her chin in a defiant gesture and suddenly Rafe wondered how he could have been so dense. *Of course she was someone*—hadn't that been apparent from the start? A diamond in the rough—that had been his initial reaction on seeing her and he had been right. And when he stopped to think about it, her high-born status had been apparent in every gesture she made. It had been there in the way she moved and the way she walked. In her flawless skin and heart-shaped face and the thick, lustrous bounce of her hair. She was a princess. Of course she was. A runaway virgin princess who had chosen him as her first lover.

Why?

'I'm still trying to get my head around what happened last night,' he said. 'About the fact that you let a virtual stranger take your virginity. And wondering if there's anything else you've omitted to tell me?'

Sophie went very still, because something in his eyes told her the game was up—but still she clung to her fake freedom for a few last, precious seconds. She tried to convince herself it was her own guilty conscience making her think he'd found out who she really was—but that was impossible. Just because he'd been deep inside her body the night before, didn't mean he'd suddenly developed the ability to read her mind, did it? How could he *possibly* know?

'Like what?' she questioned nonchalantly.

Her words seemed to make something inside him snap and he took a step towards her. 'Oh, sweetheart,' he said softly. 'Why do women find it impossible to give a straight answer? Why is deceit always their default setting? I gave you the chance to tell me the truth, but surprise surprise—you chose not to take it. I'm talking about the fact that you're a princess—and that the world's press know you're here.'

'No,' she whispered, her fingers moving from her neck to her lips.

'Yes,' he said grimly.

She shook her head. 'They can't know. I've been here for months and been left in peace. How…how did they find out?'

'Apparently, the woman who runs the store at Corksville recognised you.'

And Sophie could have wept. How could she have been so *stupid*? Why hadn't she just behaved the same way she'd always behaved with her nondescript clothes and her hair hidden beneath a big hat? But, no. Rafe Carter had returned and the lure of feminine pride had been too strong to resist. For once she'd worn a dress. For once she'd applied mascara and left her hair loose. Vanity and desire had been her downfall. She had discarded her habitual disguise and someone had identified her. She had nobody to blame but herself.

But her regret was fleeting. There was no time for regrets. No time for anything except to work out what she did next.

'I'm sorry,' she said.

'It's a bit late for that,' he snapped.

'What else do you expect me to say?' she said, and walked back inside her bedroom. 'Excuse me. I have a lot to do.'

But Rafe had followed her and was reaching out to catch hold of her wrist, and even in the middle of all her confusion and fear—*even in the middle of all that*—she could still feel her hotly instinctive response to his touch. She wanted him to pull her close. To kiss her again. To put his tongue inside her mouth and his erection deep inside her body and make her feel all those things he'd made her feel last night.

'What I can't work out is how you got here,' he bit out. 'A royal princess travelling all the way from Isolaverde to the east coast of Australia without any-one knowing.'

Sophie snatched her hand away and stared at the faint imprint his fingers had left on her wrist. Her journey here seemed like a dream now. Like some-thing out of an adventure film. But why *not* tell him? Surely it would reinforce the fact that she had been brave and resilient—and she could be those things all over again *if only she believed in herself.*

'The man I was meant to marry made another woman pregnant.'

'So my assistant just informed me.'

Sophie's mouth pleated in dismay as she expe-rienced that old familiar feeling of people talking about her behind her back. 'It was the biggest outrage to happen in years and everyone seemed to have an opinion about it,' she continued. 'It was *claustropho-bic* on the island and I knew I had to get away. No bodyguards or ladies-in-waiting, or people fussing round me. I just wanted to be on my own for the first time in my life, to lick my wounds and decide what I wanted to do next. But more than that, I wanted to feel like a normal person for once. To shake off all the royal trappings and do something on my own.'

'I'm not interested in the pop psychology behind your actions,' he said coldly. 'More the practicalities.'

'My brother was away on a hunting trip,' she said slowly. 'So I left him a note saying I was leaving and not to try to find me. And then I persuaded one of the palace pilots to fly me to the west coast of the USA.'

He frowned. 'How the hell did you persuade him to do that?'

She shrugged. 'It shouldn't take too much of a stretch of your imagination to work it out. I made it worth his while.'

'Of course you did. And you would have needed to pay him a lot of money,' he said cynically. 'Since presumably smuggling you out of there meant the end of his flying career at the palace?'

'I didn't force him to agree!' She felt a sudden flicker of rebellion. 'He was happy to do it.'

'So what happened next?' he said, in a hard voice.

'He took me to one of the smaller Californian ports and introduced me to a friend of his—a man named Travis Matthews—who had a boat big enough to cross the Pacific. And that's what I did.'

Now he was staring at her in disbelief. 'You *crossed the Pacific*?'

'I'm a good sailor,' she said defensively. 'I love boats more than anything. And there was a crew of six, so I was just an extra. It took us weeks. It was...'

As her voice faltered he frowned. 'It was what?'

Sophie swallowed. This had been the bit she hadn't counted on. The bit which had soothed her wounded ego and hurt pride and put it all in perspective. The sheer beauty of being that far out at sea—the ever-changing ocean and the bright stars at night. And a sense of freedom she'd never known before. It had been a heady experience and one she would never forget.

She looked at the sculpted lines of Rafe's hard face, at the steely grey eyes, which last night had darkened with hunger, yet today were glittering with fury. Why tell him things which would bore him rigid? Stick to the facts, she told herself fiercely. The *practicalities*.

'It was an interesting experience,' she said.

'And when you got to Australia? What then?'

She shrugged. 'We docked at Cairns where Travis had a contact of his pick me up and drive me out this way. En route I stopped off at a store and bought an entire new wardrobe.'

'Discount clothes?' he questioned dryly, with a sardonic glance at her outfit.

'Exactly that. Nothing which could possibly identify me.' Reflectively she rubbed the hem of her cheap T-shirt between thumb and forefinger. 'And you know what? That was a liberation, too. Putting on something which was indistinguishable from what the woman at the checkout was wearing made me feel that I was the same as everyone else for the first time in my life.'

Rafe shook his head. 'Except that most women at the checkout don't have a multimillion-dollar trust fund bolstering up their little *adventures*,' he said sarcastically, before something occurred to him. Something which chimed with the nagging memory in his mind. 'Did you *know* this was my cattle station?'

She hesitated and he saw an uncomfortable look cross her face. 'Why do you ask?'

'No more lies or evasion, Sophie,' he bit out. 'Just tell me the truth.'

'Yes, I'd heard about your station.'

'How?'

She shrugged. 'The man I was supposed to marry is called Prince Luc and your sister Amber's husband is an art dealer who once sold him a painting. Luc was telling me about Conall Devlin marrying into the Carter family—about how you're all scattered across the world and how none of you conform. He mentioned that you were some bigshot entrepreneur who had a huge cattle station.'

'And you liked the sound of me, did you?' he questioned arrogantly.

'Hardly,' came her frosty retort. 'The thing that attracted me was the fact that you were never here. I knew from talking to Travis that most cattle stations employed a cook and that I could probably teach myself.'

'But we already had a cook working here,' he said.

She flushed a little. 'I know you did. But I met her for a drink and...'

'Let me guess. You offered her money to go earlier than planned?'

Flushing a little, she nodded. 'That's right.'

'Oh, Sophie. How easy it is for you to delude yourself,' he said softly. 'For all your commendable announcements about wanting to be the same as everyone else, it must give you a pretty big buzz to realise you can buy pretty much anything you want if you throw enough money at it.'

'Are you telling me you've never used your own fortune to do exactly the same?'

Rafe stiffened as he met the challenge in her eyes and an unwanted feeling of regret coursed through him. How would she react if he told her that the only things he'd ever wanted were things which money could never buy? Things which could never have a price attached to them. Things he had lost and could never get back. He shook his head. 'This is your story, not mine,' he said bitterly. 'Get on with it.'

'I've told you everything you need to know.' She walked over to the top of the wardrobe to pull down a huge rucksack, which she threw on top of the bed. 'Just console yourself with the fact that you won't have to put up with me for much longer!'

'What do you think you're doing?'

'What does it look like I'm doing? I'm leaving. I can't stay here,' she said, tugging open a drawer and pulling out a stack of T-shirts, which she began to layer haphazardly in the rucksack. 'If I stay it'll be too much hassle for you.'

'Oh, please. Spare me the spin. I don't imagine you're leaving out of the goodness of your heart, are you, little Miss *Princess*?'

Sophie heard the venom in his voice and thought about the way he'd touched her last night. The way he'd made her feel so safe and *protected*. As if she was capable of anything. She remembered the way she'd trembled with delight as he'd explored her skin with his fingers and his mouth. The way she'd gasped with pleasure with each deep stroke he'd made. She had taken a long time to have sex for reasons which were complex and unique, but Rafe Carter had been the perfect lover—even if now he was looking at her as if she were something he'd found squashed beneath the sole of his shoe.

And surely what happened last night had been about more than sexual liberation. She had given herself to him freely—so didn't that give her the right to treat him as an equal and be treated as an equal herself?

'Is it fair to criticise me because I was born with a title?' she said. 'Something which is completely outside my control.'

'Would you prefer that I criticised you for your deceit instead? For failing to tell me who you really were?'

'But I couldn't tell you,' she said simply. 'How could I? I couldn't tell anyone—it would have made it impossible for me to stay here. Surely you can see that. It would have altered everything.'

'And of course, if you'd told me, particularly the part about your lack of sexual experience...' his eyes glinted '...then at least I would have had a choice about whether I wanted to be used as an experimental lover in your big round-the-world adventure.'

'It wasn't like that!' she said fiercely.

'No? You chose me because we'd forged a deep bond in less than a week of knowing one another?'

'I actually wasn't analysing it very much at all—I was just going with the flow. And aren't you forgetting that there were two people involved in what happened?' she questioned quietly. 'Or just preferring to forget your part in it?'

'So what was it? Did I tick all the right boxes, Sophie?' He began to tap each one of his fingers in turn. 'Rich, single, hot and therefore the perfect candidate to give the rejected royal her first taste of sexual pleasure?'

Flinging a belt on top of the T-shirts, Sophie lifted her head, grabbing at the streak of anger which flashed through her because surely anger was better than buckling under these sudden feelings of vulnerability and sadness which were bubbling up inside her. 'You bastard,' she whispered shakily, but Rafe Carter didn't look in the least bit shocked by her first ever public use of a swear word. The only emotion she could see flickering in his hard grey eyes was bitter cynicism.

'Yeah. For a while I was exactly that. A bastard,' he drawled. 'My father didn't marry my mother until three days after I was born. As it turned out, they should never have bothered.'

His phone started to vibrate in his pocket and he slid it out to take the call, listening in silence as Sophie continued to pack the rucksack.

'Where are you planning to go?' he questioned, once the connection had been cut.

She didn't look up, terrified now that her vulnerability would be impossible to hide. 'I haven't really thought about it.'

'Well, start thinking!' He felt a flicker of temper. 'You're not protected by your royal status now, Sophie. You're out in the middle of Queensland with a limited choice of transport available, no matter how much money you're suddenly able to produce. That was my assistant on the phone. He says your presence in my Outback home is generating a lot of interest on a quiet news day—not least because I'm just about to mount a bid for one of Malaysia's biggest cell-phone networks and there's been a lot of opposition to the deal.' His mouth twisted. 'So thanks very much for that.'

'I'm sorry this has impacted on you because it was never intended to,' she said. 'But I'll be out of your life soon, Rafe. You can put all this down to experience and forget it ever happened. Which is precisely what you wanted in the first place, isn't it?'

She zipped up the rucksack and swept her tumbled hair away from flushed cheeks and Rafe was reminded of the way she'd moved over him the night before. He remembered the brush of her pubic hair as he'd tangled his fingers in it. The beat of her heart and how tight she'd felt. The way he'd kissed away her cries of pleasure. And damn it if he couldn't feel the sudden debilitating jerk of sexual desire as he visualised pushing her down on that bed and ripping open the ugly cotton trousers and doing it to her all over again.

'If only it was that easy,' he growled. 'What do you think it's going to do for my reputation if I leave you here to fend for yourself among the rabble of newshounds who are due to arrive?'

'Heaven forbid I might damage your reputation!'

'You might not care about my reputation, sweetheart, but I do. And I'm not letting you go anywhere on your own.'

She tilted her chin in defiance. 'That sounds awfully like an order to me.'

'At least that's something you've got right. Because if that's what it takes to make you see sense, then it's an order.' His eyes bored into her. 'What's the matter, Little Princess? Not used to somebody else telling you what to do?'

She stared at the door behind him, as if planning to make a rush for it. 'If you must know, I've spent my whole life being told what I can and can't do and this is the first time I've ever been able to decide things on *my* terms. So please don't trouble yourself with concerns about my personal safety, Rafe. I can have some Isolaverdian bodyguards sent out here to look after me.'

'And how long is that going to take?' he demanded. 'Even if your rarefied palace protection people knew how to cope with life in the bush, which I doubt. The situation could dissolve into complete farce with people suffering from heatstroke or getting spooked by some animal they've never seen before, or worse. Is that what you want?'

Sophie bit her lip. She didn't know *what* she wanted. Well, in a stupid way she did. She wanted to rewind time so that she was back in his arms. She wanted to feel like a normal woman again. And that was never going to happen.

'I don't know,' she admitted, hating the sudden break in her voice.

Rafe stiffened as he steeled himself against that unexpected trace of vulnerability. Because it was all an act, he reminded himself grimly. Everything about her was false. And until her playboy fiancé had jumped ship, she'd presumably been given everything she wanted, no matter how much she might protest otherwise. Well, she was about to learn that around here he was the one who called the shots.

'You're going to have to come with me,' he said,

an idea slowly forming in his head. 'And perhaps we can each do one another a favour at the same time.'

'Come where?' She narrowed her eyes suspiciously. 'And what kind of a favour?'

Rafe stared down at the bulging rucksack as it occurred to him that this—like all bad situations—could be turned into an advantage. Couldn't the unbearable prospect of having to face Sharla again be diluted by taking Sophie to his nephew's christening? Because the presence of a beautiful princess would easily trump the fact that one of the world's most famous supermodels was going to be there.

Haunting him with what she'd done. Or, rather, what she had failed to do.

'To England,' he said. 'I have a family christening I can't get out of. This is the first time the Carters have been together in a long time and I'm not looking forward to it.'

'Why not?'

'Why is none of your business,' he snapped. 'Let's just say that family reunions have never been my thing. But since there's safety in numbers, you can be my plus one. You get safe passage out of here, and I get someone who can deflect some of the attention away from me.'

'But I don't want to go to England for a family christening—and I certainly don't want to be your "plus one".'

'No? Then what else are you going to do?'

Sophie fished around for a suitable answer but with a sinking heart realised her options were limited. They always were. She didn't want to go home—not right now, when the people of her country would still look at her with sympathy in their eyes. Yet anywhere else would only emphasise her lone status—especially around Christmas time. Wouldn't travelling with Rafe stop the press from getting too close, while she decided what she was going to do next? Hadn't she proved that she could cope with hard work and be resourceful? She was young and fit and there was a great big world out there. Why shouldn't she use this opportunity to decide how best to embrace her new life?

She met the steely gleam of his eyes, thinking about the harsh things he'd said to her. She didn't like him very much but something told her she'd be safe with him. Not because they shared a special connection because of what had happened last night, but because he was strong and powerful. A man like this could protect you, she thought wistfully. And he could make you want him, even if you knew that wanting him was the last thing you needed.

She could do nothing to stop the ripple of sexual awareness which had started spreading over her body but she did her best not to think about it. His offer made perfect sense but she could only accept it if she took it at face value. She would go along for the ride, but no further. She mustn't start yearning for things Rafe Carter was never going to give her. Because even though he'd taken her to heaven and back last night, this morning his eyes were cold and unwelcoming.

He doesn't much like you either, she thought.

And even though his opinion didn't matter, wasn't it funny how something like that could hurt?

CHAPTER FIVE

FORTY THOUSAND FEET above the South China Sea and wanting to break the hours of interminable silence, Sophie turned towards the brooding figure who was seated beside her. 'I'm surprised you don't have body-guards.'

Rafe looked up from the papers he'd been reading, his eyes narrowing, clearly irritated at having been interrupted from the work which had consumed his attention since they'd first boarded the aircraft. 'Why the hell should I have bodyguards?'

Sophie waved a hand to encompass all the luxuri-ous fittings of his private jet. 'Why not? You travel like a royal. You're rich as Croesus. Aren't you wor-ried that somebody might kidnap you and spirit away your vast fortune?'

His grey eyes glittered. 'I have a black belt in both karate and judo,' he said silkily. 'I'd like to see some-body try.'

Sophie absorbed this as he picked up his papers again and she stared at the white clouds billowing out-side the aircraft window. Her comparison hadn't been made lightly. Their journey from Poonbarra had been so smooth that at times it *had* felt like being part of a royal convoy again. Yet she'd been sad at having to say goodbye to the Outback station where everyone had just accepted her as she was. To them she was an ordinary woman who'd learnt how to cook and mop floors and use a dishwasher. She had been dreading the moment of confessing her identity to Andy and the other men, knowing it would change everything. But she had been wrong, because they'd acted as if it meant nothing. They'd gruffly told her they wished she weren't going. And hadn't tears pricked at the corners of her eyes as the car had left Poonbarra for ever, her feeling as though she was leaving behind a peace and a freedom she would never know again?

They had flown in a light aircraft to Brisbane airport, where Rafe's private jet had been fuelled and ready to go. He'd made her telephone her brother and tell him that she was flying to England under his protection. And although Myron had been angry, his relief at being able to speak to her after so long, and knowing she was 'in safe hands', was almost palpable. And now they were flying towards the UK and it felt unreal. It *was* unreal. She was going to England to meet the family of a man who clearly couldn't stand her—and she didn't have a clue what she was going to do afterwards.

Her heart sank. Everything had been fine until he'd turned up at Poonbarra. She'd thought she'd have another couple of months before she needed to make any major decisions about her future, but Rafe Carter's seduction had changed everything. Should she ask him about flights to Isolaverde once the ceremony was over? She stared at his proud, carved profile.

Maybe not right now. Why not prepare herself for what lay ahead instead?

She cleared her throat. 'Maybe you should tell me something about your family.'

He looked up, his face not particularly friendly. 'Like what?'

'A few facts would help. Who's going to be at this Christening. That sort of thing.'

Answering questions of a personal nature was an activity Rafe habitually avoided and, besides, he wasn't in the mood to talk to Sophie. He was still angry with her. For her deception. For not telling him who she really was. For coming onto him and failing to tell him she was a virgin.

Yet his body was refusing to listen to the disapproval which was clouding his mind. The single thought which consumed him was how much he wanted to have sex with her by daylight—with the sun streaming in through the cabin windows and illuminating her creamy body. His throat thickened as he imagined her arching that elegant back, those long legs stiffening helplessly as she came. He didn't usually bring lovers on long-haul flights because being trapped in an enclosed space for so many hours meant the possibility of boredom was very high. But for once there had been no other option.

Pushing his erotic thoughts away, he met the questioning look in her eyes.

'It's my nephew's christening,' he said shortly.

'Right,' she said. 'So is it your brother or your sister who is the parent?'

'My half-brother. Or at least, one of them.'

'Right. And how many half-brothers do you have?'

With a barely stifled sigh of irritation, Rafe put down his pen. 'Three. Or at least, three that I know about,' he answered. 'And a half-sister named Amber.'

'Gosh. That's a lot. How come?'

His instinct was to snap back: *how do you think?* Until he remembered that her privileged life had probably protected her from the worst excesses of relationships—of children born in and out of wedlock and illicit affairs which wrecked marriages.

'Because my father liked women. Ambrose Carter was something of a darling in his day, which is probably why he married four times and why I have so many half-siblings. There's Amber, Chase, Gianluca and Nick—he's the one who's just had the baby—or rather, his wife, Molly, did.'

'Are they're all going to be there?'

'Everyone except Chase. He's in South America, halfway up the Amazon. Molly's parents are both dead.' There was a split-second pause. 'But her twin sister is going to be there. Like I said, it's complicated.'

'Okay.' She shifted her gaze to his. 'And does your father—Ambrose—have a good relationship with his children?'

'As much as each mother would allow.' He gave a faint smile. 'Because a child's welfare is primarily down to the mother, isn't it? And the kind of woman who marries a man for the size of his wallet probably isn't going to be the kind of person who puts her child's welfare first.'

Sophie hesitated. 'And was…was your mother that kind of woman?'

'You could say that.' His laugh was bitter. 'My

mother was the kind of woman for whom the term gold-digger might have been invented.'

'I'm sorry.'

'Why be sorry? It's the hand I was dealt and I learned how to play it.'

'And was it...tough?'

For a moment he thought about ignoring her probing questions, until he reminded himself that he was over *this* stuff. He shrugged. 'A lot of her behaviour was thoughtless and I was left alone to fend for myself a lot of the time. But something like that is probably outside your level of understanding.'

'What do you mean?'

'Presumably you've always been protected from the more sordid side of life.'

Sophie hated his assumptions—the same ones people always made. As if the material wealth which accompanied a royal title made you immune to the pain and hurt every human being had to contend with. As if you lacked the imagination to realise what most people's lives were like. 'Yes, I'm just a poor little rich girl,' she said. 'Scratch my skin and I'll bleed oil.'

'If you're trying to play on my sympathy, Sophie, don't bother.'

'I doubt whether you've a sympathetic bone in your body,' she bit back. ' People think it's so easy, being a princess. That you swan around all day wearing a diamond crown.'

'Poor you,' he mocked.

She glared at him, wanting to make him see the reality, wanting him to *understand* instead of being so damned *judgemental*. 'Try to imagine never being able to go anywhere without people knowing who you are. Everyone listening to what you say so that they can tell their friends—or a reporter—what they thought you meant. Imagine people watching every move you make. Analysing you. Assessing you. Obsessing about your weight. Working out where you bought your outfit and how much it cost and deciding *that* colour makes you look washed out, or plain, or fat—and then writing a whole article about it. Imagine everyone knowing that you'd been saving yourself for your fairy-tale prince, only he decided at the last moment to have his fairy tale with someone else and their new baby.'

'I can imagine that must have been difficult,' he conceded.

She stared down at her bare hands, before lifting her gaze to his once more. 'Imagine suddenly realising that the sweet woman you bought a pair of earrings from is now using your photograph on her website to promote her brand.'

'Oh, I can imagine that pretty well,' he said, and suddenly his voice hardened. 'Somebody who wasn't everything they seemed. Ring any bells, Sophie?'

Sophie met the accusation which burned like hot steel from his eyes. 'I thought I explained why I didn't tell you who I am.'

'I'm just amazed that I fell for your story,' he said. 'Amazed I should have thought you were different from any other woman with your lies and subterfuge. And you aren't, are you? So maybe it's time I started treating you in the way I know women like to be treated…'

She didn't realise what he was going to do until he pulled her across the seat onto his lap and her eyes widened as she felt the hard throb of his erection pushing against his trousers.

'Rafe?' she breathed uncertainly.

'Do you like that?' he taunted.

She wanted to say no, but she couldn't—even though she didn't like the look in his eyes. But the hot rush of desire flooding through her body was powerful enough to make her forget about his anger and his mockery. All she wanted was to press her groin against that throbbing ridge of hardness which had brought her so much pleasure last night.

'Rafe,' she said again, her voice sounding thick as she struggled to get the word out.

'Shh. You don't have to say anything.'

Deliberately, he tilted his pelvis, so that she could feel his erection pushing against where she was hot and wet and aching, and Sophie's throat dried. It was scary and exciting all at the same time. It was making her aroused, but, more importantly, it was blotting out the pain of thinking about Luc's new baby, which she *wasn't* over—no matter how hard she tried to be.

'I'm still very angry with you, Sophie,' he said softly. 'But that doesn't stop me wanting you. Can you feel how much I want you?'

She swallowed. 'I…yes…'

'And you want me, don't you? Even though you're trying very hard not to?'

Hating him for his perception, Sophie found herself powerless to push him away. 'Yes,' she said, between gritted teeth.

'Then we'd better do something about it, hadn't we? And very quickly, I think.'

Now the excitement was unbearable. Sophie felt

honeyed heat rush to her groin—but social conditioning went deep as he spread his fingers over one aching breast. 'The...crew?'

'Don't worry your pretty head about the crew.
They're trained never to disturb me unless I call them.
Satisfied?' he questioned, rucking up her T-shirt to reveal the cotton bra she'd bought at the discount store,
and Sophie gasped as he cleaved his thumb across a
nipple which was straining frantically against the thin
material. 'Because I'm sure as hell not.'

Insecurity made her say it, even as he impatiently
tugged the T-shirt over her head and tossed it aside.
'I expect you do this kind of thing all the time? Make
love on planes?'

His hand stopped from where it had been just
about to undo her bra and his eyes darkened with
an emotion which went deeper than desire. 'Don't
ask,' he said. 'And don't project, because if you can't
enjoy this for what it is, then it isn't going to happen.
Understand?'

And suddenly she couldn't bear not to do it. Who
cared how many women had come before her, or
how many would inevitably follow? Why couldn't
she just live in the moment and take what he was offering? And what he was offering was sex. Amazing and beautiful sex for the second time in her life.
'Yes,' she whispered. 'Yes.'

He didn't say anything more, just reached down
to unfasten the button of her jeans before sliding the
zip down and dipping his hand beneath the elasticated edge of her panties. His middle finger tangled
luxuriously in the soft fuzz of hair there, before
beginning to stroke rhythmically at her slick, wet

flesh and she couldn't stop the small yelp of pleasure she gave.

'No!' Frustratingly, his fingers stilled. 'I choose my staff for their discretion, but I have no desire to provide a floorshow by having you moan out loud when I make you come,' he ground out. 'So either you enjoy this in silence or we're both going to have a very frustrating journey ahead of us.'

His clipped words were so outrageous that Sophie was tempted to tell him to forget the whole idea, but the sensation of his fingers against her aroused flesh was much more tempting and suddenly the last of her pride shrivelled beneath the heat of her desire. Did he sense her capitulation? Was that why, with a sensual dexterity which dazed her in every which way, he laid her down on the floor of the aircraft and tugged her panties and jeans down to her ankles. She waited for him to tug them off but he shook his head and answered her unspoken question.

'No. The jeans stay. You'll be able to spread your legs for me, but only so far. It'll make you feel... *wicked*, which is exactly how I'm feeling right now.' He unzipped himself and pulled his trousers down, his erection springing free as he lowered himself down to position himself between her restricted legs. 'You need to try dirty sex—'

'D-dirty sex?'

'Mmm.' He stroked on a condom. 'Surreptitious, partially clothed and very...' he thrust into her suddenly '...*urgent*.'

He powered deep inside her and Sophie gripped onto his broad shoulders as her body began to accommodate his stroke. *He was still almost fully clothed,* she thought, yet somehow that only added to her mounting excitement. Some of what she was experiencing was the same as last night—that blood-racing exhilaration and rapid acceleration of pleasure—but some of it was radically different. And he was right. The fact that her jeans were restricting her movements only added to the excitement of what was happening. She was his prisoner, she thought weakly. His willing prisoner.

She lifted her face, her lips seeking his, eager for a kiss which would blot out the urgent cries which wanted to bubble up from her throat. But there were other reasons for wanting to kiss him. She liked the way his lips made her feel. Because even if it was nothing but an illusion, they made her feel cosseted. But it was too late for kisses because suddenly her body began to spasm and just as suddenly he began to buck inside her with a ragged groan of his own, as he made those last few, final thrusts.

She waited for him to say something which might imply an ending of the undoubted hostilities which were still shimmering between them. Something to acknowledge that what had just happened had been beyond fantastic. *Again.* He'd told her she didn't have the experience to know that the sex was amazing, but she could just about work out for herself that it was.

'Better go and freshen up,' he suggested softly, giving her bare bottom a light tap. 'And then I'll ring for some coffee.

Her heart contracted with disappointment at his careless reaction but she made sure she didn't show it, silently picking up her rucksack and carrying it to one of the bathrooms at the far end of the cabin.

She emerged some time later, with her hair neatly brushed and a clean T-shirt tucked into her jeans, but the cursory gaze he flicked over her wasn't particularly warm.

'You're going to need something to wear for the ceremony,' he said. 'I don't suppose you've got anything suitable in your rucksack?'

'Not a thing, I'm afraid.' She forced a smile, wishing he would at least *acknowledge* the intimacy they'd just shared, instead of staring at her so coolly. 'I left all my silks and satins behind at the palace.'

Rafe nodded as he reached for the phone. 'In that case I'll contact one of my assistants and arrange to have some suitable clothes brought to the aircraft when we land.' He paused. 'And in the meantime, perhaps you could find something to amuse yourself with for the rest of the flight. Something which doesn't involve looking at me alluringly with those big blue eyes and asking personal questions. Because I have work to do and you're distracting me, Sophie.'

CHAPTER SIX

THEY ARRIVED AT just past midnight when huge white flakes were tumbling from the night sky as if someone were having a celestial pillow fight. Rafe's limousine negotiated the final bend of the narrow road and it began to inch its way up the long drive towards his brother's Cotswold mansion.

Sophie peered out of the window at the night-time English countryside, thinking that if circumstances were different she might have enjoyed the snowy beauty of rural England—especially in contrast to the beating heat of Australia. But for now she was just grateful for the fact that the big house was shrouded in darkness—the faint, fairy-lighted glow gleaming behind the glass over the front door indicating that everyone had gone to bed. Thank heavens. She wasn't sure if she could face a reception committee and wondered if Rafe had arranged that deliberately by insisting they stop at a small pub for dinner on the way here. Perhaps he'd been delaying the inevitable meeting with his family because he didn't know how to introduce her. It meant she'd eaten her first ever meal in a British pub, enjoying the shepherd's pie the landlord had recommended though less keen on the warm beer Rafe had insisted she try.

In the back of the car were a large selection of clothes which he'd ordered to be delivered to the plane when they touched down in England—and she was now wearing some of them. Gone were the cheap jeans and T-shirt and in their place was an exquisite cashmere dress, which clung to every curve of her body, along with a pair of beautiful leather boots. They were the kind of clothes she was used to wearing, but along with her sudden change of image came that familiar sense of being *on show* again. She stared straight ahead, realising how much she had enjoyed her uncomplicated life of anonymity and realising it was about to come to an abrupt end.

'You okay?' Rafe questioned as the car slid to a halt in front of the house.

'Not really. I feel as nervous as hell,' she said truthfully.

'You?' In the shadowy light, his eyes narrowed. 'But you must have met hundreds of new people over the years.'

Probably thousands, she thought—but never like this. Meeting somebody's family on equal terms was something she'd never had to do before. Mostly people knew who she was and had prepared accordingly and everyone was always on their best behaviour when a princess was around. She stared out of the window again and it seemed that the sleeping house had been nothing but an illusion, because the moment their car swished to a snowy halt the front door opened and a woman appeared in the doorway as if she'd been listening out for them. Her greying hair matched a dress which was clearly a uniform and Sophie saw immediately what the glow behind the front door had been—a giant Christmas tree, dominating a vast and imposing wood-panelled hall.

Rafe smiled as the woman in the uniform stepped forward.

'Sophie, I'd like you to meet Bernadette, our housekeeper,' he said, 'who has been with different factions of this family for many years. And if she wasn't the soul of discretion, she could earn a living writing about the exploits of the infamous Carter family, couldn't you, Bernadette?'

'Sure, and who would want to read anything about you lot?' answered Bernadette, her accent warm and Irish. 'And aren't you forgetting your manners? Who's this beautiful young lady?'

Rafe introduced her simply as 'Sophie' and Bernadette seemed content with that. And at least Sophie was able to chat easily to the housekeeper. Six months ago and her observations would have been stiff and formal, but working at Poonbarra meant she could now identify with the housekeeper in a way which would have been unthinkable before. She had learnt how to mix with ordinary folk, she realised—and for that she must be grateful.

'Is everyone else here?' Rafe was asking.

'No. You're the first.' Bernadette closed the heavy oak door on the snowy night. 'Some of the others are flying in tomorrow. Your father's got the four-by-four so he'll be okay. And Sharla rang to say she's coming by helicopter, so she'll be here about midday.'

Sharla.

It was an unfamiliar name which sounded vaguely

familiar, but Sophie's interest was heightened by the sudden tension which had made Rafe's body stiffen. She glanced up to see a hardness distorting his taut features—and a darkening look which made him seem like a stranger.

But he *is* a stranger, she reminded herself fiercely. *You don't really know anything about him.* All they'd done had been to fall into bed where he'd made her feel stuff she hadn't thought she was capable of. *Made her long for things which were way out of her reach.*

A sense of unease whispered over her but she said nothing as they were shown up a grand staircase into an enormous bedroom, dominated by a king-size bed covered with a brocade throw in deep shades of claret and gold. Beside the bed, crimson roses glowed in a bronze bowl and, against huge windows, velvet curtains were drawn to blot out the snowy night. A huge crackling fire had been lit in the grate, scenting the air with the crackle of applewood, and the glitter of the flames was reflected in the overhead chandelier. The overall effect was almost medieval and Sophie unbuttoned her new coat and hung it up in the old-fashioned wardrobe before slowly turning round.

'Who's Sharla?' she questioned.

Rafe was reading something on his cell-phone and didn't look up as he answered. 'You've probably heard of her. She used to be a model.'

Wondering if his reply had been deliberately casual, Sophie nodded as she realised why she'd half recognised the name. Of course. How could she have overlooked that rare level of fame achieved when somebody was known simply by their first name? 'You mean *the* Sharla?' she questioned. 'The supermodel with the endless legs—the one who's married to the rock star?'

'That's the one.' He looked up then and the expression in his grey eyes was curiously flat. 'And just for the record, she isn't married to him any more.'

'Right.' She looked at him. 'But why is she here? I thought you said it was just family. A low-key affair.'

'She *is* family.' There was a pause. 'I told you. She's my sister-in-law Molly's twin, although I don't tend to think of her as family.'

She wondered how he *did* think of her. Why a sudden harshness had distorted his voice and why he'd tensed when Bernadette had mentioned the supermodel's name. But it was none of her business. She was here because they were supposedly doing each other a favour. And yes, they'd had sex on the plane, but that didn't mean anything—he couldn't have made that more apparent if he'd tried. He hadn't exactly pushed her away afterwards but he might as well have done. His attitude had been cool and distant. *Careless* might be the best way to describe it, as he'd tapped her bottom in that rather insulting way— which hadn't stopped her wanting his fingers to linger there a little longer. So did sexual intimacy give her the right to quiz him about his thoughts or his feelings? It did not.

She peeped out behind one of the heavy velvet drapes. The snow was coming down hard now—great drifts swirling down and covering the ground by the second. Rafe switched on one of the bedside lamps and the rich brocade of the counterpane was illuminated by a golden glow. Yet Sophie felt awkward as she watched him moving around the elegant room.

He looked so far away, she thought. Any closeness they had shared now seemed to have been forgotten. He hadn't touched her once in the car and now she was supposed to be sharing a room and a bed with him and she didn't have a clue how that was going to work. How any of this was going to work. What did other women usually do in this kind of situation? But she had wanted normality, hadn't she? Maybe now was the time to embrace it.

Pulling the band from her hair, she shook her ponytail free. 'What have you told them about me?'

'Nothing. I told my brother I was bringing someone, but that's all. They can find out who you are when they meet you.' His eyes gleamed. 'Given your great love of understatement, I thought you'd prefer no forewarning.'

'And they won't think it's odd that you've turned up with a runaway princess?'

He gave the ghost of a smile. 'I come from an unusual family, Sophie. Where the odd is commonplace and people break the rules all the time. They might remark on it but they certainly won't have their heads turned by it. And don't worry—people won't bother you or ask you predictable questions, if that's what you're concerned about. Now,' he added softly. 'It's late. Aren't you going to get ready for bed?'

His words sounded scarily informal, which seemed crazy when she remembered being pinned to the floor of the plane, her jeans trapped around her ankles. But that didn't prevent a sudden flash of nervousness as Sophie grabbed her wash bag and went into the bathroom. The clothes which Rafe had ordered to be delivered to the plane contained nothing as warm or practical as a nightshirt—but there was no way she was walking back out there naked. So she kept her knickers on and pulled a T-shirt over her head. Rafe's eyebrows rose when she returned and climbed quickly into bed, though he said nothing as he went into the bathroom himself.

She switched off the bedside lamp and lay shivering beneath the duvet, listening to the sounds of taps being run and teeth obviously being brushed. The minutes ticked by excruciatingly slowly before the bathroom light was eventually turned off and Rafe came back into the bedroom. But it was long enough for her to see that he had no similar qualms about nudity and the image of his powerful naked body seemed to burn itself indelibly onto the backs of her eyes.

His words filtered through the air towards her. 'Why are you hiding away in the darkness?'

'I'm not hiding.'

'Really?' A hint of amusement touched his voice. 'Are you suddenly turning shy on me, Sophie?'

'Of course not.' How could she tell him that this felt...*weird*? That she didn't want to leave the light on because she didn't know what to say or what to do. She wondered what had happened to the woman who'd been so uninhibited on the plane. Why she'd suddenly morphed into someone who was feeling swamped by hazy fears. The bed dipped beneath his weight and she held her breath as she heard the rustle of bedclothes.

'Maybe you're jet-lagged?' he suggested.

'I think I am, a little,' she said hopefully, because surely sleep would blot out the tension which was growing by the second and making even the tiniest sound seem amplified. Surely the best thing would be to close her eyes and pray for oblivion to come, so she could wake up in the morning refreshed and able to cope with what lay ahead.

But sleep didn't come. She lay there stiff and un-moving, terrified to move in case she rolled against his hard, warm body—wondering how she was going to get through a whole night like this—when a soft laugh punctured the semi-silence.

'I know you're not asleep.'

'How?' she questioned indignantly, before realis-ing that her answer had given the game away.

'Because you're trying to make your breathing sound regular and shallow and people don't really breathe like that when they're asleep.'

'I suppose you're an expert on women's breathing habits in bed?'

'I do have some experience.'

'I'll bet you do.'

And then his hand slid around her waist and So-phie froze.

'Just relax,' he said softly, as he cupped her breast with his other hand. 'Lie back and think of Isolav-erde.'

And unexpectedly, Sophie started to giggle. 'You're...*oh*!' His thumb grazed across her nipple and she swallowed. 'You're outrageous.'

'So they tell me. Now, isn't that better?' he said as his hand slid down over her belly, and then down further still. 'Why are you wearing knickers in bed? They're going to have to come off.'

'Rafe,' she said thickly.

'Shh. What did I just tell you?'

'I…d-don't remember.'

'Then try.'

He slithered the panties down over her thighs and, with his foot, kicked them away from her ankles. But he left the T-shirt on as his fingers returned to burrow in the tangle of hair at her groin before slipping down to find her molten heat. Now the only sound in the room was the increasing rise of her unsteady breathing. He didn't say a single word, just continued to touch her with a lightness and delicacy which was sending her out of her mind.

'Rafe,' she said again, only now an urgent desperation was making her voice crack.

'What?'

'I…*oh*!' Her nails dug into his shoulders. 'Oh, oh, *oh*!'

Her hips arching upwards, her body jerked with helpless spasms as he lowered his head to kiss her. She felt the honeyed rush of heat as reality splintered into countless unbearably bright pieces and then dissolved into a dreamy daze. Afterwards she lay there, sucking ragged breaths of air back into her lungs. She felt lazy. Luxurious. Heavy and wonderful—but as her eyelids began to grow weighty, some nagging notion of inequality made her stir. Peeling her lips away from where they were glued to his bare shoulder, she touched her fingertips to the rough rasp of growth at his jaw.

'You must show me how to…' She hesitated, too shy to say the words. Or maybe it was because she didn't know *how* to say the words, and maybe he guessed that.

'Pleasure me?'

She licked her dry lips. 'Yes.'

'Go to sleep, Sophie.' He sounded almost *kind* as he brushed away the lock of hair which had fallen over her cheek and dropped the briefest of kisses onto her nose. 'Just go to sleep.'

CHAPTER SEVEN

WHEN RAFE WOKE next morning it took him a minute to work out where he was—a habitual dilemma for someone who travelled the globe as frequently as he did. But usually he liked that sense of uncertainty. Transitory was his default setting. Most people were fearful of change but he wasn't one of them. It was the only thing he'd ever known.

He hadn't been lying when he'd dismissed Sophie's sympathetic words after he'd told her what a gold-digger his mother had been. It didn't hurt. How could something hurt if you had nothing to compare it with? Just as it didn't hurt that he'd always been pushed aside whenever the latest love interest had appeared in his glamorous parent's life. Why he'd spent school holidays in vast and empty hotel rooms, while his mother went out on the town. He'd learned to order room service and put himself to bed when there were no more cartoons on TV. He *had* learned to play the cards he'd been dealt and he'd done it by building a wall around his heart. At first the foundations had been rocky, because what did a small boy know about emotional protection and self-reliance, when it went against the natural order of things? But

the more you did something, the better at it you got—
and these days nothing touched him. His mouth hardened. *Nothing.*

He glanced around the bedroom, realising he was
in his brother's Cotswold home. Only then did he acknowledge the warm and sated feeling which came
after a night of particularly good sex. He turned his
head to find Sophie's side of the bed empty.

Lazily he stretched, his body hardening as he listened for sounds of running water or any suggestion
she might be tidying her hair in preparation for an
early morning kiss, but there was nothing. He bashed
one of the pillows with his fist and comfortably rearranged his head on it, thinking maybe it was better
this way. Better than her snuggling up close trying
to do that thing women always did after a night like
that—stroking their finger in a slow circle over his
belly and wondering what made him tick.

Because they had reached for each other in the
darkness before dawn—caught in that strange half-
world between waking and sleeping. Two naked bodies, doing what came naturally. He stared up at the
ceiling—at the fractured light and shadows cast by
the antique chandelier. Only it hadn't felt like that.
Her skin had been silky-soft and her body as warm as
soft candle wax you could mould with your fingers.
She'd felt so tight when he entered her.

Briefly, he closed his eyes. Almost as tight as the
first time. And she'd started saying things in Greek
as she came. Soft things. Things he didn't understand
but which instinctively made him wary—because
when a woman starting talking in that tone of voice
it usually meant trouble. He hoped her inexperience

didn't mean she'd started to misinterpret the impact of a powerful series of orgasms. He hoped he wasn't going to have to make it clear that it was a waste of time for her to develop *feelings* for him.

Pushing back the rumpled bedcovers, he got out of bed and walked over to the window, blinking a little at the starkness of the tableau outside. He spent so little time in England these days that he'd forgotten how beautiful the countryside could look in thick snow. For a moment he stood, transfixed by a landscape which was almost unrecognisable—the long drive and other familiar landmarks obliterated by a thick blanket of white. It must have been coming down all night long—and it was still snowing, great flakes of the stuff hurtling down from the sky. It was the kind of white-out you usually only found in a ski resort and Rafe's eyes narrowed as he took in the heavy clouds overhead. It wasn't the best day for a christening, not by any stretch of the imagination.

Sophie hadn't returned by the time he'd showered and dressed and it was after ten when he headed downstairs, where he could hear the sound of voices coming from the direction of the dining room. He walked along the long corridor, unprepared for the sight which greeted him.

Because it was Sophie who was the centre of attention—and not because she was behaving in a princessy kind of way. On the contrary. She was sitting cross-legged on the floor right next to another big glittering Christmas tree, and she was playing with his nephew. Against the sparkle of tinsel and the gleam of fairy lights, she lifted the baby high in the air before bringing him down towards her, rubbing her nose against his tummy and making him gurgle with delight as she made a squelchy sound. And sitting watching them, with an overwhelming look of pride on her face, was the baby's mother, Molly.

Rafe wasn't expecting the painful shaft of ice which speared its way through his heart as he stood watching her play with the baby—he was outside the charmed circle but had no desire to enter it. But maybe his breathing had altered fractionally or maybe he moved, because both women turned round and saw him. He saw the uncertainty which crossed Sophie's face as she lowered the baby to rest against her shoulder, but her uncertainty was quickly forgotten as she fielded the playful swipe of a chubby fist as the baby urged her to play on.

'Rafe!' said Molly, getting to her feet and coming towards him with open arms and a wide smile on her face. 'Here you are. Awake at last! How lovely to see you. And Sophie seems to have made a huge fan of Oliver as you can see for yourself.' She tilted her head. 'But you really are naughty—why didn't you tell us who you were bringing?'

Rafe felt his body grow tense, but he kept his smile bland. 'Because Sophie prefers to keep her status low-key, don't you, Sophie?' He sent her a mocking glance as he gave his sister-in-law a hug. 'And besides, I can see she's made herself perfectly at home. She has a knack of doing that. Where's Nick?'

'Gone to speak to the vicar and to investigate how bad the roads are. Nobody else has arrived and they're all supposed to be here soon.' Molly scooped the baby from Sophie's arms. 'Here, let me take him and put him down for a quick nap before all the fun starts. You've been brilliant with him, Sophie—thanks.'

'You're welcome,' said Sophie. 'He's absolutely gorgeous.'

'I know he is—although I'm heavily biased, of course!' Molly gave a wide smile. 'I must say, it makes a nice change to meet one of Rafe's girl-friends—we only ever get to read about them in the papers.'

But Sophie became aware of the silence which fell like an axe between them the instant Molly carried the baby from the room. She met the silvery glint of Rafe's shadowed gaze, wondering if she was imag-ining the unspoken undercurrents which suddenly made the atmosphere seem so hostile.

'I like your sister-in-law,' she said.

'I'm sure she'd be delighted to have the royal seal of approval.' His voice grew rough. 'But you didn't think it might be wise to wait for me before coming down to breakfast?'

From the way he was glowering at her, Sophie felt as if she were in the dock. Yes, she probably should have waited so they could come down to breakfast together, but she'd *needed* to get away from him this morning. Needed to get her head straight and her senses back to something like normality. She'd been terrified of being caught staring dreamily at him when he opened his eyes, which had been what she'd wanted to do. She'd wanted to stare at him and stroke her fingertips over his skin and never stop, because what had happened during the night had thrilled and scared her in equal measure. The sex had been...

She swallowed. It had been *unbelievable*. Different

from the first time and from the time on the plane. She hadn't known it could be like that. So dreamy. So close. Just as it was *supposed* to be…as if two people really had become one.

She remembered his arms wrapping around her and how unbearably excited she'd felt as he'd pulled her close. His kisses had been barely there at first— his mouth grazing over hers as if he had all the time in the world. As if he were exploring her in slow motion and bringing her to life—cell by delicious cell. And when at last he'd entered her, his penetration had been deep. So deep that she had gasped and murmured his name. But she'd murmured a lot of other stuff too, after he'd brought her to that seemingly endless orgasm which had left her feeling blindsided. Things she hadn't been planning to say but which had suddenly seemed to spring from her lips. Did he understand Greek? She sincerely hoped not. Or perhaps he did. Perhaps he'd guessed she'd been murmuring sweet nothings and that was why he was glaring at her in that accusatory way.

'I thought it might be easier if I introduced myself, rather than you having to explain it. Get the whole Princess thing out of the way.' She shrugged. 'I have to say that both Molly and your brother took it very much in their stride. And besides,' she added, when his expression still showed no sign of softening, 'I didn't want to disturb you. You were sleeping like a baby.'

'Really?' Dark brows arched upwards. 'You seem obsessed by babies.'

'I was playing with your nephew, Rafe,' she said, from between gritted teeth. 'That's what people do when they meet a baby for the first time. What am I supposed to have done which is so wrong?'

'Did you tell them why you were here?'

'Yes. I explained I was hiding from the press and you were helping me. Was that the right thing to say—or the wrong thing? Should I have run a list of correct responses before you? Perhaps you could have written me a few guidelines.'

But he was saved from having to answer by the return of Nick, his half-brother—who was brushing stray flakes of snow away from his face and hair.

Tall as Rafe and almost as eye-catching, Nick Carter had the same black hair and sculpted features as his brother. Sophie watched as the two men greeted each other.

'How are the roads?' Rafe asked.

'What roads? It's like a wasteland out there,' said Nick grimly. 'And I've just heard they've closed all the major airports.'

'You're kidding?'

'I wish I was. I haven't dared break the news to Molly.'

'Can't you postpone the service?'

'At this time of year? With non-stop carol services and a vicar who's run ragged?' Nick pulled a face. 'Fat chance. Which means most people aren't going to be able to get here in time. Just Dad and whoever his current squeeze is.'

'And Sharla, of course,' said Rafe, after a barely perceptible beat. 'She's coming by helicopter.'

Something in his tone alerted Sophie's senses again. Something which had started troubling her last night though she couldn't for the life of her work out what it was. *What wasn't he telling her? What was it about Sharla which was making him so edgy?* Or was she simply in danger of reading too much into a casual conversation because she wasn't used to being inside a private home like this? Sharla was probably as lovely as her twin sister—and Molly was a complete delight.

So she sat and chatted as Rafe ate buttered eggs and he and Nick drank their way through a pot of strong black coffee. And when Nick said he was going to speak to Molly, Rafe suggested to her that they go back upstairs. Sophie nodded, but her emotions were all over the place. He'd been very cool with her and she needed to remember that. To remind herself that he could be cold and curt, and it was only during sex that he seemed to show any emotion. But they weren't *real* emotions. She needed to remember that, too. Even she, with her laughable lack of experience, could work that one out.

Back in their room the bed had been made and a fresh fire lit in the grate. Someone had put a huge spray of seasonal holly in a jug on one of the window ledges—its spiky green leaves and scarlet berries contrasting with the dramatic whiteness of the snow outside. It looked beautiful, almost tranquil, but tranquil was the last thing Sophie was feeling as Rafe closed the door. She went straight over to the dressing table, sat down in front of the mirror and started to unpin her hair.

In the reflection of the glass, she saw him frown—as if her reaction wasn't what he'd been anticipating. He walked across the room and put his hands on her shoulders, starting to caress them in a way which instantly made her want to melt, but she forced herself to wriggle away.

'Don't,' she said.

'Really?'

She supposed it was an indication of his arrogance that the note of surprise in his voice sounded genuine. 'Yes, *really.*' Meeting his gaze in the mirror, she picked up the brush and began to attack her hair.

'You're bored with sex already?'

She gave a short laugh. 'Don't be disingenuous, Rafe. I'm sure there isn't a woman alive who wouldn't find you physically attractive but my emotions aren't something you can turn on and off, like a tap.'

'Why bring emotion into it?' he questioned carelessly.

'Well, what about simple manners, then?' She put the brush down and turned on him. 'You were cold and accusatory towards me downstairs, yet the minute we get back to the bedroom I'm supposed to fall straight into your arms?'

He seemed taken aback by her frankness. 'You seemed to be getting very cosy with my family.'

'So? Would you have preferred it if I'd been aloof? Don't you realise that's what people *expect* me to be? It was actually lovely to meet people who treated me normally. People I didn't have to put at ease, the way I usually do. Who didn't seem to *care* that I was a princess. What's your problem with that?'

'I just don't want them getting any false ideas about our relationship,' he growled.

'Oh, I wouldn't worry your head about that.' She gave a short laugh. 'I'm sure your attitude towards me will be enough to convince them that we have no lasting future. It's just a pity you're managing to ruin the present in the process. Great way to live your life.'

For a moment he stilled, as if he was going to object to her making such a personal comment, but he didn't. Instead his eyes narrowed. 'Is that what I'm doing?'

'Yes.' She could hear the powerful pounding of her heart as it slammed against her ribcage and knew she couldn't keep avoiding the question she was burning to ask. 'Tell me, do you and Sharla have some kind of history?'

There was a fraction of a pause.

'What makes you say that?'

'It was a simple question, Rafe. A yes or a no will do.'

Rafe heard the persistence in her voice as he looked into her luminous blue eyes. At those rosy lips, which were plump and parted. He could lie to her—of course he could. She'd told a few lies herself, hadn't she—so what would a few more matter? Except that their conversation on the plane had made him understand why she'd been so reluctant to reveal her identity. Even why her virginity had become a millstone around her neck—something which had been saved for a man who had ultimately chosen someone else. Maybe there had been some *justification* for those lies she had woven, but the same could not reasonably be said of him if he chose not to answer her question directly.

And surely he could give her the bare facts. He didn't have to give her chapter and verse.

'We were an item a long time ago.' He drew in a

deep breath. 'Over a decade ago, in fact, and it lasted less than a year.'

'And did you—?'

'No, Sophie,' he said, because he was discovering that some things *could* still hurt, no matter how deeply you buried them. That when you pulled them to the surface they could still seep like a dark stain over your skin. Still make you want to smash a frustrated fist against the nearest wall. 'That was a lot more than the yes or no you initially demanded and it's all you're going to get.'

He saw confusion on her face along with a softness which affected him even though he didn't want it to. And although he knew he should resist touching her when she was trying to unpick him like this, something made him override his instincts. Was it comfort he sought, or oblivion? Reaching out, he pulled her to her feet and brought her up close against his body, his hands cupping her buttocks so that she could feel the hardness of his erection. And she did. He could tell from the sudden dilation of her eyes and he half expected her to object as he bent his head to kiss her. To pull away and demand to know more about Sharla, because curiosity was part of human nature and women were far more curious than men.

But she didn't. Was she intuitive enough to guess that right then he needed her kiss, in the way a starving man needed food? Was that why her lips parted, as if silently begging him to crush them with his own? And why, when he did, she kissed him back with a hunger which matched his, as if realising that in this, at least, they were properly equal? His tongue laced with hers and he could feel the urgent rush of blood to his groin as he skated his palm down over her hips. 'Sophie—'

'Shh,' she said urgently, pushing her breasts hard into his chest, her breath hot against his. 'Just do it.'

The unexpected earthiness of her response only fuelled his spiralling hunger and Rafe tugged the cardigan over her head, not bothering with the tiny buttons. Granted access to the silky camisole beneath, he rubbed his palm over her hardening nipple and felt her shiver as she began tugging urgently at his belt. His mouth dried. She might be a novice, but she certainly wasn't shy. He liked the murmuring sound of approval she gave as she tugged down the zip of his jeans and wrapped her hand around his rock-hard shaft. But when she started to slide her fingers up and down, he gave a swift shake of his head to stop her.

Picking her up, he carried her over to the bed, his hands unsteady as he laid her down and pulled off the rest of her clothes. Curve after silken curve was revealed and he resisted the urge to let his fingers linger and caress her until they were both naked and warm beneath the duvet. He wanted to put his head in between her legs but he wanted to be inside her even more. Somehow he found a condom and although she seemed eager to take responsibility for the task, he shook his head.

'No,' he said. 'Let me do it. I don't trust myself if you put your hands anywhere near me when I'm in this state.'

Moments later and she was giving an exultant gasp as he thrust deep into her moist heat and that wild little sound set off something deep inside him. It kick-started a level of lust which grew and grew, threatening to blow him away. He did it to her hard and then he did it to her slow. He licked her skin and sucked on her flesh. He was on the very edge of control as he cupped her buttocks and drove into her, deeper and deeper and deeper. He never wanted it to end and yet for once he found he couldn't hold back any longer. His body stilled for one exquisite split-second before finally he began to jerk inside her.

Eventually he turned his head and looked at her lying back against the pillows, her eyes closed. His voice sounded as if he was speaking from a long way away.

'Did you come?'

'Yes.' Her eyelids fluttered open and she smiled. 'Didn't you notice?'

Rafe stared up at the ceiling. Not really. It had been... He shook his head. He thought a burglar could have walked in and ransacked the room and he doubted he would have noticed. What was it about Sophie Doukas, this woman who'd had sex just a handful of times who could *bewitch* him like this? Lifting his forearm, he forced himself to glance at his wristwatch and to ignore the renewed lust which was hardening his groin again. He yawned. 'I ought to go and help my brother clear the snow from the paths.'

'Can I help?'

He turned to look at her, propped up on one elbow, her glossy hair spilling down all over her bare shoulders and flushed face.

'You?' he said.

'Is that such an extraordinary proposition?'

'Are you serious?'

'Totally serious. What's the matter, Rafe—do

you think the Princess isn't capable of hard, physical work?' Her blue eyes gleamed. 'I travelled halfway across the globe to get to Poonbarra. Even you were surprised that I'd sailed across the Pacific. Shifting a little snow will be child's play.'

CHAPTER EIGHT

IT WAS EASY to be nonchalant about your lover's ex-girlfriend when he had just given you the most amazing orgasm, but not quite so easy once that euphoric blitz of hormones had subsided and you were confronted with the reality. And the reality was sitting right in front of her in church—an ex-girlfriend known as one of the most beautiful women in the world, and Sophie could instantly see why.

She tried to focus her attention on baby Oliver, who was swathed in a shawl of cobwebby white, and not stare at the eye-catching vision who was drawing her gaze like a magnet, but it was proving impossible. She'd seen pictures of Sharla, of course—who hadn't? You didn't get to command thousands of dollars a day without having a high profile, but nothing could have prepared her for actually seeing the supermodel in the flesh. Sophie had met some beautiful women in her time—indeed, her brother had dated a seemingly endless stream of them—but Sharla was in a league of her own. Sophie found herself thinking how weird it was that twin sisters with identical colouring could look so different. Molly was exceptionally pretty, with her strawberry-blonde hair, pale skin and wide green eyes—but Sharla took those same characteristics and turned them into something quite breathtaking.

Maybe it was the high maintenance of her appearance which made her so mesmerising, because she looked as perfect and as glossy as an airbrushed magazine photo. Unlike Molly, Sharla's hair was shot with highlights of deep gold and rippled down to her waist. And unlike Molly, her endless legs were enhanced by a tiny pair of leather shorts and black thigh-length boots. This bizarre combination was topped with an iconic Chanel jacket and a kooky hat, which was an explosion of black and dark pink feathers. It should have looked ridiculous for a family christening in a small country church and in a way it did—yet the overall effect was one of beauty and originality. In her ice-blue cashmere jacket and skirt, Sophie felt strait-laced and conservative in comparison.

She risked a glance at Rafe but, judging from his cold expression, it was difficult to believe that a little while ago he'd been making love to her. Back then he had been animated and alive but he now seemed to have been carved from a block of dark and unforgiving stone. The ebony material of his overcoat hugged the broad width of his shoulders and echoed the blackness of his hair. There was stuff going on— she could tell. Stuff to do with Sharla. And much as she had been longing to ask more questions about the relationship he'd had with the supermodel, Sophie had bitten them back. She'd sensed he would tell her only as much as he wanted to. That she should be careful how far she pushed him because his defences were up and she wasn't sure why.

She had seen the unfathomable look Sharla had

slanted him when she'd sashayed into the fairy-tale church with its high grey walls and flagstone floors. Was that a normal look for a former lover to give? Sophie didn't know. Would she, one day—in the unlikely event of ever running into Rafe Carter again—give him a similar look?

Apart from the godparents, the only other guest who had made it through the snow in time for the ceremony was Rafe's father, Ambrose, a towering man with greying hair and piercing eyes, which were very like those of both his sons. Sophie felt as if she was being given a glimpse of what Rafe might look like one day and she was unprepared for the wistful way that made her feel. Afterwards, as they crunched their way over the salt-sprinkled path back to the house, Ambrose confided in her that he'd recently called off his engagement to a young yoga teacher.

'I'm sorry to hear that,' said Sophie cautiously, not quite sure about the protocol of discussing romance with your lover's father. And people randomly confiding in her like this was something else she'd never encountered either, since normally her status kept her well away from idle chatter. It was yet another thing she was getting used to, along with sex straight after breakfast and sharing a shower with a man when you were both damp with melted snow and red-cheeked with exertion.

'Yes,' said Ambrose thoughtfully. 'I decided maybe I should throw in the towel and admit that, after four failed attempts, I'm just not husband material. I always thought marriage avoidance was more Rafe's bag than mine, but maybe I was wrong.' He shot her a mischievous smile. 'He hasn't ever brought a woman to a family function before and I'd be lying if I said I wasn't impressed that he's turned up with a beautiful princess.'

Sophie knew this was her opportunity to make light of her relationship with Rafe and tell his father she was only there because of circumstance, but something stopped her. She told herself it was pointless to start a conversation which would only generate curiosity and more questions, but wasn't the truth rather different?

Wasn't she enjoying being Rafe's lover and revelling in the fantasy while it lasted? Why end it before she needed to?

So she offered Ambrose no explanation about her role in his son's life. She didn't tell him that she had put her decisions about the future on hold. She simply smiled and said how pretty the house looked. And it did. The two Christmas trees glittered with rainbow fairy lights and somebody had lit tall red candles, which flickered all along a wide mantelpiece decked with garlands of greenery. Old-fashioned carols sung by a visiting group of singers provided just the right amount of nostalgia and Sophie watched Bernadette serving drinks and food—along with some young girls who must have been drafted in from the village to help.

She thought about the total lack of formality which existed here, despite the fact that Nick Carter was obviously a hugely successful man. It was nothing like her own home life back in Isolaverde. There was no procedure which had to be followed. No rigid timetable worked out to the nearest second. And best of all, she wasn't weighed down with the family jewels she was always expected to wear. She felt light. Free. Fulfilled. And more than a little wistful.

Her gaze strayed across the room to Rafe, thinking how gorgeous he looked as he stood next to the Christmas tree, deep in conversation with his father. She was doing her best not to think about the powerful body which lay beneath his charcoal suit. Just as she was trying not to constantly hover at his side, telling herself he wouldn't thank her for behaving like a *real* girlfriend. But once again she'd noticed the undeniable tension as Sharla had strutted up to him earlier, minus her hat and jacket, her perfectly toned arms glowing in the firelight. Whatever they'd said to one another had been brief but tense and there had been an angry glitter in the supermodel's eyes as she'd marched from the room afterwards, announcing that she needed to make a phone call.

Sophie saw Molly go over to Rafe and hold out his nephew towards him. But although Rafe gave an emphatic shake of his head, Molly wasn't having any of it and laughingly placed the baby in his arms. And it was as if someone had turned him to stone. The sudden tautness of his face and tension in his body sent a chill of apprehension down Sophie's spine. She looked at him uneasily. What was the *matter* with him? Did he really dislike babies so much that he couldn't even bear to hold one for a couple of minutes?

On the other side of the room, Rafe felt the baby wriggling against his chest and a dagger of pure pain lanced through his heart. His forehead was beaded with sweat and he felt an overwhelming desire to escape—even though on one level he could acknowledge the undeniable cuteness of his young nephew.

But that didn't take away the complicated feelings of regret and guilt which still raged inside him. It was the reason why he never held babies. Because it hurt. Because it made him remember and think, *what if*? Because, because, because…

Did Oliver sense his tension? Was that why the infant suddenly screwed up his little face, as if he was about to cry?

'Bounce him up and down a bit,' advised Ambrose, and Rafe shot him a silent look over the top of Oliver's curly hair.

'What do you know about dealing with babies?' he questioned, as he tried to replicate what he'd seen Sophie doing that morning. 'You certainly weren't around for any of your own. Do you remember the time you turned up unexpectedly and Chase thought you were the postman?'

'I know. I know. I hold my hands up to all accusations of being a bad father,' said Ambrose, with a sigh. 'I married too young and too often and behaved like a fool. But at least you've taken your time choosing a wife, which might mean you've got a better chance than I had.' He looked across the room. 'And she's very beautiful.'

Rafe froze as the door swung open, and as Sharla reappeared he thought about the things she'd said to him earlier. 'Sharla?' he demanded, his mouth twisting.

'No, not Sharla.' Ambrose snorted. 'Sharla's like one of those hothouse plants you see—requires constant maintenance and remains as unpredictable as hell. I'm talking about your blue-eyed princess, who, for all her upbringing, seems surprisingly normal.'

Rafe opened his mouth to say that Sophie wasn't 'his' anything, but something stopped him. He certainly wasn't in any position to be able to offer any definitive judgement of the Princess, but privately he found himself agreeing with Ambrose. She *was* surprising, that was for sure, and not just because she hadn't pulled rank—not once. Or because she'd amazed them all by shovelling her way through an icy bank of snow, wearing some of Molly's old ski clothes and an unflattering woollen hat. Or even because she was fast proving the most enthusiastic lover he'd ever known as her acrobatic feats in the shower a while back had proved. One who had, despite her inexperience, chipped away at his habitual cynicism and reawakened a sexual appetite which had been in danger of becoming jaded.

Oliver began to wriggle in his arms and as Rafe lifted him up in the air again the baby gave a gurgle of pleasure. Grey eyes not unlike his own met his and Rafe felt a powerful pang of something inexplicable as he stared at the newest member of the Carter family.

'Ever thought about having children of your own?' questioned Ambrose, with a sideways look.

'No,' said Rafe as Oliver's chubby little fingers strayed towards his face, seemingly fascinated by the tiny cleft in his chin which all the Carter men carried.

'Or thought about who you're going to leave your fortune to if you don't have children of your own?' Ambrose continued.

Rafe stared down into the baby's trusting eyes, trying to ignore the sudden ache in his heart. 'There are countless charities who will be glad to benefit from my wealth.'

'But that isn't the same thing,' said Ambrose. 'Believe me when I tell you that it all boils down to flesh and blood. And that, in the end, nothing else matters.'

The sudden reedy quality in his father's voice made Rafe realise that the old man was thinking about the end of his own life and it was a sobering thought. He reflected on Ambrose's words during the champagne toast and the cutting of the cake afterwards. It had never particularly bothered him to think that he would not pass on his own genes, but suddenly a wave of emptiness and futility swept over him. Would he one day stand in a room like this, as his father was doing? Only the difference would be that he wouldn't have adult children of his own. He would be standing there protected by the icy shell he had constructed—a lonely old man with nobody to leave his vast fortune to.

The walls seemed to be closing in on him and he found himself walking across the room to where Sophie stood, chatting to one of the godparents. Sliding his arm round her waist, he manoeuvred her away from the conversation, wanting the oblivion-giving warmth of her body to chase away some of these damned demons.

'Come upstairs,' he said, his lips close against her scented hair.

She drew back, eyebrows raised. 'Won't people miss you?'

'Now.'

Sophie hesitated, thinking how autocratic he sounded—and wondering if he always got his own way. But why refuse to accompany him just to make a point? She'd had enough of meeting the occasional baleful stare from Sharla, even though the model had been nothing but steely politeness when they'd been introduced.

She didn't say another word until they were back in their room and she pulled the pashmina from her neck, letting it flutter into a pale blue heap on a nearby chair. 'So why the sudden masterful display of bringing me up here before the party's properly ended?' she questioned. 'Was that all for Sharla's benefit?'

'For Sharla's benefit?' He frowned. 'What's that supposed to mean?'

Sophie stared out of the window, at the black snake of the newly shovelled driveway she'd helped clear, before meeting Rafe's shuttered gaze. 'I don't have any ex-lovers to base my hunch on but I've been observing people for as long as I can remember.' She sucked in a deep breath. 'And for someone you split up with such a long time ago, there seemed a lot of underlying *stuff* going on between you both. What did she say to you downstairs?'

'That's none of your business.'

'I thought you might say that. What's the matter, Rafe—are you still in love with her?'

He clenched his fists. 'In love with Sharla?' he demanded hotly. 'Are you out of your mind?'

'What, then?' she persisted. 'Because there's *something* there.'

'Something? Yeah, you could say that.' He took a step towards her. 'You want to know what she said? Do you? Would it make you feel better if I told you that she made it very clear she'd like to be back in my bed again?'

She flinched. 'And that's all?'

How many more questions was she going to ask? Rafe wanted to tell her to mind her own damned business or maybe silence her with a kiss. But Ambrose's words and the memory of the baby who'd been wriggling in his arms had loosened the floodgates he'd kept in place for so long. Too long. He gave a bitter laugh as he removed his tie with a violent tug and slung it at a nearby chair. 'You want the truth about my relationship with her?'

He saw the faint concern which clouded her eyes before she nodded. 'Yes,' she said quietly. 'Yes, I think I do.'

She sank down on one of the armchairs by the blazing fire and looked up into his face. And although the idea of sharing confidences was alien to him, something told him he could trust Sophie. He sensed she could be properly discreet as her upbringing had taught her to be, but it was more than that. Something strong and sure was shining from her blue eyes to cut through his usual icy reserve. But as that reserve melted, he could feel the heaviness in his heart—so painful and tight in his chest that it was hurting him just to breathe. If he'd thought the years might have lessened the sorrow then he'd been wrong. So maybe it really *was* time he talked about it, instead of letting it gnaw away inside him, like some dark cancer.

He drew in a ragged breath. 'My brother Nick was going out with Molly for years before they married, and I first met Sharla at a party when we were in our early twenties. I'd left university and was a couple of years into my telecommunications business and she'd already done several magazine covers. My career was taking off and so was hers. In many ways it was a very satisfactory relationship.'

'Satisfactory?' she echoed cautiously. 'That's an odd word to use.'

'I can't think of a better one. I was young and horny and she was hot. I thought we were both giving the other what they most needed.'

'You mean sex?' she questioned baldly.

'I mean sex,' he echoed as he stared at her. 'Sorry if that offends your sensibilities, Sophie—but that's the truth.'

He watched her teeth digging into her bottom lip, as if she might be having second thoughts about hearing this, and maybe this was his opportunity to stop and change the subject. But he was on a roll now and the words were streaming out of that dark place inside him, where he'd buried them all those years ago. 'Right from the start I was honest with her. I said that if she was looking for permanence—for babies and wedding bells—then she should look elsewhere,' he said. 'We both had worlds to conquer and we were both so young. I remember she laughed when I told her the door was open any time she chose to walk away. But she didn't.'

There was silence as he stared at her, but she didn't break it—she just carried on looking at him with those bright blue eyes. And now the flood of dark memories were swamping him in a foul tide.

'One day she came to me and asked whether I'd ever consider changing my mind. Whether I thought I could love her or think about marrying her. To be honest, I was confused. I thought we understood one another. I asked why she was saying all this stuff and I remember the look on her face. The way she said, *A woman needs to know these things, Rafe.* And because I thought she was being practical and because I knew the rock star was pursuing her, I told her no, and that if she wanted commitment, she was free to go and find it with someone else. And then...'

His voice faltered. With shock? Or surprise? That he, who had always tried to distance himself from the conflict of relationships, had become an unwilling victim of one and as a consequence was plagued by a guilt and bitter regret which wouldn't seem to go away?

'What, Rafe?' she whispered, her soft voice carrying across the room towards him. 'What happened?'

He swallowed and it felt as if a ball of barbed wire were trying to force its way down his throat. 'She was carrying my baby,' he said. 'But she never told me that. She didn't give me the chance to change my mind, or come to some mutual agreement which would have worked for us all. I didn't know and I didn't find out. At least, not until afterwards, when she told me what she'd done.'

'Oh, no.' Her face blanched as the true meaning of his words sank in. 'Oh, Rafe.'

'Yes.' He looked at her quite calmly and then his voice broke. 'She killed my baby.'

Sophie's heart squeezed painfully as she heard the rawness in his voice and she wanted to jump up from the chair and wrap her arms tightly around him. To stroke his ravaged face with all the tenderness she possessed until some of his unbearable grief had subsided. But something held her back, some bone-deep instinct which told her to go easy around this damaged man. He had confided in her. Had told her the dark secret it was clear still haunted him. Wasn't it enough to be understanding and kind and calm? Not go over the top with an emotional response which would help no one, least of all him.

'I'm so sorry,' she whispered.

'Yeah. Me, too.' He swallowed before rasping out the next words. 'I would have supported her. Provided for her. Even married her. Done any damned thing she might reasonably have wanted. But I never got the chance.'

'Because you were powerless,' she said slowly. 'A man always is in a situation like that. She didn't want you to know and there was nothing else you could have done. You answered her questions truthfully because you didn't know why she was asking them.'

'And maybe I should have guessed,' he said bitterly.

'But you didn't have that kind of relationship, did you? It was supposed to be upfront and honest, but that only works if both parties want the same thing. Was that around the time you left England?'

He nodded. 'I couldn't wait to get away. To leave the old, tainted life behind me. I went to Australia and started a new life there. I set up offices in Brisbane and bought the cattle station. I just happened to be in the right place at the right time—because the country was ripe for new technology. The money started pouring in and the work provided a distraction, but whenever I could I would spend any spare time I had at Poonbarra, working on the land.'

It must have been a kind of escape for him, thought Sophie, to muster those cattle and build those fences. To toil and sweat beneath the fierce and unforgiving sun. A new life, far away from the pain of the old one. Just as it had been for her.

She guessed that was why he'd rarely returned to England and why he hadn't seen much of his family over the years, because the chance of running into Molly's twin must have filled him with horror. She thought about what he'd said about his mother. Women hadn't done right by Rafe Carter, had they? No wonder he'd stayed away from commitment and why he regarded them as nothing more than sexual playthings.

But today he had confronted all the darkness of his past. Did that mean he had drawn a line in the sand and could finally leave it behind? 'Rafe—'

'No.' His voice was harsh now. 'I don't want to talk about it any more, Sophie. Do you understand?'

Oh, she understood, all right. How could she fail to? She nodded as he began to walk towards her and knew from the dark look on his face that he wanted to take out his pent-up anger and frustration on her and just how he intended to do it. Was he treating her as a convenience, using her to blot out the bitter memories of what another woman had done to him, and shouldn't she object to that? Yet the moment he pulled her into his arms and kissed her, she didn't care. Who cared if his passion was fuelled by anger? Was it so wrong to want him this badly?

She acknowledged the brutal hardness of his kiss, but when her hands reached up to cradle his head, he groaned and softened it. He unzipped her skirt so that it pooled around her ankles and she stepped out of it and pulled at his trouser belt, as intent on quickly removing his clothes as he was hers. But she could feel something deep in her heart being tugged as he drew her against his naked body. Some stupid little ache that made her long for something more than the satisfaction of the physical.

The rug in front of the blazing fire wasn't particularly soft but Sophie didn't care about that either. All she could feel was the warmth from the flames licking over their bare skin as their bodies met. Wordlessly she moved over him, straddling him. She could feel the hard bones of his hips against the softness of her thighs—and he felt very big as she brought him deep inside her. They'd never done it in this position before and her initial tentativeness was instantly banished by the smoky look of pleasure on his face as he filled her. He spread his fingers over her breasts and played with her hardened nipples as she rode him with a total lack of inhibition. And when her body began to tighten with the now familiar shimmerings of orgasm, his hands anchored her so that he went deeper still until she gasped out loud, in Greek.

She must have drifted off to sleep because when she opened her eyes, it was to find that Rafe had covered them with a blanket and his naked body was pressed against her bare back. For a moment she just revelled in the feel of his warm flesh next to hers and the way he'd slung his arm over her hips, so that his fingertips rested carelessly in the cluster of curls at her thighs. She remembered the things he'd told her about his past. The way he'd unburdened himself. Did it mean something that he'd chosen to confide in her, or was she in danger of reading too much into the situation? No matter. The future could wait. Lying there together like that was just about perfect and as she stirred a little she could feel his hand automatically begin to drift downwards, when there was a loud banging at the bedroom door.

'Rafe?' It was Nick's voice.

'Go away,' Rafe mumbled, his breath warm against the back of her neck.

'I need to speak to you. *Now.*'

Cursing a little beneath his breath, Rafe got to his feet and pulled on a pair of jeans, still doing up the zip as he walked over and opened the door, behind which his half-brother was standing. He didn't invite him in and Sophie couldn't hear what was being said—only the low murmur of their voices before Rafe quietly closed the door and came back into the room.

She looked up into his face, but if she'd been hoping for some new kind of openness after the things they'd talked about, then she'd been way off mark because his features were as dark and as unreadable as ever. 'Is something wrong?'

'You could say that.' His voice sounded grim. 'My brother's had a phone call from the landlord of the local pub. The snow has started to melt and a man and woman have checked in. He thinks they may be journalists.'

She sat up, clutching onto the blanket. 'How—?'

He shrugged. 'I suspect Sharla let them know you're here—inadvertently or not, I don't know. The question is how we deal with it.'

Sophie shook her head. 'There's only one way

to deal with it and I can't keep avoiding it for ever. There's no point in me trying to concoct another life—it won't make any difference. And maybe it's time to stop running.' She clutched the blanket a little tighter to her breasts. 'To let Myron know I'm a grown-up now and can make my own decisions. To tell him that I need to forge a new future for myself.'

His eyes narrowed. 'And do you know what that future will be?'

'Not yet. I'd just hoped…'

'Hoped what?' he questioned as her words tailed away.

She shrugged. 'I don't know. After my fairly successful stab at independence, it's a pity I have to return being pursued by the press. I'd hoped to make a more…*controlled* arrival.'

'Unless you refuse to play ball,' he said slowly.

'What do you mean?'

'Why *should* the damned press back you into a corner?' he demanded. 'Why go back earlier than originally planned?'

'That was pretty much on the cards the minute you returned unexpectedly to Poonbarra. I don't really have any alternative, Rafe. I can't stay here. And I can't face the thought of turning up somewhere else just before Christmas, with a load of news-hungry journalists on my tail.'

There was a pause. 'Unless you came to New York with me for Christmas.'

Sophie tried to squash the leap of hope in her heart as she met his shadowed gaze. 'But you must have plans?'

'None I can't get out of. The only thing set in stone

is my Boxing Day ski trip to Vermont. But New York is the most anonymous city in the world and I can have my PR people make sure nobody bothers you.'

'I don't know,' she said, even though she was filled with an excitement she was trying very hard to contain.

'The city is beautiful during the holidays,' he continued softly. 'And I think there's a lot more sex we need to have before I'm willing to let you go. I'm not offering you a home, Sophie—as long as you understand that. Just a temporary shelter.'

Her smile didn't falter, even though the baldness of his statement left her in no doubt of his feelings for her. But surely it was better to know exactly where she stood. And he was offering her a solution, wasn't he? Practical help in the form of a Christmas break in a city she'd never visited, rather than a scandal-wrapped return to her island home. There was no contest, really.

'I'd like that,' she said.

'Good. In that case, I'll have my jet prepared.' His eyes gleamed as he unzipped his jeans and started walking towards her. 'And in the meantime…why don't you lose the blanket?'

CHAPTER NINE

THIS HIGH UP, the snowy winter light was on the harsher side of bright. A penthouse apartment high in the sky—far above the streets and away from the sounds of the New York traffic. Chosen specifically for its isolation and for the fact that nobody could see you, or hear you. An apartment Rafe had never shared with anyone.

Until now.

He stared at Sophie's back, silhouetted against the Manhattan skyline as she watched the ant-like people far below. His home, his space, his *life*. A fortress of a place which up until now had always been inviolate. People came here rarely because hospitality on home turf had never been his thing. He preferred to take people out to dinner, rather than be stuck with guests who wouldn't take the hint and go home. The same with lovers, too. Not for him the awkward morning ritual of trying to remove a woman who wanted to stay.

Why *had* he invited Sophie here? He ran his gaze over the gleam of her bare legs. Because he felt partly responsible for the arrival of the press in the Cotswolds? Yes. And the sexual chemistry between them had been an added incentive. Why turn his back on a physical compatibility which was as good as theirs? But it was more than that. He'd confided in her. Told her stuff he'd never told anyone else. Stuff which had stirred up feelings inside him which had left a raw and gaping void. He'd thought exposing his secrets would make the darkness go away, but he had been wrong. He told himself he just needed time. And that maybe having Sophie here with him was nothing but an insurance policy. A charm offensive to get her onside and make sure she kept those secrets close to her heart.

He acknowledged another stir of lust as she shifted her weight from one leg to the other. This morning she was wearing one of his shirts which came to just below her bottom as she surveyed the cityscape. One hand was planted on her hips as she watched the snow tumbling towards the city streets. It was a pose designed to show off her long legs to their best advantage—something he suspected she knew very well, despite her relative inexperience. But she was a fast learner, he thought approvingly. She'd learnt to remove her clothes and tantalise him better than any of those high-class strippers he knew rich out-of-towners visited down on Midtown West.

His groin throbbed with a relentless beat as he walked over to her and slid his arms around her waist, lifting aside the still-damp curtain of dark hair to plant a lingering kiss at the base of her neck.

'Good swim?' he murmured.

'Fifty lengths—and all I had to do was take the elevator.'

'That's the beauty of having a pool in the basement.'

'Yes. Rafe,' she added indistinctly as he cupped his hands over her breasts and began to massage them through the cotton of her shirt. 'You do realise I'm standing in front of the window?'

'I do. And you're nineteen floors up.'

'Somebody might have a pair of binoculars.'

'The glass is mirror-coated,' he said, moving one hand down. 'Which means nobody gets to see—although, if it turns you on, you can always pretend someone is watching me slide my hand down between your legs and easing you open like this.'

'You are...' she gasped as he slipped his finger inside her '...incorrigible.'

'Am I?' He moved his finger against her, loving the way her head fell helplessly back against him, the scent of her sex heavy in the air as he brought her to a shuddering climax right where she stood. He felt the buckling of her knees as she slumped back against him and thought about carrying her over to the sofa. But she was nothing if not surprising because she quickly gained her equilibrium and turned around, her face flushed and a small smile on her lips as she ran the flat of her palm experimentally over his groin.

'Oh,' she said, digging her teeth into her bottom lip almost shyly as she explored the hard and throbbing ridge covered by the denim of his jeans. 'I see. You are a *very* excitable man, aren't you, Rafe Carter?'

He gave a low and exultant laugh. 'Is that what I am?'

'Among other things.'

The rasp of his zip sliding down was the only

sound other than his ragged breathing as she sank to her knees in front of him and teased him with her fingers, before putting the moist tip against her lips.

'Sophie,' he groaned as her tongue gave a playful lick.

Sophie lowered her lips onto him, loving the sensation of sucking this most intimate part of him. She liked having the silken thickness of him deep in her mouth, just as she liked tasting that first salty bead of moisture which showed he was close to climax. He'd taught her so much. About her body. About his. Sometimes she wished she could grab hold of time and freeze it because the clock was ticking down towards Christmas and once the holiday was over, she'd be far away from here. From him.

But her thoughts were forgotten as his hands clamped around her head and his fingers dug into her scalp as his excitement grew. She could feel him tense and hear that distinctive choking sound he made, just as he flooded her mouth and she drank him in.

She opened her eyes and looked up to find him staring at her and she slid her tongue slowly over her lips, which were still sticky with his salty essence. His eyes darkened but his hands were gentle as he pulled her to her feet and led her into the huge wet room adjoining his bedroom, where he turned on the warm jets of the shower.

'Where do you want to go for lunch?' he questioned, slicking thick soapy foam over her body.

'I'd love to go to that lovely restaurant in Gramercy again.'

'Then that's where we'll go.'

'Won't you need to book?'

His smile was wolfish as he sluiced suds from her skin, paying specially close attention to her thrusting nipples. 'I never need to book.'

Overlooking a snowy courtyard garden, the restaurant was exquisite and afterwards they went to an art gallery in Chelsea where a friend of Rafe's was exhibiting his sculptures. Sophie drank champagne and chatted with the artist and decided she liked New York, a city where it was possible to blend in and lose yourself. She liked it nearly as much as Poonbarra. Her heart missed a beat. The two places which had felt most like home had one thing in common.

Him.

She glanced across the gallery, where Rafe was standing studying a sculpture, his thumb rubbing thoughtfully at his chin while close by a striking-looking blonde in a mulberry-coloured velvet coat was trying to catch his eye.

Sophie thought about how it would be once she had returned to Isolaverde. That one day soon, this blonde—or someone like her—wouldn't just be chatting to Rafe about a marble figure, but would be accompanying him back to his gorgeous penthouse, to do to him what Sophie had been doing earlier. A sickening image sprang to her mind—of somebody else unzipping his jeans. Somebody else taking him so intimately into her mouth…

Sophie's heart clenched as she put her glass down on the tray of a passing waitress and waited for the feeling to pass. But these pangs of longing and possession had been getting more and more frequent as the days had ticked by. Was it sexual jealousy she was experiencing, or something else? Something she was too scared to acknowledge because it was as futile as expecting the sun to rise at midnight. That her feelings for Rafe were becoming more complicated than either of them would ever have anticipated.

Far more than he would ever have wanted.

She wondered if he'd noticed her attitude towards him softening, or whether she'd managed successfully to hide her growing feelings. She suspected he would push her away if he got an inkling she'd started to care for him in a way he had warned her against, right from the start.

She tried to pinpoint when her attitude had slid from lust into tenderness and then into a wistful longing for a future which could never be hers. Was it when he'd protected her from the press and continued to protect her, here in his adopted city? Or when he'd made love to her and shown her that sex could be about tenderness as well as hot, hard passion? She swallowed.

No. She knew exactly when it had been. When he'd opened up his heart and told her about the baby he'd lost and she'd seen the raw pain on his face and heard the bitter heartbreak in his voice. In that moment he had revealed a vulnerability she'd never associated with a man like him, and that had changed everything. And she didn't want it to change.

Because she couldn't afford to fall in love with Rafe Carter.

On Christmas morning, Sophie woke first—slipping from the bed and disappearing into one of the dressing rooms before starting to busy herself in the kitchen. She gave a smile of satisfaction as she cracked the first eggshell against the side of the bowl. Six months ago and she hadn't known one end of a frying pan from the other and now she made the best omelette in Manhattan. Well, that was what Rafe said. She was humming beneath her breath when he came out of the bedroom in just a pair of boxers, the hand which had been raking back his mussed hair suddenly stilling.

He ran his gaze over her. 'Sweet heaven. What's this?'

She did a twirl. 'You don't like it?'

Rafe felt a shaft of lust arrowing down to his groin. She was like every male fantasy come to life and standing in front of him, wearing a short baby-doll nightdress in scarlet silk, trimmed with fake white fur. The tiny matching knickers—which showed as she moved—were the same bright red and a Santa hat was crammed down over her dark hair. 'Santa, baby,' he murmured. 'Come here.'

'It's my Christmas present to you,' she said, walking over to loop her arms around his neck. 'Because I couldn't think what else to get you. The man who has everything.'

'Best gift I've ever had,' he said unevenly. 'Which I'm now about to unwrap.'

The eggs were cold by the time they got around to eating them and afterwards they walked through the snow to Central Park, going by Grand Army Plaza and ending up in Bryant Park. Sophie's cheeks were glowing by the time they got back and Rafe made steak and salad. They ate their meal beside the tiny Christmas tree they'd put together with decorations bought from Bergdorf Goodman And when they'd cleared away the dishes, he handed her a curved package, wrapped in holly-covered paper.

'Happy Christmas, Sophie,' he said.

Her fingers were trembling as she opened it and, even though it was probably the most inexpensive gift she'd ever been given, she couldn't remember receiving anything which had given her quite so much pleasure. It was a snow globe. A miniature version of the Rockefeller Christmas tree, which he'd taken her to see the moment his jet had touched down in the city. She shook it and the rainbow sparkle was momentarily obscured by the thick white swirl of flakes.

'Oh, Rafe,' she said, trying not to let emotion creep into her voice. 'It's...beautiful.'

'To remind you of New York,' he said. 'When you're back in Isolaverde.'

'Yes.'

The word fell between them like a heavy stone. What was it going to be like? she wondered and now the pain in her heart was very sharp. It wasn't settling back into life as a princess after all this that she was worried about—it was the thought of not having Rafe which was making her feel so utterly wretched. She tried to imagine waking up in the morning and him not there beside her and she thought how quickly you could get used to something, which had been the very best thing in your life.

'Have you considered what you're going to do?' His question cut into her troubled thoughts. 'Are you going to be content spending your days cutting ribbons and pulling curtains away from little bronze plaques?'

'No. I've realised that things are going to have to be different.' She forced herself to think about her royal life. A life which was a whole world away. 'I don't just want to be a royal clothes horse any more. I want to do more behind-the-scenes work with my charities, and I'm going to have to work out some kind of satisfactory role for myself.'

'That's the professional Sophie talking,' he said. 'But what about the personal one?'

She stared at him. 'What do you mean?'

'Isn't it obvious? Has what happened with Luc scarred you? Or do you want to meet someone one day and marry them, and have children of your own?'

She shifted her position on the sofa, flinching as if he had scraped his fingernails over an open wound. She realised that nobody had ever asked her such a bluntly personal question before because nobody would ever have dared. And somehow his words got to her. They made her want the impossible and the resulting pain was so deep that she spoke straight from the heart.

'Of course I want that. Most women do,' she admitted quietly, her cheeks colouring a little, because she realised there was only one man she wanted to do that with and he was right in front of her. 'But there are all kinds of obstacles to that happening so it's unlikely I'll ever get it.'

'What kind of obstacles?'

She chose her words carefully. 'Well, meeting a man is fraught with difficulties. It would really only work if I married someone suitable and the pool of eligible princes isn't exactly big.' She could feel her skin colouring as she stared at the tumbling snowflakes outside the window. 'Anyway, that's all in the future, which starts tomorrow. Because tomorrow's Boxing Day and while I'm heading for the Mediterranean, you'll be hurtling down the side of some snow-covered mountain in Vermont. Lucky you. You hadn't forgotten, had you?'

'No, I hadn't forgotten,' he said, turning her face towards his so that his silver gaze was on a collision course with hers. 'But right now, the thought of skiing is less appealing than taking you back to bed for the rest of the day.'

'Making the most of the few hours we have left, you mean?' she questioned brightly.

'No. Not just that.'

His voice had hardened and Sophie screwed up her nose in confusion. 'What, then?'

Rafe shook his head. He'd tried to blot it out. To make like it didn't matter, but he was discovering that this new yearning deep inside him *did* matter. And maybe it would always matter unless he did something about it. *So do it. Do it now.* He cleared his throat. 'What if I came up with an alternative solution? Something which meant you wouldn't have to go back to your old life. A solution which might suit both our...*needs*?'

She stared at him. 'I don't understand.'

'Then hear me out.' He paused. 'I've been doing some thinking. In fact, a lot of thinking. About something Ambrose said to me at the christening.'

He met the question in her blue eyes as the enormity of what he was about to do hit him and his heart clenched with something like pain as he realised he was on the verge of doing what he'd spent his life trying to avoid. But even the fear wasn't enough to stop him. He remembered holding his little nephew. The warmth and milky smell of him. The curly hair which had brushed against his cheek. Most of all, he remembered the sudden rush of yearning which had flooded through him and the realisation that having a child would be the only way he could heal the scars of his past. 'My father asked who I was going to leave my fortune to and I told him that I was planning for it to go to charity,' he said. 'But in that moment I realised that I wanted what I'd never had.'

'I don't understand,' she whispered.

There was another pause before he said it. Words he knew would create a line in the sand which he could never step back from.

'A family,' he said. 'A real family.'

She leaned forward, her hand reaching out to take one of his. 'Tell me,' she whispered.

And suddenly Rafe needed no prompting. He felt her fingers curling around his. Heard the loud beat of his heart. And the words just came tumbling out. 'Although come from a big family, I grew up not knowing my brothers or sister. My father kicked my mother out because of her behaviour and as a consequence, she and I were estranged from the rest of the Carter clan for years.'

'Because of her behaviour?'

His mouth twisted. 'Just how open-minded are you prepared to be, Sophie? How easily do you shock? My mother liked men. She liked them a lot. More than anything else.' There was a pause and his mouth flattened. 'Much more than me.'

'Oh, Rafe.'

He shook his head to silence her. 'After her divorce, she wasn't looking for a replacement husband because her divorce payment had set her up very nicely. Her idea of fun was having the freedom to ensnare some hot young lover.'

She nodded, as if she was absorbing his words. 'And what happened to you, while she was doing that?'

He shrugged. 'I used to sit alone in hotel suites,' he said. 'Watching as she appeared in the tightest dress she could get away with—usually with her second or third martini in her hand. Sometimes she would come back that night, but often she didn't rock up until the morning. I can't count the number of strange men I encountered the next day amid the empty champagne bottles and cigarette butts.' His words grew reflective. 'Most kids hate being sent away to boarding school, but you know something? I loved it because it was safe and ordered and structured. It was the holidays I dreaded.'

'Of course you did,' she said, her gaze meeting his. 'But why are you telling me all this?'

He didn't look away, just stared straight into her bright, blue eyes. 'Because when I held Nick and Molly's little boy in my arms, I realised what I'd been missing. I realised I wanted what I'd never had. A family of my own.' His voice deepened. 'And I think I could have one with you.'

Sophie's heart began to pound, not sure whether to feel elated or confused. Dared she hope that *his* feelings had been changing, too? Was he hinting at the kind of future she had secretly started to wish for? Oh, please, she prayed. Please. 'Me?'

He nodded. 'Yes, you. You told me you'd like a family one day, well, so would I. You told me all the reasons that might not happen and I'm giving you all the reasons why it could. I can't offer you love, but maybe that isn't necessary since you are obviously a pragmatic woman. You told me you didn't love Luc but you obviously recognise that arranged marriages can and do work.'

'Did you say marriage?' she echoed cautiously.

'I did,' he agreed, and now his voice deepened. 'Because I can't see that it could happen any other way.'

'You would marry me simply to achieve your dream of having a family?'

'Your dream, too,' he pointed out. 'And no, not just that. There are plenty of other reasons why it could work. We are compatible in many ways, Sophie— you know we are.'

Sophie was so appalled by how badly wrong she'd got it. She'd been thinking about love and clearly he was focussed on sex. 'In bed, you mean?'

'Yes, in bed. I have never wanted a woman as much as I want you. I only have to look at you to... well, you know what happens to me when I look at you.' He smiled. 'But this is about more than sex. You don't bore me or rely on me to entertain you. And if you agree to marry me, I will promise to be faithful to you—of that I give you my vow. To be a good husband and a good father to our children. To support you in whatever you want to do.' His eyes were as bright as quicksilver as they burned into her. 'So what do you say? Will you be my wife, Sophie?'

It was a big question and Sophie knew the importance of taking your time with big questions, just as she knew you should never let your expression give away what was going on inside your head.

She'd often thought a royal upbringing would have been great preparation for a career as a professional poker player and, although she'd never been remotely tempted by gambling, she was able to draw on those skills now.

So she hid her bitter disappointment that there had been no breakthrough in Rafe's emotions. Was she deluded enough to think he'd started to care for her, just because her own feelings had started to change? Hadn't he told her right from the start that he didn't *do* love? Now she knew more about him, she could see why. She could understand his trust issues and the reason why he'd never settled down. His childhood sounded grim and the cushion of his parents' wealth had probably made it worse. If he'd been abandoned by his mother and left to fend for himself in some grimy tenement block, the authorities would have stepped in and acted. But in the protected air-conditioned world of the luxury hotel suite, nobody would have even known.

And then there had been another betrayal—an even greater one, by Sharla. Wouldn't a child of his own help him get over that terrible loss?

She looked into his grey eyes. He had vowed to be faithful and she believed him. He wouldn't do what Luc had done and lose his heart to someone else. During his own childhood, he'd seen the devastation that infidelity could wreak and he wouldn't want to replicate that. He'd never had a chance to create a family unit of his own and yet that was what he yearned for above all else. This powerful man with so much wealth at his disposal wanted nothing more than a baby.

And so did she.

His baby.

Why *shouldn't* an arranged marriage work? Some people considered romantic love to be an unrealistic ideal and maybe they were right. The marriage of her own parents had been arranged, and theirs had been a long and happy union. Why couldn't she have that with Rafe—and all the things which went with it? The companionship and the sex, and the feeling safe. Better no love than pretend love, surely? And sometimes love could grow...

She looked at him. 'But what would I do—as your wife?'

His grey eyes gleamed. 'You can do what the hell you want, Sophie. Just think about what you achieved on Poonbarra.'

'You mean I progressed from being unable to recognise a tin-opener to making a pie which apparently you described to Andy as "ordinary"?'

He laughed. 'He wasn't supposed to tell you that. I just don't like pie. But you're capable of anything you want to be.'

And it was that which swung it for Sophie. It was the same feeling which had come over her when she'd looked up at the stars, on that ocean-going yacht travelling out to Australia. That same sense of wonder and, yes...*hope.* It was the most empowering thing anyone had ever said to her and she could hear the ring of sincerity in his voice.

'Then yes, I'll marry you,' she said, in a low voice. 'And have a family with you and be faithful and true to you. Because I think you're right. I think we *are* compatible in many ways.'

He looked down into her face. 'We will make a good life together, Sophie,' he said. 'I promise you that.'

The effect of his smile made her emotions dip and wobble. And too much emotion was dangerous. She needed to remember that. This was only going to work if she kept it real. So she sucked in a deep breath and gave a cool smile. 'Yes, we will,' she said.

'Now, isn't it customary to seal an engagement with a kiss?' He pulled her into his arms, his mouth hovering close to hers. 'And then to buy a ring worthy of a princess?'

She brushed an admonitory finger over his lips, even though her body had begun to prickle with anticipation. 'Not quite so fast. The ring we can deal with but there's a protocol to marrying someone like me. Before we do anything, you're going to have to come to Isolaverde and ask my brother for his permission.'

CHAPTER TEN

SOPHIE'S HEART WAS racing as they were summoned into the throne room of the Isolaverdian palace. She could hear her high heels clipping over the polished marble floor, past all the beautiful oil paintings of her ancestors towards the dais at the far end.

It felt like forever since she'd last been here and the significance of the magnificent setting was never lost on her. It was where her brother had been crowned after the sudden death of their father and where their grief-stricken mother had sat, keeping vigil over the late King's coffin.

As she heard the heavy clang of the double doors slamming shut behind them, Sophie thought about everything she'd seen and done since she'd last seen her brother. California and an ocean crossing. The heat and dust of the Australian Outback, the silent snow of the Cotswolds and then the high-octane holiday glitter of New York. And now she was back on her island home, feeling a bit like a stranger on her home territory with the man beside her about to ask the King for her hand in marriage.

As they took their seats she wondered if Rafe was dazzled by the twin thrones before them—where diamonds, rubies and emeralds as big as gulls' eggs glittered in the winter sunshine. One throne sat empty—waiting for the wife her brother seemed so reluctant to find, for it was rumoured he had a mistress who was preventing him from fulfilling his destiny. Not for the first time, Sophie acknowledged the inequality of one rule for royal men and a different one for women. Myron had been allowed to have as much sex as he wanted, while she'd been supposed to save her virginity until her wedding night. How unfair was that? She moistened her lips with her tongue as she stared at the imposing figure of her brother, his dark face stern, his legs crossed with the carelessness of a man born to rule, as he leaned back against his throne.

'I understand that you have provided both sanctuary and protection for my sister,' said the King, without preamble. 'For which I owe you a great debt as well as my thanks, and for which you will be rewarded accordingly. The Princess has behaved in a way which was undoubtedly headstrong, but she is home now and everything is as it should be. Whether your desire is for land or capital, I shall endeavour to grant you your wish, Carter.' He gave a wry smile. 'Within reason, of course.'

Rafe smiled back. 'I'm very honoured to receive Your Majesty's offer,' he said diplomatically. 'But it was no hardship to give your sister my protection and, indeed, she fended for herself most admirably for many months. Months during which my men assured me she was the best cook they've ever had on the station.'

A glitter of irritation iced the King's blue eyes. 'I

have no desire to imagine the Princess in a position of such servitude. Let us discuss how best you will be recompensed instead.'

'But, Your Majesty,' said Rafe silkily, 'I have no need or desire for any financial reward. I have no desire to accept payment for what was my pleasure.'

Nervously Sophie resisted the invitation to chew the inside of her mouth. Didn't Rafe realise that refusing Myron's offer was the last thing he should do if he wanted to keep him onside? That it was bad form to refuse the King *anything*?

Nothing was said for a moment as both men engaged in a silent battle of wills.

'As you wish,' said Myron eventually, unable to hide another flicker of irritation when it became clear Rafe had no intention of backing down. 'But on the other matter you brought to my attention when you first arrived, I'm afraid I cannot be quite so reasonable. You say you wish to marry my sister?' He raised his eyebrows before shaking his head. 'I'm afraid this will not be possible, for reasons I'm sure I don't need to spell out for you.'

Rafe nodded and then, very deliberately, reached out and put his hand over Sophie's. Had he done that to hide the sudden trembling of her fingers from her brother? she wondered.

'I completely understand your reservations, Your Majesty,' Rafe said. 'Because Sophie is your sister and you love her and care about her welfare and, obviously, I'm not the prospective husband you would have chosen—mainly, I suspect, because I am not royal. But I have a vast fortune at my disposal as well as the ways and the means to protect the Princess as she has always been protected. You need have no fears about her future.'

'That is not the point,' snapped Myron, uncrossing his legs and sitting up, ramrod-straight. 'I have had you investigated.'

'Of course you have,' put in Rafe calmly. 'I would have done exactly the same in your position.'

Myron's face darkened. 'And your family is...disreputable, to say the least.'

'We have a somewhat colourful history, that I won't deny,' said Rafe wryly. 'But I won't do wrong by your sister and nothing you can say or do will change my determination. Because I intend to marry her, with or without your permission—although it would be better if we could do it with your blessing. Obviously.' His fingers tightened around Sophie's as he gave her hand a squeeze. 'Back in New York, I made a vow to the Princess that I would be faithful and true and I am repeating that vow today, in your presence. For I intend on being the best husband I can possibly be.'

Sophie felt quite faint. Nobody ever talked to Myron like that. *Nobody.* And nobody ever kept interrupting him that way either. She looked into her brother's face, expecting to see the first hint of the simmering rage which his courtiers knew to beware of, but to her astonishment there was nothing but a flicker of frustration in his eyes, which gradually became a gleam of reluctant acceptance.

'You are a strong man, Carter,' observed Myron slowly. 'And a woman needs a strong man. Very well. You have your permission to marry my sister. She will come to you with a generous dowry.'

'No.' Rafe's voice was firm. 'Sophie will bring to the marriage only what she wishes to bring. Some sentimental trinkets or the like, but nothing more than that.'

Some sentimental trinkets?

For the first time since she'd accepted his proposal, Sophie felt a shimmer of apprehension as Myron stepped down from his throne and she watched as the two men shook hands, almost as if they were sealing some kind of business deal. And the thought which had taken root in her head was now stubbornly refusing to shift, because wasn't that *exactly* what they were doing? The shimmer became a shiver. What she'd just witnessed had been a kind of battle between two very alpha men who were both used to getting their own way.

She realised now that if Rafe had backed down or buckled underneath the weight of her brother's arrogant royal power—or greedily accepted a reward—then the marriage would never have taken place. Somehow, Myron would have put a stop to it. He might have threatened to destroy Rafe's company or found an area of his life to target, an area which was ripe for exploitation. She would put nothing past him, for he had been furious when Prince Luciano had announced that he could no longer marry her. He had been angry on behalf of his jilted sister but there was no denying that he had seen the move as a slight to the royal house of Isolaverde.

But Rafe hadn't buckled. He had shown himself to be powerful and indomitable. He had stood up to Myron in a way she'd never seen anyone do before and he had won her, as a man might win a big prize at a game of cards.

Pressing her fingernails into the palms of her hands, she told herself to *stop wishing for the impossible*. To get real instead of trying to spoil her enjoyment before it had even started. Because this was what she wanted, wasn't it? She wanted Rafe—a man who made her feel alive. Who made her senses sing. Who made her think she was capable of *anything*. Hadn't he told her that, back in New York, and hadn't she been almost hugging herself with delight as they'd flown to her island home? And yes, there were limitations to the way he felt about her—he'd been completely upfront about that. He wasn't promising her love and fairy-tale stuff. He wasn't spinning lies and pretending to have feelings which were alien to him. And shouldn't she be *grateful* to him for that?

But as Myron stood up and prepared to take his leave of them Sophie was aware that gratitude was the very last thing on her mind.

'Thank you, Myron,' she said, aware that her voice was lacking the joy she'd expected to feel. All she could feel was a sudden and uncomfortable sensation of *flatness*.

'I have put Rafe in the Ambassadorial suite,' said Myron, his eyes glittering. 'Even though I understand you've been living together in New York, I suggest we don't bombard the palace staff with too many changes all at once. A commoner husband is going to take some getting used to and I think it's best you don't share a room until after your marriage. Let tradition reign supreme. I think we should adopt a softly-softly approach.'

Sophie glanced up at Rafe, expecting him to object to this as well. To a man with his healthy sexual appetite it would seem old-fashioned and hypocritical to be put in separate rooms. But to her astonishment, he simply nodded.

'That sounds perfectly agreeable,' he said.

'Good. And I should be honoured if you would be my guest at the New Year's Eve ball we hold here in the palace each year. It will be a good time to introduce you to the great and the good of Isolaverde. We can announce your engagement on New Year's Day.' Myron looked straight into Rafe's eyes. 'If that also meets with your approval?'

'Absolutely,' answered Rafe. 'I should be honoured.'

But as the King swept from the throne room Sophie couldn't shake off a distinct feeling of *disenchantment*—remembering the way the two men had talked about her as if she were nothing but an object to barter. Suddenly, it felt as if she had been slotted straight back into her familiar restricted role of *princess*. As if the stiff mantle of being a royal had settled over her shoulders and was threatening to stifle her. The woman who had shovelled show and beaten eggs while wearing a silly little Santa outfit now seemed as if she belonged to another life.

She accompanied Rafe and a small convoy of servants through the maze of palace corridors to the luxurious Ambassadorial suite and when they were alone at last, and the servants dismissed, he took her in his arms. It should have felt like heaven to be this close to him again, but Sophie couldn't shake off the notion that it just didn't *feel* right.

'Now,' he said, his thumb grazing over her breast and the warmth of his breath fanning her lips. 'What shall we do next? Any ideas?'

She swallowed. 'We'll have to get ready for dinner and my rooms are at the opposite end of the palace to yours, so I'd better…I'd better get going.'

'Dinner can wait,' he murmured as he ran his other hand down her spine to cup the curve of one buttock.

This was the point when she normally began to dissolve, when her blood would grow heated and her skin sensitive as she anticipated his lovemaking. But all Sophie could feel was an acute self-consciousness, the easy familiarity all but gone. She felt as if people were watching. Listening. Wondered if the servants were hovering in the vicinity, eager to know if the Princess was being intimate with the commoner she had brought into their midst. She froze. Rafe's fingers felt alien against her skin as he popped the buttons on her shirt and it flapped open. She felt as if this were all happening to someone else as he unclipped the front fastening of her bra and her breasts tumbled free.

'Dinner can't wait.' She swallowed as she stared down at his fingers—olive-dark against her paler skin as he stroked her breast—but for once her knees weren't growing weak and her nipples weren't tingling. For once she could feel *nothing*. 'That's something you'd better get used to,' she added. 'It is always served on the stroke of eight and to be late will be seen as an insult to the King.'

'So? That gives us a couple of hours.' He nuzzled her neck with a lazy kiss. 'Plenty of time for what I have in mind. I haven't made love to you in hours, Sophie—and I'm beginning to get withdrawal symptoms. But if you're telling me that we're on a tight schedule, then maybe we won't bother with bed. Maybe we'll do it…right here.'

She couldn't stop him. She told herself she didn't *want* to stop him and that much was true. Because she kept thinking that her familiar passion would return as his lovemaking progressed. So she let him push her up against the wall and slide her panties down over her thighs, and helped him as he carefully tugged the zip down over his straining erection. She even stroked on the condom just as he'd taught her to, but she didn't get her usual thrill of pleasure as he made that first stifled groan when he entered her.

She did everything she always did, wrapping her legs around his back, feeling the swing of her skirt against her naked thighs and burying her face in his neck as he thrust deep inside her. But today she couldn't free herself of a slight sense of *guilt*. She'd always seen herself as others saw her, because that was the way she'd been brought up.

Always be aware that someone could be watching you, Sophie, her mother used to say primly. *Because someone usually is.*

So that now, part of her was observing a princess pressed up against the wall with her panties down by her ankles, as Rafe thrust in and out of her.

She felt him begin to shudder and she whispered soft and muffled words in Greek to him. Words of excitement and encouragement and she kissed his lips hard and passionately when he came, hoping that would disguise her own lack of orgasm.

Neither of them spoke for a moment and when

the last of his spasms had died away, she pulled out of his embrace. Awkwardly, she stooped to pick up her panties, her hair falling over her flushed face as she stepped into them again. 'I'd...I'd better go,' she said. 'And...settle in.'

'Sure.'

His face was curiously guarded as she put her bra and shirt back on and tidied up her hair, but he said nothing more as she left for her own section of the palace. And even the sight of her familiar rooms did little to soothe feelings which were ruffled by more than her scary lack of reaction to Rafe's lovemaking. Was her prolonged taste of freedom responsible for the sense of alienation she now felt in the environment she'd grown up in?

She looked at the canopied white bed, positioned beneath a soaring golden ceiling which had seemed so impossibly high when she was a little girl. She picked up a photo of her parents at a ball they'd attended before she was even born, her mother wearing the dazzling ruby and diamond necklace which Sophie had been destined to wear when she married Prince Luc. A necklace which now belonged to another woman...

Putting the photo back down, she showered Rafe's scent from her skin and then walked over to the wardrobe. The lavish clothes she found inside were worlds away from the cheap shorts and T-shirts she'd worn at Poonbarra, where she'd blended in and felt like everyone else. Running her fingertips over the soft fabrics, she put on a floaty dress of a blue so pale it was almost white, and went down to dinner.

The meal was held in the State banqueting room—

a setting designed to show the palace at its most splendid. Old gold and cream roses were massed into glittering crystal vases and tall gold candles flickered all the way along the centre of the table. It felt like a jolt to be back amid all this lavish and very obvious luxury again and Sophie tried to shake off the feeling of being on show. She was next to Myron, who she could tell was making a big effort to be nice to her. She kept expecting him to berate her for her impetuosity in running away, but instead he asked her about life at Poonbarra—and it was all she could do to keep the wistfulness from her voice. And she detected an undeniable sense of *relief* in his attitude towards her. Was the King glad that his troublesome little sister was soon to be off his hands at last—passed from the care of one powerful man to another?

Rafe was seated next to Mary-Belle—with the Isolaverdian Prime Minister on the other side. Sophie watched as he charmed both her little sister and the high-ranking politician who had recently approved an extension to the country's world-famous oceanographic museum. Who knew Rafe was such an expert on marine science, or that he'd once scuba-dived in the Galapagos? She sat and listened as he made her sister giggle. Over the top of her golden goblet she saw him smile at something the premier had said and Sophie's heart began to pound beneath the delicate material of her silk-satin dress. He looked so gorgeous sitting there, but she thought he also seemed...distant. There were no meaningful looks slanted at her from across the wide expanse of the table. No suggestive smile. *And whose fault was that?* Had he noticed her lack of response earlier, or had he been so caught up in his own passion that he hadn't noticed? She wondered if she should have faked an orgasm, yet something deep inside her baulked at the thought of doing that—because wasn't this relationship of theirs supposed to be based on honesty?

Except it didn't feel so honest right then. It felt as if she was hiding stuff away from him. As if she knew it would appal him to realise the direction of some of her thoughts.

It was no better when the evening broke up and they were each assigned a servant to take them to their separate suites. Rafe gave her only the briefest of kisses before they parted—but what else could he do in front of all those silent, watching faces?

She slid between the cool sheets, wondering if he would steal through the vast palace to find her, so that they could try to make right that awkward one-sided coupling of earlier. She stared up at the ceiling, realising that this was the first night they'd spent apart since that moonlit seduction in the swimming pool. Were these cold and gilded walls responsible for deadening her physical response to her lover, or was it that a lifetime of conditioning was hard to throw off overnight?

Eventually she fell into a fitful sleep, thinking about the sparkling engagement ring which Rafe would slide on her finger on the first day of the new year.

And she couldn't shake off the thought that it seemed all *wrong*.

CHAPTER ELEVEN

UNDER THE CURVING arches of a galleried ballroom an orchestra played and Rafe looked around him. Beneath the low murmur of voices, he could hear the occasional aristocratic laugh and bell-like sound of champagne glasses being chinked. Even for a man who had attended more than his fair share of dazzling occasions, the Isolaverdian New Year's ball was quite something.

He could sense people's eyes on him—at least, everyone's except Sophie's. She seemed to be avoiding his gaze as much as possible. He wondered if she was remembering that unsatisfactory episode of lovemaking yesterday, when she'd been about as responsive as a block of ice in his arms. His mouth flattened because that had never happened to him before—a woman staying ice-cool even while he was deep inside her body. And Sophie wasn't some random lover he could just forget about, or decide that maybe they weren't so compatible after all. He shook his head as someone offered him a glass of champagne. She was the woman he had vowed to make his wife and he knew it was a lifelong commitment.

A middle-aged blonde—a fortune in emeralds

dazzling around her neck—was making no attempt to hide her interest and even though he was used to being stared at, it had never felt like this before. He was aware that his every movement was being observed, his every comment noted and analysed. Was this what being royal was all about—along with all the damned rules and endless protocol which seemed to make this palace seem like a giant institution? Was that the reason Sophie had been so uptight the moment she'd stepped back on familiar territory? Why she was scarcely recognisable as the warm woman he'd grown to know?

He glanced across the ballroom as she strayed into his line of vision. She was easily the most beautiful woman in the room, her dark hair studded with sapphires and a matching midnight-blue gown hugging her slim figure. But she looked cool and aloof as she greeted the high-born guests and once again that feeling of unease settled over him.

He had asked her to be his bride but he couldn't deny that doubts had started to creep into his mind since they'd arrived here in Isolaverde. Back in New York, it had all seemed ridiculously simple. He'd been on a high—amazed to find a woman whose company didn't irritate him and dazed from the non-stop and amazing sex. They'd each dragged out their demons and shone daylight on them and confronting them had seemed to diminish them. She'd told him she wanted a family and marriage; well, so did he. And the cherry on the cake as far as he was concerned was that neither of them was chasing after that disappointing fairy tale known as love.

But in the high-octane buzz of the city it had been

easy to forget that Sophie was a royal, while here it had been in his face from the moment they'd touched down. And nothing was ever going to change that. He wanted children of his own—but hadn't he overlooked the fact that any child he sired with Sophie would be royal by birth? As soon as they were born, wouldn't expectation be heaped all over their innocent heads? Could he willingly subject any child of his to a life beneath the glare of the spotlight?

Sophie was walking towards him and he could see people bobbing into curtseys as she moved past. 'So. There you are,' she said.

'Here I am,' he agreed, his eyes capturing hers. 'And I'm all yours. Dance with me?'

She nodded, a small smile tugging at her lips as he took her into his arms and the orchestra swelled into a slow and sensuous waltz. He could smell a different scent on her skin, something warm and spicy, and he felt the punch of his heart as he drew her close.

'Having fun?' he questioned.

'Of course!' Her voice sounded bright. 'How about you?'

'This is certainly a very elaborate production,' he said dryly.

Now what did he mean by *that*? Sophie glanced up into Rafe's hard-boned face but his shuttered features gave her no clues. She thought how *unapproachable* he looked this evening, even though she kept trying to tell herself she was imagining it. But deep down she knew she wasn't. Things had been awkward between them since that disorientating episode of sex when she hadn't felt a thing. They hadn't discussed it because neither of them had acknowledged it—and hadn't she been secretly praying he might not have even noticed? That his own pleasure had been powerful enough for it to have passed him by? But the truth was that he hadn't laid a finger on her since.

Yet while his lack of attention had removed her fear of a repeat episode of unresponsiveness, it did nothing to lessen her dread about what was happening to them. Her growing fear that this was how it was going to be from now on. Her stomach tied itself up in knots as they moved around the dance floor. Because what if she was one of those women who couldn't sustain sexual enjoyment? She'd read about that kind of thing happening. Women whose senses shut down for whatever reason, leaving their highly sexed menfolk aching and frustrated.

And she wasn't stupid. There were plenty of reasons why a rift should have appeared between them and it wasn't just because they weren't having sex. She'd seen the expression on Rafe's face when he wasn't aware she was watching him. He reminded her of a person walking around a zoo and observing all the exhibits with a wry and faintly disbelieving look on his face. What if he'd changed his mind about wanting to marry her, now that he had seen her in her natural habitat of the royal palace?

She lifted her gaze towards his shadowed jaw and asked the question she had been dreading. 'You are still happy for the marriage announcement to be made tomorrow?'

The look he slanted down at her was unfathomable. 'I gave your brother my vow, didn't I? And I never go back on my word.'

But Sophie took little comfort from his response.

Why, that was the most lacklustre endorsement she'd ever heard! The dance finished and an Isolaverdian nobleman she'd known since childhood stepped forward to take Rafe's place. With a smile, she shook her head, taking a glass of punch from the tray of a passing waitress instead. But she wanted a drink even less than she wanted a dance. It was more of a distraction—a stalling device—something which enabled her to observe Rafe as he headed over towards a nearby beauty to ask her to dance.

The beauty was a Duchess, an ethereal blonde who'd been sitting near Rafe at the pre-ball dinner, and she accepted his offer immediately. Sophie felt her heart plummet. Of course she did. What woman wouldn't want to be in the arms of Rafe Carter? Despite the fact that he had no royal title, he was easily the most attractive man in the crowded ballroom. She watched him move the Duchess round the floor, wondering if she was imagining that he seemed more relaxed than he'd been during his dance with *her*. But could she blame him? It couldn't be much fun dancing with a woman who had suddenly turned to ice in his arms.

She tried not to react but she couldn't seem to quash the sheer, blinding jealousy of seeing him so close to another woman. She told herself not to be so stupid—that it was all completely innocent. And it *was* innocent. Logically, she knew that. She believed in his vow of intended fidelity, just as she believed he was a man who wouldn't go back on his word.

But that was before she had shut down in his arms, wasn't it? Before he'd seen at close quarters just what it meant to marry into the pomp and ceremony of the Isolaverdian royal family.

Feeling as if someone were pressing their fingers against her throat, Sophie turned away and found herself a hiding place behind a tall marble pillar, dejection washing over her as she leaned back against the wall. Because nothing had changed, had it? Despite her daredevil stab at gaining some independence, everything was as it always had been. She had tied up her future with a man who'd promised her the security of marriage but without the cushion of love. Just as Luc had done.

And she was just as trapped as before!

Only this time it was worse.

Much worse.

She'd known all along that her feelings for Luc had been tepid, because they'd never been given the freedom to get to know each other properly. But she *did* know Rafe. More intimately than she'd known anyone. She'd been his lover. She'd shared his bed. She'd cooked him meals and vice versa and she'd lain face down on the pillows of his New York bed while he had carefully massaged her shoulders and then, afterwards, eased himself inside her aching body. He'd taken her to parties, and shows. They'd shopped together and walked for miles through the snowy streets of New York City. And if the truth were known, she'd fallen in love with him along the way, hadn't she?

Hadn't she?

The music changed to a lively foxtrot as she tried to tell herself she was panicking unnecessarily. That tomorrow Rafe would slide on the huge ruby and diamond ring they'd chosen together on Madison Avenue and the people of Isolaverde would be delighted that their princess had found her own happy ending at last.

But she hadn't, had she?

She was still that same dumb, docile princess who thought she couldn't exist without the patronage of a powerful man. She was about as modern as one of the ancient suits of armour which stood in the palace entrance hall! How could she knowingly walk into such a one-sided relationship and open herself up to all the potential pain of such a union? How could she force that on Rafe when the agreement had been that neither of them was asking for love?

Thought after disturbing thought rushed through her head, but she kept them hidden behind a careful smile as she went through the motions expected of her. She danced with the prime minister, with assorted Dukes and a visiting Sheikh. She even danced with Rafe again, trying not to indulge in a rush of jealous questions about his many dance partners.

And this was what her future would be like, she realised. Life with a man who couldn't love her. A man every woman would see and want and probably make a play for.

And she would be left watching from the sidelines, not daring to show him her feelings because they didn't have that kind of marriage.

'Relax,' he said, his thumb making idle little circles at her waist.

'I'm trying.'

'Then try a little harder.' He smiled. 'Because soon this will all be over.'

The decision she'd been trying her best to avoid could no longer be ignored and Sophie wondered if

Rafe had any idea how eerily accurate his words were. Because suddenly she knew she couldn't keep running from the truth. Running only got you so far. Sooner or later you had to stop and face what was troubling you—and what was troubling her was that she couldn't let this fantasy marriage go ahead. For all their sakes, she needed to stop it. She swallowed. 'Rafe, I need to talk to you.'

'Then talk.'

'No. Not here. It's too public. Can we go somewhere more private? Please.' She hesitated. 'It's important.'

He loosened his hold on her fractionally, pulling back from her so that his silver-grey gaze clashed with hers. 'But the ball hasn't finished.'

It felt like a reprimand. It *was* a reprimand. How ironic that the commoner was giving the Princess a lesson in etiquette. 'After the fireworks and once my brother has left, can you meet me in the Ruby Drawing Room?' she questioned breathlessly. 'Do you know where that is?'

He nodded, but now his gaze was thoughtful as it rested on her. 'Sure.'

Somehow Sophie got through the remainder of the evening. At midnight the French windows were opened and everyone moved onto the terrace as bells peeled out all over the island to celebrate the coming of the new year. It was always an emotional time but tonight it seemed even more poignant as Sophie thought about what lay ahead. She could feel the prick of tears as the sky exploded in a spectacular display of fireworks—silver, gold, cobalt and pink flowering against an indigo backdrop—all reflected in the dark gleaming waters of the Mediterranean. She heard the collective gasps of the ball-goers echoing around the vast terrace as the fireworks whirred and whistled in the air, but somehow she didn't feel part of it.

And then the evening became nothing more than an endurance of clock-watching. All she wanted was for Myron to retire, because nobody was allowed to move until after the King had taken his leave. At last the King whispered into the ear of a stunning redhead before sweeping with his entourage from the room and, a few moments later, Sophie saw the woman follow him.

Sophie's heart was thumping as she made her way to the eastern side of the palace. The Ruby Drawing Room was one of her favourite places in the palace, its décor overseen by her late mother, whose favourite colour and gemstone it had been. Hers, too. The walls and floor were in restful shades of darkest pink and only the ornate ceiling was gold—its intricate mouldings picked out with dazzling precision. It was a room which made her feel emotional for all kinds of reasons and therefore probably not the best choice for the kind of talk she and Rafe needed to have, but it was quiet and far away from the hustle and bustle of the ball.

She walked in and saw that Rafe was already there, tall and magnificent as he stood beside the marble fireplace, his grey eyes watchful as she pushed the door shut.

'So what's with all the cloak and dagger stuff?' he questioned.

She drew in a deep breath, her heart pounding

with nerves. 'I've brought you here to tell you I can't marry you, Rafe.'

She searched his face for a trace of emotion. Something which might hint that her words had surprised him, even if they hadn't actually wounded him. But no. There was nothing. Those dark features remained impenetrable. And somehow that made her decision easier. It reinforced that she was doing the right thing—because he could turn it on and off like a tap, couldn't he? The man he'd been in New York seemed to have vanished. He seemed more of a stranger even than the day she'd first met him. 'I wanted to tell you tonight...' she stared into his eyes '...so we can stop the announcement being made.'

Not a trace of emotion showed on his face as he shot out the single word. 'Why?' And then his face darkened. 'Surely one episode of disappointing sex isn't enough to make you have cold feet?'

'It's a contributory factor, yes.'

He slanted her another unfathomable look. 'You want me to lock the door and make you come? Will that make you feel better?'

Sophie could feel her cheeks growing hot. 'No, of course not. It's about much more than that.'

'Like what?'

She bit her lip. She could do the easy thing of telling him she'd changed her mind and didn't want marriage after all. She could even pretend that she'd been sucked back into palace life and had decided that she liked it too much to ever leave. Except she suspected he was intuitive enough to know that wasn't the case—and besides, why on earth did she think any such option would be easy? None of this was ever going to be *easy*.

'Because we want different things.'

His brow darkened. 'I thought we'd already thrashed this out and decided that ultimately we wanted the same things. A family life together. Wasn't that what we both agreed, Sophie?'

And Sophie knew then that nothing would do except for the truth, no matter what the cost to her own pride. She kept her voice very low. 'I can't marry you, Rafe, because I've fallen in love with you. And I can see from your face how much that horrifies you.'

'Because love was never part of the deal,' he ground out.

'I realise that.' She licked her lips. 'Do you really think I want to feel this way? Because I don't—but I needed to be honest with you. I lied to you in the past about stuff and I think you realised I had reasons for keeping the truth hidden. But I don't ever want to do that again. And since our relationship is supposed to be based on truth then you need to hear it. And the truth is that I've fallen in love with you, Rafe. I've tried my best to stop myself but there doesn't seem to be a thing I can do about it.'

She stared straight into his face, willing him to say something, but she was met only with silence.

'Only something tells me that love won't work in a marriage which was only ever supposed to be practical,' she continued unsteadily. 'I thought...I thought I could do practical, but I was wrong. I'm not going to opt for second best. Call me stupid or unrealistic, but I'd rather hold out for love—even if that never happens.'

He nodded his head like a mathematics teacher
who'd just been presented with a tricky equation and
as Sophie waited, didn't part of her hope her words
might have struck a chord, even if it was just a little
one? That there might be a platform from which to
springboard her growing feelings. What if he told
her that he was receptive to the *idea* of love—would
that be enough for them to go on? Wouldn't the tiniest crack in his armour mean that some of her love
might be able to slip inside and warm him? She kept
her eyes fixed on his face and watched as something
in his expression changed. And it was as if the shut-
ters had suddenly been lifted for there was no disguising the sudden hostility which gleamed so hard
and silver from his eyes.

'I told you emphatically that I didn't do love,' he
said. 'And you know why? Because it means nothing. *Nothing.* I've seen greed and lust and ambition,
all masquerading as *love.* Did you really think that
your words might bring about a fundamental change
of heart, Sophie? That I was going to have a personality change just because you looked at me with
those beautiful blue eyes and told me words I never
wanted to hear?'

Sophie felt that little spark of hope crumble inside
her, like a heap of dust onto which a heavy boot had
just stamped. She wanted to break down. To sink to
her knees and let the great slurry of dark emotions
come sliding down onto her head. But she would not.
She could not. She was going to walk away from this
relationship with her heart shattered, but she would
make sure that her dignity was kept intact.

'No, Rafe,' she said quietly. 'I didn't think that, although I'd be lying if I denied that's what I was hoping for. I thought you might be open-minded enough to the idea that feelings can sometimes grow if you let them—but maybe you won't let them. Or maybe you can't.' She met his stony gaze and nodded her head. 'We need to tell the King so that no announcement of our engagement will be made. We need to end it, as of now. Well, not tonight, obviously. But first thing tomorrow.'

'So I'm to go to your brother and tell him that my vow was worthless?'

'Oh, don't worry. I'll tell him. I'll make sure he knows that you didn't break your precious word and that the fault was all mine. I should... I should never have agreed to it.'

'Another marriage which has fallen by the wayside just before it reached the altar,' he observed. 'Are you really prepared to go through with the damage to your reputation, Sophie?'

'Better a brief spell of shattered pride than a lifetime of disillusion,' she flared back. 'Of always having to hide my feelings for fear that you might mistake them for *lust* or *greed* or *ambition*.' She swept the palm of her hand back over her chignon, checking that her appearance was pristine enough to face any servant she might encounter on the way back to her room, and then lifted her chin to direct one final look at him. 'Your words can sometimes be cruel, Rafe—but I suppose I should be grateful for your candour. Because, for the moment at least—I'm finding it very easy not to love you.'

CHAPTER TWELVE

HE HAD EVERYTHING he wanted. *Everything.* So why wasn't it enough?

Rafe paced the floor of his Manhattan apartment, where outside the glitter of skyscrapers meant you couldn't really see the darkness of the night sky. A bit like him. He was functioning as normal. Closing deals and starting new ones. Working out and going to parties. Life had to go on in every sense. He knew that. He'd even taken a woman to the theatre last night.

He stopped his relentless pacing and gave a ragged sigh. She must have thought he was crazy. Successful and beautiful, she'd made it plain she'd like nothing more than to have him share her bed.

And just the thought had left him cold. Worse than cold. His skin had crawled at the thought of touching a woman. Any woman.

Except Sophie.

Damn her.

His pacing resumed. Why the hell couldn't he stop thinking about her, despite his conviction that this was the best thing for both of them? Because if he couldn't give her what she really wanted then neither of them would be satisfied.

An image of her face swam into his mind. Her eyes as blue as a Queensland sky. Her dark hair threaded with sapphires or tumbling free over bare shoulders. The cool smile she'd given him as he'd left Isolaverde. He'd thought the flatness in her eyes had been for the benefit of her watching brother, who was clearly irritated by this latest turn of events. But then Rafe realised it was all for him. There had been no reproach in her gaze—just a quiet dignity, which had preoccupied him all the way home to America and continued to preoccupy him.

So what was he going to do about it?

His mouth tightened.

He had a problem. Wasn't it about time he started seeking a solution?

Bright sunlight flooded into the breakfast room of the Isolaverdian palace and the King sat back and regarded his younger sister.

'I wondered if you might take a run out to Assimenios Beach today,' said Myron.

Sophie pushed away her half-eaten dish of grapefruit segments and forced a smile to her lips. The one which seemed to split her face in half but which she hoped Myron found convincing. He probably did. He wasn't exactly the kind of man who spent his life analysing the facial expressions of women, especially not those of his sister. Why should he care if she was happy or not?

'Any particular reason?' she questioned.

'Could be. I'm thinking of building a house there,' said Myron. 'And I'd like your input.'

'Mine?'

'Sure. Why not?'

Sophie opened her mouth to say she wasn't sure her opinion was up to much at the moment, then quickly shut it again. Because wasn't this another sign that Myron was being more inclusive—something she had told him she wanted? It wasn't *his* fault that she wasn't firing on all cylinders, she thought as she went to her room and crammed on a light straw hat over her ponytailed hair. It wasn't anybody's fault except for...

She stared into the mirror, aware of the new definition of her cheekbones and the shadowed hollows of her eyes. She had to stop thinking this way. She couldn't blame Rafe. She really couldn't, because he'd been honest with her from the start. If there was any blame to be apportioned, she should heap it all on herself because *she* had been the one who had been unable to settle for what he was offering. *She* was the one who'd wanted more than he was capable of giving. He'd ruled out love from the start but she had demanded it—a bit like someone walking into a fish restaurant and demanding to know why there was no steak on the menu.

And it wasn't as if she were without choices. She might have yet another failed love affair behind her, but things had changed. She was getting stronger by the day. Sometimes she even managed a whole fifteen minutes before Rafe's shuttered features would swim into her mind and she'd be reminded of everything she'd lost. No, not *lost*, she reminded herself fiercely. She hadn't lost something. She had walked away from something which would ultimately damage her and bring her pain—a one-sided marriage with a man

incapable of love. She had been strong, not weak—
and one day she would be grateful for that strength.

Just not today.

Myron had agreed to expand her royal role and to
give her more responsibility. Just as he had agreed
that if she wanted to go abroad and forge a career for
herself, she would have his blessing. Because after
Rafe had gone and she'd cried the last of those bitter
tears, Sophie had realised she needed to take control of her own life and that running away to sail a
boat over the Pacific wasn't the answer this time.
She needed to stop letting herself be moved around
by these powerful men, like a token on a gaming
table. So she had gone to Myron and told him she
was planning to enrol on a cookery course in Paris
in late spring.

And Myron had just nodded his head and agreed!

Maybe independence had always been that simple,
she mused as she climbed behind the wheel of her car,
which had been brought round to the front of the palace by one of the servants. Maybe all she'd needed
to do was to have stood up for what she wanted from
the start. Trouble was that she hadn't really known
what she wanted until she met Rafe, and now she was
going to have to learn to want other things. Different
things. Things which were nothing to do with him.

Reminding herself of his impenetrable eyes, she
headed off on the coastal road towards the eastern
side of the island. The sky was a shimmering bowl
of palest blue, contrasting with the much deeper blue
of the Mediterranean which glittered far below. The
roadsides were thick with early spring flowers and the
distinctive and unique yellow and white bloom known

as the Isolaverdian Star shone out from the grassy
verges as far as the eye could see. Sophie glanced
into her rear mirror, the bodyguard's car further away
than usual, thinking they were giving her a lot of lee-
way today.

Assimenios was the most picturesque spot on an
island not exactly short of picturesque spots—a private beach of pure white sand, which was used only
by the royal family and their guests. Crystal waters
lapped against the sheltered bay and it was as stunning as any Caribbean getaway. She parked her car
and began to scramble down the sandy incline, reminded of childhood holidays when she, Myron and
Mary-Belle would play beneath the wide beach um-
brellas.

The beach should have been deserted but as her
canvas shoes sank into the soft sand she looked up
and saw a yacht in the water, lazily swinging to her
anchor in the gentle breeze. Her expert eye ran approvingly over the boat's beautiful curved lines and
even from here she could see the glint of sunlight
on varnished wooden decks. Her eyes narrowed, because on the beach a short distance away from the
boat stood a man. And not just any man.

She knew straight away it was Rafe. She didn't
need to see the broad shoulders or powerful physique or the black hair glinting in the sunlight; it was
much more visceral than that. Every pore of her body
screamed out to her in shocked and delighted recognition, but she fought back the latter feeling, resisting the desire to kick off her shoes and go running
towards him with her arms spread wide.

Because they were over and she didn't know why

he was here—appearing in front of her and taunting her like this. Had he constructed some kind of elaborate charade with her brother to be allowed to come here? He must have done. She told herself that the anger which followed this surprising realisation was healthy. That it would help her stay focussed and she needed that. Because they were over. They needed to be over.

So why was he here, making her heart squeeze with pain all over again?

The Sophie of a year ago might have turned away, got back into her car and driven at speed to the palace. Because no matter what Rafe's sudden new influence with her brother was, he would be unable to access the Princess if she refused point-blank to see him. But that would be running away and she was through with that.

So she took off her shoes and began to walk across the silver sand towards him, her heart pounding out a powerful rhythm in her chest as she got closer and closer.

'Hello, Rafe,' she said, when she was near enough for him to hear.

'Hello, Sophie.'

Rafe's breathing was shallow as she stopped right in front of him but she wasn't looking at him. She was staring out to sea as if she preferred to look at the yacht bobbing in the lapping water rather than look at him. 'Whose boat is that?'

'Yours. I bought it for you.'

She turned then and he could see fury spitting from her blue eyes. 'You bought me a *boat*? What's this—the billionaire's equivalent of a bunch of flowers to say you're sorry?'

'In a way. But also because she's the loveliest boat I've ever seen and one I thought a sailor of your calibre might enjoy. I cleared it with your brother—'

'I managed to work that out all by myself and I don't give a damn about my brother,' she hissed from between clenched teeth. 'I want to know what you're doing here. Turning up like this out of the blue—appearing on a private family beach without any warning!'

It was the most difficult question he had ever been asked and Rafe knew that he had to get the answer right or risk everything. He wanted to pull her into his arms and kiss her and let his lips demonstrate just how much he'd missed her. But that would be cheating. Even if she allowed him to kiss her, which—judging by the look on her face—he doubted. She needed to hear his words and he needed to speak them. But even so, a lifetime of conditioning was hard to break. 'I'm here because I miss you,' he said. 'Because I've been a fool. A stubborn, unimaginative fool.'

Angrily, she shook her head. 'I don't have to listen to this…rubbish,' she hissed. 'You made your decision, so stick with it! I'm getting my life back together and I don't need you.'

'Don't you?' he questioned. 'Then you are very lucky, Sophie, because I sure as hell need you. Nothing is the same without you. I have a whole world at my feet. I can go anywhere I want. Manhattan, Poonbarra, even England—but I don't want to go anywhere which doesn't have you.'

'Tough. Go away, Rafe,' she said tiredly. 'And take your meaningless words with you.'

'If that's what you really want, then I will go.' He narrowed his eyes. 'But before I do, I need you to listen to what I have to say. Will you at least do that for me?'

He could sense her struggle as she turned her face away from him to look out at the water again.

'Hurry up, then,' she said abruptly. 'Because I want to go.'

He drew in a deep breath. 'I never really believed in love. I wasn't even sure it existed—'

'I remember,' she interrupted acidly. 'You'd seen it masquerading as *lust*, or *greed*.'

'Yes, I had. I'd seen nothing but chaos in its wake,' he continued. 'And that made me determined to control my own life and destiny. That's why I steered clear of any emotional entanglements and it had always worked just fine. And then I met you.'

'Don't.' He could see her jaw working now. 'Don't tell me things you don't mean.'

'I won't. Because what's in it for me to make this admission, unless to admit that I'm fighting like mad to try to get you back, Sophie? To tell you that you appeal to me on every level which matters? You didn't just break through the glass ceiling of my life—you smashed your way in, without even seeming to try. Somehow you made me confide in you. Made me realise that talking about painful stuff was the only way of letting it go. You gave me your body in the most beautiful way I could have imagined. You made the hard-bitten workers at Poonbarra fall completely under your spell, because despite everything this princess has the common touch. I fought it as hard as I knew how and I'm through with fighting because I love you, Sophie.'

'I don't believe you,' she said.

'You can't choose who you love,' he continued doggedly. 'But if you could, I would still choose you. Even if you tell me you never want to see me again, I will never regret loving you, Sophie. Because somehow you've made me come alive. You've made me experience joy—only the flipside of that is the pain of missing you.'

He saw in her eyes the gleam of unshed tears, and a sudden unbearable thought occurred to him. Maybe he really *had* blown it with his arrogance and his fear. He felt the raw aching of his heart and then she started to speak.

'All my life I've been put on a pedestal, like some kind of marble statue,' she said. 'And when you made love to me, you made me feel like a real woman. Only then I realised that you've imposed all these rules and guidelines about what I'm allowed to do and what I'm allowed to say. I'm not allowed to love you, but presumably I was going to be allowed to love our children. Only love isn't something you can limit, or siphon off. It's supposed to grow, Rafe. We're supposed to spread as much of it around as we possibly can.'

'Then spread some over me,' he said softly, but still she shook her head.

'What if I'm frigid?' she demanded. 'If that night we had sex at the palace is the way it's going to be from now on?'

'You think that?'

'It's *your* opinion I'm asking, Rafe.'

'I thought you must be uptight about being in the palace and so I decided to back off—to give you the space you needed.'

Her voice trembled. 'I thought you'd gone off me.'

'Gone off you? Are you out of your mind? We were having a communication breakdown, which wasn't exactly helped by palace protocol.'

He met her gaze and wondered if she could read the longing in his. She still hadn't touched him and he thought there was still some defiance in her attitude.

'I'm going to Paris next month. I'm taking a professional pastry course to capitalise on all the cooking I did at Poonbarra.'

'Then I can come to Paris and work from there.'

'Maybe I want the chance to spread my wings and live on my own for a while.'

'Then I'll wait until you're ready to fly back to me.'

'You're so sure I would?'

'That's a risk I'm prepared to take.'

She looked at him. 'Do you think you have the answer to everything, Rafe Carter?'

'I hope so,' he said, his voice suddenly serious. 'Because I feel like I'm fighting for my life here. All I'm asking for is one more chance, Sophie. A chance to make it right. A chance to show you just how much you mean to me.'

Her lips pressed in on themselves but he could sense she was softening.

'If you ever, *ever* hurt me—'

'I won't ever hurt you again,' he vowed. 'I will love and cherish you for the rest of my days. Just so long as you...' His words tailed off, but he knew that he had to say them. Because they were equals. Because his love for her was fierce and strong, but that didn't make *him* any less vulnerable. And because there was no shame attached in admitting that to the woman you loved. He swallowed. 'Promise never to hurt me either.'

'Oh, Rafe.' And now the unshed tears were spilling down her face and she brushed them away as she shook her head from side to side. 'I will never do that,' she whispered. 'Never.'

His own eyes were pricking as he framed her face in his hands and a swell of emotion so powerful came over him that the world seemed to tilt on its axis. For a moment there was nothing but stillness as their gazes met.

His voice was full of tenderness. 'Do you want to sail your yacht off into the sunset?'

She smiled as she lifted her face to his. 'It's a long time until sundown. I think I'd rather kiss you instead.'

EPILOGUE

A GHOSTLY WAIL shattered the night calm and Sophie rolled over lazily to curl her naked body comfortably against Rafe.

'That's a curlew,' she murmured sleepily, her breath warm against his chest.

'Congratulations.' He kissed the top of her head. 'Soon you'll be eligible for membership of the Australian Ornithological Society.'

'That's not fair,' she protested. 'I know lots about the indigenous birdlife. I can easily recognise a bowerbird.'

He kissed the tip of her nose. 'Only because their colouring is as blue as your beautiful eyes.'

'Oh, Rafe,' she whispered as she wriggled luxuriously against him. 'I do love you.'

'Well, that's good,' he said steadily, though he could do nothing about the sudden lump which had risen in his throat. 'Because I love you too.'

He pulled her closer, reflecting on the last three eventful years. It had been an *interesting* road they'd travelled together before Princess Sophie of Isolaverde had finally consented to become his wife. She'd meant what she said about doing a cookery course in

Paris, but Rafe had quickly established a branch of Carter Communications in the Eighth Arrondissement and they had set up home nearby.

Sophie had graduated from the famous patisserie school with honours and soon afterwards they had married in the Isolaverdian cathedral in a ceremony which included royalty, magnates and film stars. But the glittering congregation might as well not have existed, because all Rafe had been able to see was his beautiful bride, wearing the ruby and diamond necklace which had belonged to her mother and which he had presented to her the day before their wedding, to the accompaniment of her tear-filled eyes and trembling lips. Rafe had been planning to pay any price to get it back from Prince Luc, but the Mardovian royal had insisted on gifting it to them.

'It is yours,' he'd said gruffly. 'For it was always intended for Sophie.'

But there were no hard feelings between Sophie and the man to whom she had once been betrothed— and Luc and his wife Lisa were both guests at the royal wedding. So was Amber, with Conall. Nick, Molly and Oliver. Chase had defied logic and schedules and somehow managed to get himself there from the depths of the Amazonian rainforest and Gianluca was there, too. Even Bernadette had accepted an invitation and Ambrose surprised them all by spending most of the evening dancing with the Irish housekeeper.

And when Rafe had laughingly enquired whether there was some kind of romantic attachment brewing, Bernadette had silenced him with a stern look.

'There is *not*!' she'd declared. 'Sure and all he wants to talk about is his gout!'

After the wedding, Rafe had asked Sophie where she wanted to live, telling her that they could go anywhere she wanted—but her answer hadn't really surprised him. For although they visited Europe and America from time to time, their main base was in Poonbarra, where the skies were huge and the air was clean. It was the only place she'd ever really felt free, she told him. And he felt the same. It was *their* place, now shared with their firstborn— a beautiful bouncing baby boy they named Myron Ambrose Carter.

But before she'd become pregnant, Sophie had experimented with everything she'd learned in Paris and added a few twists of her own—which was how Princess Pastries had come about. Her second cookbook had just been published to great international acclaim and had become an instant bestseller, with all the profits going to an Isolaverdian children's charity. Despite a lot of pressure from the major networks, Sophie had refused all offers to do her own television show. Why would she want to do anything which took her away from her family? she'd asked Rafe quietly.

Why, indeed?

Rafe stroked the hair which lay so silkily against his skin. Family. And love. It was that simple. He sighed. How could something so simple be this good?

'What time is it?' Sophie murmured, her arms tightening around him.

The dawn had not yet streaked the sky and it would be several hours before the wild and beautiful Australian bush sprang into new life. But for now they had the night and they had each other.

Always.

'Time to kiss me,' he said throatily.

And in the darkness, she raised her face to his.

* * * * *

THE PATERNITY
CLAIM

For my wonderful aunt, the gypsy-hearted
Josephine "Dodie" Webb

CHAPTER ONE

COME on, come *on*! With a frustration born out of fear, Isabella jammed her thumb on the doorbell one last time and let it ring and ring, long enough to wake the dead—and certainly long enough to rouse the occupant of the elegant London townhouse. Just in case he hadn't heard her the first time round.

But there was nothing other than the sound of the bell echoing and her hand fell to her side as she forced herself to accept the unthinkable. That he wasn't there. That she would have to make a return journey—if she could summon up the courage to come here for a second time.

And then the door was flung open with a force of a powerhouse—and one very angry man stood looking down at her, his crisp dark head still damp and shining from the shower. Tiny droplets of water sparkled among the brown-black waves of his hair. Lit from behind, it almost looked as though he were wearing a halo—though the expression on his face was about as unangelic as you could get.

His black eyes glittered with irritation at this unwelcome intrusion and Isabella felt her heart begin to race. Because even in her current nerve-jangled state of crisis his physical impact was like a shock to the senses.

He was wearing nothing but a deep blue towel which was slung low around narrow olive hips and came to midway down a pair of impressively muscled thighs. Half of his chin was covered with shaving foam and in his hand he held an old-fashioned cut-throat razor which

5

glinted silver beneath the gleam of the chandelier overhead.

Isabella swallowed. She had seen his magnificent body in swimming trunks many, many times—but never quite so *intimately* naked.

'Yes?' he snapped, in an accent which did not match the Brazilian ancestry of his looks and a tone which suggested that he was not the kind of man to tolerate interruption. 'Where's the fire?'

'Hello, Paulo,' she said quietly.

For the split second before his brain started making sense of the information it was receiving, Paulo stared impatiently at the woman who was standing on his doorstep looking up at him with such wary expectation in her eyes.

He ignored the sensual, subliminal messages which her sultry beauty was hot-wiring to his body, because his overriding impression was how ridiculously *exotic* she looked.

She wore a brand-new raincoat which came right down to a pair of slender ankles, so that only her face was on show. A face covered with droplets of rain from the summer shower, her dark hair plastered to her head. Huge, golden-brown eyes—like lumps of old and expensive amber—were fringed with the longest, blackest lashes he had ever seen. Her lips were lush, and unpainted. And trembling, he thought with a sudden frown. Trembling...

She looked like a lost and beautiful waif, and a warning bell clanged deep within the recesses of his mind. He knew her, and yet somehow he also knew that she shouldn't be here.

Wrong place. Definitely.

'Hello,' he murmured, while his mind raced ahead to slot her into her rightful place.

'Why, Paulo,' she said softly, thinking for one unimaginable moment that he actually didn't *recognise* her. 'I wrote and told you that I was coming—didn't you get my letter?'

The moment she spoke a complete sentence, the facts fell into place. Her accent matched her dark, Latin looks—although her English was as fluent as his. The almond-shaped eyes set in a skin which was the seamless colour of cappuccino. The quiet gleam of black hair which lay plastered against her skull by the rain.

The last time he had seen her, she had been standing illuminated by the brilliant sunshine of a South American day. Her silk shirt had been stretched with outrageous provocation over her ripe, young breasts and there had been the dark stain of sweat beneath her arms. He had wanted her in that moment. And maybe before that, too.

Resolutely he pushed that particular thought away, even as his eyes began to soften with affection. No wonder he hadn't recognised her, against the grey and teaming backdrop of an English summer day, looking cold and hunched. And dejected.

'Isabella! *Meu Deus!* I can't believe it!' he exclaimed, and he leaned forward to kiss her on each cheek. The normal and formal Latin American greeting, but rather bizarre and unsettling—considering that he was wearing next to nothing. He noticed that although she offered him each cool cheek, she shrank away from any contact with his bare skin. And he offered up a silent prayer of thanks.

'Come *in*,' he urged. 'Are you on your own?'

'M-my own?'

He frowned. 'Is your father here with you?'

Isabella swallowed. 'No. No, he's not.'

He opened the door wider and she stepped inside.

'Why on earth didn't you tell me you were coming?' he demanded. 'This is so—'

'Unexpected?' she put in quickly. 'Yes, I know it is.' She nodded her head in rapid agreement—but then she was prepared to agree to almost anything if he would only help her. She didn't know how—she just knew that Paulo Dantas was the kind of man who could cope with anything that life threw at him. 'But you got my letter, didn't you?' she asked.

He nodded thoughtfully. It had been an oddly disjointed letter mentioning that she might be coming to England sometime soon. But he had thought of soon in terms of years. He certainly wasn't expecting her *now*, not yet—when she was still at university. 'Yeah, I got your letter. But that was a couple of months back.'

She had written it the day she had found out for sure. The day she realised the trouble she was in. 'I shouldn't have just burst in on you like this. I tried ringing, but the line was engaged and so I knew you were here and I...I...'

Her voice faded away, unsure where to go from here. In her mind she had practised what she was going to say over and over again, but the disturbing sight of a near-naked Paulo had startled her, and the carefully rehearsed words were stubbornly refusing to come. Not, she thought grimly, that it was the kind of thing you could just blurt out on somebody's doorstep.

'I thought it might be nice to surprise you,' she finished lamely.

'Well, you've certainly done that.'

But Isabella saw his sudden swift, assessing frown. 'I'm sorry, I've come at an awkward time—'

'Well, I can't deny that I was busy—' he murmured, as the hand which wasn't holding the razor strayed down to touch the towel at his hips, as if checking that the knot remained secure. 'But I can dress and shave in a couple of minutes.'

'Or I could come back later?'

'What, send you away when you've travelled thousands of miles?' He shook his crisp, dark head. 'No, no! I'm intrigued to discover what brings Isabella Fernandes to England in such dramatic style.'

Isabella paled, as she tried to imagine what his reaction would be when she told him her momentous piece of news. But there was one more obstacle to overcome before she dared accept his offer of hospitality. What she had to tell him was for his ears alone. 'Is Eduardo here?'

And some sort of transformation occurred. A face which was fundamentally hard and uncompromising underwent a dramatic softening, and a smile of pure pleasure lifted the corners of his mouth—making him look even more outrageously handsome than he had done before.

'Eduardo? Unfortunately, no.' The mouth curved into heart-stopping grin. 'Ten-year-old boys prefer to play football with their friends rather than keep their father company—and my son is no exception. He won't be back until later. A—' Inexplicably, he hesitated. 'A friend of mine is bringing him home.'

'Oh.' The word came out with just the right amount of disappointment, but Isabella wondered if the relief showed on her face. She also wondered who the friend was, as she quickly wiped a raindrop off her cheek.

Paulo watched the jerky little movement of her hand. She seemed nervous, he thought. Excessively nervous. Not a quality he had ever associated with Isabella. She could outshoot most men—and ride a horse with more grace than he had ever seen in another human being. He had watched her grow from child to woman—in the condensed, snap-shot way you did when you only saw someone once a year.

'You'll see him later. Come on—take off that wet raincoat. You're shivering.'

She was shivering for a variety of reasons—and coldness was the least of them.

'Th-thank you.' She stood blinking beneath the glow of the artificial light which danced overhead, frozen by the strangeness of this new environment. And the fact that Paolo was standing next to her, still wearing next to nothing, a faint drift of lemon about him—as indolently at ease with his semi-naked state as if he had been wearing a three-piece suit.

With numb fingers, she began fumbling with the buttons of her coat and Paulo felt the strongest urge to unbutton it for her, as you would a child—except that the first lush glimpse of her T-shirted breasts reinforced the fact that she was anything but a child. And that if he didn't put some decent clothes on in a minute...

'I can't believe you didn't buy an umbrella, Bella?' he teased, in an attempt to divert his uncomfortable thoughts. 'Did nobody tell you that in England it rains and rains? And then it rains some more—even in summer!'

'I thought I'd buy one when I got here, and then I...well, I forgot,' she finished lamely, although an umbrella had been the very last thing on her mind. She had spent weeks and weeks just wearing her father down.

Telling him that it was *her* life and her decision. And that lots of people of her age dropped out of university. She had told him that it wasn't the end of the world, but the look on his face had told her otherwise. Isabella shivered. And he didn't the know the half of it.

He felt the slight tremor in her body as he tugged the cuff of her jacket over her wrist and hung the garment on a peg above a radiator. 'There. You're dry underneath. Come into the sitting room.'

Reaction set in. He was letting her stay. Her teeth started to chatter but she clamped them shut. 'Thank you.'

'Need a towel for your hair?' he asked, shooting her a quick glance. 'Or maybe borrow a sweater?'

'No. Honestly. I'll be fine.' But she didn't feel fine. Her limbs felt stiff and icy as he led her along a wide, deep hallway and into a large, high-ceilinged room, its cool, classic lines made warmly informal by the pulsating colours he had chosen.

Isabella looked around her. It was a very *Latino* colour scheme.

The walls were painted a rich, burnt orange colour and deepest red and covered with vibrant pictures—there was one she instantly recognised as the work of an up-and-coming Brazilian painter. Two giant sofas were strewn with scatter cushions and a low table contained magazines and papers and a book about football. Dotted around the place were photographs of a young boy in various stages of growing up—Paulo's son—and a black and white studio portrait of a cool, beautiful blonde, her pale shining hair held close to a little baby. And that, Isabella knew, was Elizabeth—Paulo's wife.

'Make yourself comfortable,' he instructed, 'while I

get dressed and then I'll make you some coffee—how does that sound?'

'Coffee would be lovely,' she replied automatically.

Paulo went back upstairs and into the bathroom to finish shaving and frowned at himself in the mirror. Something was different about her. Something. And not just that she'd put on a little weight. Something had changed. Something indefinable… And it was something more than the dramatic sexual flowering he had noticed a few short months ago. He moved the blade swiftly over the curved line of his jaw.

He had known her for ever. Their fathers had been friends—and the friendship had survived separation when Paulo's father had eventually settled in England, the home of his new wife. Paulo had been born in Brazil, but had been brought to live in London at the age of six and his father had insisted he make an annual pilgrimage back to his homeland. It was a pilgrimage Paulo had carried on after the deaths of his parents and the birth of his own son.

Every year, just before Carnival erupted in a blaze of colour, he and Eduardo would travel to the Fernandes ranch for a couple of weeks and Paulo had seen Isabella grow up before his eyes.

He had watched with interest as the little girl had blossomed to embrace the whole spectrum of teenage behaviour. She had been stubborn and sassy and sulky, like all teenage girls. By seventeen she had begun to develop a soft, voluptuous beauty all of her own, but at seventeen she had still seemed so *young*. Certainly to him. Even at eighteen and nineteen she had seemed a different generation to a man who was, after all, a decade older, already widowed and with a young son of his own.

But something had happened to Isabella in her twentieth year. In the blinking of an eye, her sexuality had exploded into vibrant, throbbing life and Paulo had been touched by it; his senses had been scorched by it.

He had lifted her down from her horse and there had been a split-second of suspended movement as he held her in his arms. He had felt the indentation of her waist and the dampness of her shirt as it clung to her sweat-sheened skin. Their laughter had stilled and he had seen the suddening darkening of her pupils as she had looked into his eyes with a hunger which had matched his own.

Desire. Potent as any drug.

And his conscience had made him want no part of it.

He removed the towel from his hips, staring down at himself with flushed disbelief as he observed the first stirring of arousal. He scowled. Because that was the whole damned trouble with sexual attraction—once you'd felt it, you could never go back to how it was before. His easy, innocent relationship with Isabella had been annihilated in that one brief flash of desire. *That* was what was different.

His mouth twisted as he crumpled up the towel and hurled it with vicious accuracy into the linen basket, then gingerly stepped into a pair of silken boxer shorts.

Isabella wandered distractedly around the sitting room, going over in her head what she was going to say to him, forcing herself to be strong because only her strength would sustain her through this. 'Paulo, I'm...'

No, she couldn't come straight out with it. She would have to lead in with a casual yet suitably serious statement. No matter that deep down she felt like howling her heart out with shock and disbelief...because indulging her feelings at the moment would benefit no one. 'Paulo, I need your help...'

She heard the jangle of cups and looked up, relieved

to find that he had covered up with a pair of jeans and a T-shirt. On his chin sat a tiny, glistening bead of scarlet and it drew her attention like a magnet.

He saw the amber brilliance of her eyes as she stared at him and felt the dull pounding of his heart in response. 'What is it?' he asked huskily.

'You've cut yourself,' she whispered, and the bright sight of his blood seemed like a portent of what was to come.

Paulo frowned, lifting a fingertip to his chin. 'Where?'

'To the right. Yes. There.'

The finger brushed against the newly shaven surface and drew it away; he looked at it with a frown. Had his hand been shaking? He couldn't remember the last time he'd cut his face. 'Right,' he said, absently licking the finger with a gesture which was unintentionally erotic. 'Coffee.'

She tried for the light touch but it wasn't easy when all the time she felt the weight of the great burden she carried. 'I haven't had a decent cup since I left home.'

'I can imagine.' He smiled.

She watched as he slid onto the sofa, moving with the inborn grace of an alley cat. Back home they always called him *gato*, and it was easy to understand why. The word in Portuguese meant 'cat' but it also meant a sexy and beautiful man—and no one in the world could deny that Paulo Dantas was just that.

Tall, dark and statuesque, he was a matchless mix of English mother and Brazilian father. His was a spectacular face, with an arrogant sweep of cheekbones which could have been sculpted from some gold-tinted stone and hooded eyes more black than brown. The luscious mouth hinted at a deeply sensual nature, its starkly defined curves making it look as if it had been created to inflict both pleasure and pain in equal measures.

She took the coffee that he offered her with a hand which was threatening to tremble. 'Thank you.'

This was *crazy*, thought Paulo, as he observed her unfamiliar, frozen smile and her self-conscious movements. It was like being in a room with a stranger. What the hell had happened to her? 'How is your father?' he enquired politely.

'He—he's very well, thank you.' She tried to lift the coffee cup to her lips but now her fingers were shaking so much that she was obliged to put it down with a clatter. 'He says to say hello to you.'

'Say hello back,' he said evenly, but it was difficult to concentrate when that shaky movement made the lush curves of her body move so uninhibitedly beneath the T-shirt.

Isabella wondered if she was going mad with imagining, or had his gaze just flickered over her breasts? She wondered how much he had seen—and Paulo was an astute man, no one could deny that. Had he begun to guess at her secret already? Unobstrusively she glanced down at herself.

No, she was safe. The hot-pink T-shirt was relatively loose and the matching jeans were far from skin-tight. Nothing clung to the contours of her body. And besides, there was no visible bump yet. Nothing to show that there was a baby on the way, bar the aching new fullness of her breasts and the sudden nausea which could strike her at any time. And frequently did.

She tried a smile, but felt it wobble on her lips. 'I expect you're wondering why I'm here.'

At last! 'Well, the thought *had* crossed my mind,' he said, managing to turn curiosity into a teasing little com-

ment. 'People don't just turn up from Brazil unannounced—not as a rule. Not without phoning first. And it's
a pretty long way from Vitória da Conquista.'

Isabella turned her head to glance out of the uncur-
tained window into the rain-lashed sky. It certainly was.
Back home the temperature would be as warm as kisses,
the land caressed by a soft and sultry breeze.

'And shouldn't you be at college? It's still term-time,
isn't it?'

She started to tell the story, though not the whole
story. Not yet. 'Actually, I've dropped out of college.'

His body shifted imperceptibly from relaxed to watchful. 'Why?' he drawled coldly. 'Is that what every fashionable student is doing this year?'

She didn't like the way his mouth had flattened, nor
the chilly displeasure in his eyes. 'No, not exactly.'

'Then why?' he demanded. 'Don't you know how important qualifications are in an insecure world? What are
you planning to do that's so important that it can't wait
until the end of your course?'

She opened her mouth to tell him about her dreams
of travelling, of seeing a world outside the one she had
grown up in—and then she remembered, and hastily shut
it again. Because that would never happen now. She had
forfeited her right to do any of that. 'I had to…get
away.'

Paulo frowned. Her anxiety was almost palpable, and
he leaned forward to study her, finding his nostrils sud-
denly filled with the warm, musky note of her perfume.
He moved out of its seductive and dangerous range.
'What's the matter with you, Bella?' he asked softly.
'What's happened?'

Now was the time to tell him everything. But one look
at the disquiet on his face, and the words stuck in her

throat. 'Nothing has happened,' she floundered. 'Other than the fact I've left.'

'So you said.' He felt another flicker of irritation and made sure that it showed. 'But you still haven't come up with a good reason why—' A pause, while the black eyes bored into her. 'Mainly, I suspect, because you don't have one.' Normally, he wouldn't have been so rude to her—but then this was not a normal situation. 'So, Isabella,' he said silkily. 'I'm still waiting for some kind of explanation.'

Tell him. But, faced with the iron disapproval in the black eyes, she found that her nerve had crumbled again. 'I was bored.'

'You were bored.' He tapped the arm of his hair with a furious finger.

'OK, stressed then.'

'Stressed?' He looked at her with disbelief. 'What the hell has a beautiful young woman of twenty got to be stressed about? Is it a man?'

'No. There is no man.' And that *was* the truth.

'For God's sake, Bella—it isn't like you to be so fickle! I can't believe that an intelligent girl—*woman*—' he corrected immediately and a pulse began a slow, rhythmical dance at his temple, 'like you should throw everything away because you're "bored"! So what? Stick it out for a few months more—because believe me, *querida*,' he added grimly, 'There's nothing quite so "boring" as a dead-end job—which is all you'll get if you drop out of college!'

And suddenly she knew that she couldn't tell him. Not now. Not in ten minutes' time—maybe not ever. How could she risk the contempt which would follow as surely as night followed day? Not from Paulo, whom she'd adored as long as she could remember.

'I wasn't looking for your approval,' she said woodenly.

'You don't seem to be looking further than the end of your nose!' he snapped. 'And just how are you planning to support yourself? Expecting Daddy to chip in, I suppose?'

She glared at him. 'Of course not! I'll take whatever I can get—I'm young and fit. I can cook. I'm good with children. Fluent in English and Portuguese.'

'A very commendable CV,' he remarked drily.

'So you'd recommend me for a job, would you, Paulo?'

'No, I damned well wouldn't!' His voice deepened into a husky caress. 'But I would do everything in my power to make you change your mind.' There was a pause, and then he spoke to her with the ease and affection which had always existed between them, until temptation had reared its ugly head.

'Go home, Bella. Complete your studies. Come back in a couple of years.' His eyes glittered as he imagined what two years would do to her. 'And *then* I'll find a job for you—on that I give you my word.'

She glanced down at her hands, unable to meet his eyes as his voice gentled. In a couple of years her world would have altered out of all recognition, in a way that she still found utterly unimaginable. 'Yes, you're probably right,' she lied.

'So you'll go back to college?'

'I'll…think about it.' She made a pantomime of looking at her watch, affecting a look of surprise. 'Oh, look—it's time I was going.'

'You're not going anywhere,' he protested. 'You've only just arrived. Stay and see Eddie—he'll be back soon.'

'No, I don't think I will.' She rose to her feet, anxious now to get away. Before he guessed. 'Maybe another day.'

'Where are you staying?'

'Just down the road,' she said evasively.

'Where?'

'At the Merton.'

'At the Merton,' he repeated thoughtfully.

He walked her to the front door just as they heard the sound of a key being slotted into the lock, and for some reason Paulo felt extraordinarily guilty as the door opened and there stood Judy—so cool and so blonde, wearing something soft and clinging in pale-blue cashmere, and a faint look of irritation on her face. Next to her stood his son, and the moment the boy saw Isabella his dark eyes lit up like lanterns.

'Bella!' he exclaimed, and immediately started speaking in Portuguese as he hurled himself into her arms. 'What are you doing here? Papa didn't tell me you were coming!'

'That's because Papa didn't know himself,' said Paulo, in the same language. 'Bella just turned up unannounced while you were out!'

'Are you coming to stay with us?' demanded Eddie. '*Please*, Bella! Please!'

'Eduardo, I can't,' answered Bella, her smile one of genuine regret. She had bonded with Eduardo from the word go—maybe because they had both had motherless childhoods. She had helped him with his riding and with his Portuguese and seen him grow from toddlerhood to a healthy young boy. And before very long, he would be towering above her as much as his father did. 'I'm going to be travelling around. I want to see as much of the country as I can.'

'Is this a private conversation,' asked the woman in blue, 'or can anyone join in?'

Paulo gave an apologetic smile and immediately switched to English. 'Judy! Forgive me! This is Isabella Fernandes. She's visiting England from Brazil. Isabella, this is Judy Jacob. She's—'

'I'm his girlfriend,' put in Judy helpfully.

Isabella prayed that her smile wouldn't crumple. 'Hello. It's nice to meet you.'

Paulo shot Judy a look which demanded co-operation. 'Isabella is a very old friend of the family—'

'Not *that* old,' corrected Judy softly, as she chose to ignore his silent request. 'In fact, she looks incredibly young to me.'

'Our fathers were at school together,' explained Paulo smoothly. 'And I've known Isabella all my life.'

'How very sweet.' Judy flashed a brief smile at Isabella and then leaned forward to plant a light kiss on Paulo's lips. 'Well, I hate to break the party up, sweetheart, but the show starts at—'

'And I really must go,' said Isabella hastily, because the sight of that proprietorial kiss was making her feel ill. 'Goodbye, Paulo. Goodbye, Judy—nice to have met you.' Her voice barely faltered over the insincere words. 'Goodbye, Eduardo.' She ruffled the boy's dark head and smiled down at him.

'But when will we see you?' Eduardo demanded.

'Oh, I'll be in touch,' she lied, but as she looked into the black glitter of Paulo's eyes she suspected that he knew as well as she did that she would not come back again. Because there was no place for her in his life here. No convenient slot she could fill—pregnant or otherwise. And if there had been the tiniest, most pathetic hope that she meant something more to him than just friendship... Well, that hope had been extinguished by a girlfriend who was the image of his late wife. A girlfriend who called him 'sweetheart' and who owned a key to his flat.

But then, what had she honestly expected? That she could turn up unannounced and tell him she'd run away from home—pregnant and alone—and that he would give that slow, lazy smile and solve all her problems for her?

She didn't stop for the traditional kissing of the cheeks—she didn't want to annoy Judy more than she already seemed to have done. Instead, she wrapped her coat tightly around her as she stepped out into the early evening and wondered just where she went from here.

CHAPTER TWO

'ISABELLA!' screamed a female voice from the bottom of the stairs. 'Can you get down here straight away?'

In her room at the top of the ugly, mock-Georgian house which stood in an 'upmarket estate', Isabella sighed. She was supposed to be off duty. Getting the rest which her body craved, and the doctor had demanded on her last visit to him. But that was easier said than done.

What did they want from her now, this noisy and dysfunctional family? she wondered tiredly. A pound of her flesh—would that be enough to keep them off her back for more than five minutes?

Wasn't it enough that she worked from dawn to dusk, looking after the lively twins who belonged to the Stafford family? Au pairs were supposed to *help* look after the children and engage in a little light housework, weren't they? And to have enough time for their own studies and recreation. They weren't supposed to cook and clean and iron and sew and babysit night after night for no extra money.

Sometimes Isabella found herself wondering just why she put up with treatment which clearly broke every employment law in the book. Was she weak? Or simply a fool?

But it didn't take long for her to realise exactly why she was willing to put up with such shoddy behaviour— one look in the mirror reassured her that she was not in any position to be choosy. The curve of her belly was

as ripe as a watermelon about to burst, and Mrs
Stafford—for all her faults—was the only prospective
employer who'd agreed to take her baby on, as well.

Of course, there'd always been the option of going
home to Brazil, or returning to the ranch. But how could
she face her father like this?

When her furtively conducted pregnancy test had
turned out to be positive, she'd been so stunned by disbelief that she hadn't felt strong enough to present her
father with the unwelcome news.

And the longer she put off telling him—the more difficult the task had seemed. So that in the end it had
seemed easier to run to England. To Paulo. Never
dreaming that her life-long infatuation with the man
would render her too proud to tell *him*, either.

Coming to the Staffords had seemed the only decision
which made any sense at the time, but she'd lived to
regret it since.

Or maybe the regret had something to do with letting
down the two men who she knew adored her.

'Isa-*bella*!'

Resisting the urge to yell back at her boss to go away,
Isabella levered herself off the bed and slipped her stock-
inged feet into a pair of comfortable slippers. If there
was one thing she enjoyed about being pregnant—and
so far it was the only thing she had enjoyed—it was
allowing herself the freedom to dress purely for comfort.
Elasticated waists and thick socks may have made her
resemble an enormous sack of rice, but she felt too cum-
bersome to care.

'Coming!' she called, as she carefully made her way
downstairs.

The twins came running out of the sitting room, their
faces working with excitement. Charlie and Richie were

seven year-old twins whose mission in life seemed to be to make their au pair's life as difficult as possible. But she'd grown fond of these two boys, with their big eyes and mischievous grins and excessively high energy levels.

Rosemary Stafford's methods of childcare had not been the ones Isabella would have chosen, but at least she was able to have a little influence on their lives.

She had tried to steer them away from the video games and television shows which had been their daily entertainment diet. At first, they'd protested loudly when she had insisted on sitting down and reading with them each evening, but they had grown to accept the ritual— even, she suspected, to secretly enjoy it.

'You've gotta vis'tor, Bella!' said Richie.

'Oh? Who is it?' asked Isabella.

'It's a *man*!'

Isabella blinked. Like who? 'But I don't know any men!' she protested.

Richie's mother appeared at the sitting room door. 'Well, that's a *bit* of an exaggeration, surely!' she said in a low voice, looking pointedly at Isabella's swollen belly. 'You must have known at least one.'

Isabella refused to rise to the remark—but then she'd had a lot of practice at ignoring her boss's barbed comments.

Ever since she'd first moved in, Rosemary Stafford had made constant references to Isabella's pregnant and unmarried state, slipping easily into the role of some kind of moral guardian.

Isabella thought this was rather surprising, considering that Mrs Stafford had become pregnant with the twins while her husband was still living with his first wife!

She gave a thin smile. 'Who is it?'

Mrs. Stafford was trying hard not to look impressed. 'He *says* he's a friend of the family.'

She could see Charlie and Richie staring up at her, but Isabella's smile didn't slip. Even though a thousand warning notes were playing a symphony in her subconscious. 'Did he give his name?'

'He did.'

'And?'

'It's Paulo somebody-or-other.'

Isabella's mouth froze. 'Paulo D-Dantas?' she managed.

'That's the one,' said Mrs Stafford briskly. 'He's in the drawing room. You'd better come along and speak to him—he doesn't seem like the kind of man who likes to be kept waiting.'

Isabella's hand strayed anxiously to her hair. What was he doing here? And what must she look like? Her eyes flickered over to where the hall mirror told its own story.

Her thick dark-brown hair had been carelessly heaped on top of her head, secured by a tortoiseshell comb. Her face was pale, thanks to the English winter—a pallor made more intense by the fact that she wasn't wearing a scrap of make-up.

'Why on earth didn't you tell me?' hissed Mrs Stafford.

'Tell you what?'

'That a man like *that* was the father of your child?'

Isabella opened her mouth to protest, but by then her employer was throwing open the door to the sitting room and it was too late to do anything other than go in and face the music.

The room seemed darker than usual and Isabella wondered why, until she saw that Paulo was standing staring out of the window and seemed to be blocking out much of the light.

He turned slowly as she came into the room and she saw his relaxed pose stiffen into one of complete disbelief as he took in her physical condition. The exaggerated bulge of her stomach. The heavy weight of her breasts.

She saw his black eyes glitter as they hovered on the unfamiliar swell, and she tried to read what was written in them. Shock. Horror. Disdain. Yes, all of those. And she found herself wishing that she could turn around and run out of the room again or, better still, turn back the clock completely. Something—anything—other than have to face that bitter look in this sorry and vulnerable state.

'Isabella.' He inclined his head in formal greeting, but the low-pitched voice sounded oddly flat.

He was wearing a dark suit—as if he had come straight from some high-powered business meeting without bothering to change first. The sleekly cut trousers made the most of lean, long legs and the double-breasted jacket hugged the broad shoulders and chest. Against the brilliant whiteness of his shirt, his skin gleamed softly olive. She had never seen him so formally dressed before, and the conventional clothes seemed to add to the distance between them.

Isabella felt the first flutterings of apprehension.

'Hello, Paulo,' she said steadily. 'You should have warned me you were coming.'

'And if I had?' His voice was deadly soft. 'Would you still have received me like this?'

She saw from the dark stare which lanced through her like a laser that it was not a rhetorical question. 'No. Probably not,' she admitted.

Mrs Stafford, who had been gazing up at Paulo like a star-struck schoolgirl, now turned to Isabella with a look of reprimand. 'Isabella—where are your manners? Aren't you going to introduce me to your friend?' She gave Paulo the benefit of a sickly smile.

Isabella swallowed. 'Paulo, this is Rosemary Stafford—my boss. Paulo is—'

'Very welcome,' purred Mrs Stafford. 'Very welcome indeed. Perhaps we can offer you a little refreshment after your journey? Isabella, why don't you go and make Mr Dantas a drink?'

Paulo said, in Portuguese. 'Get rid of her.'

Isabella felt inexplicably nervous. And certainly not up to defying him. 'I wonder if you'd mind leaving us, Mrs Stafford? It's just that I'd like to talk to my…friend—' she hesitated over a word which did not seem appropriate '—in private.'

Rosemary Stafford's pretty, painted mouth became a petulant-looking pout. 'Yes, I expect you do. I expect you have many issues to resolve,' she said, with stiff emphasis, and swept out of the sitting room, past where Charlie and Richie were hovering by the door, trying to listen to the conversation inside.

Paulo walked over to the door and gave the boys a slight, almost apologetic shrug of his shoulders, before quietly closing the door on them. And when he turned to face Isabella—she almost recoiled from the look of fury which burned from his eyes.

As though she were some insect he had just found squashed beneath his heel and he wished she would crawl right back where she had come from. But what right did he have to judge her? She thought of all she'd endured since arriving in England, and suddenly Paulo's anger seemed little to bear, in comparison. She drew her shoulders back to meet his gaze without flinching.

'You'd better start explaining,' he said flatly.

'I owe you no explanation.'

A pulse began a slow beat in his temple. 'You don't think so?' he said quietly.

'My pregnancy has nothing whatsoever to do with you, Paulo.'

He gave a hollow, bitter laugh. 'Maybe in the conventional sense it doesn't—but you involved me the moment you told your father that you were going to pay me a visit.'

She screwed her eyes up and stared at him in confusion. 'But that was months ago! Before I left Brazil. And I did visit you. Remember? That day I came to see you in your flat?'

'Oh, I most certainly do,' he said, grimly resurrecting the memory he had spent months trying to forget. 'I wondered then why you seemed so anxious. So jumpy.' He had been intensely aroused by her that day, and had thought that the feeling was mutual—it had seemed the only rational explanation for the incredible tension between them. But he wasn't going to tell her that. Not now. 'I also sensed that you were holding back—something you weren't telling me. And so you were.' He shook his head. 'My God!' he said slowly.

'And now you know!'

'Yes, now I know,' he agreed acidly. 'I put your tiredness down to jet-lag—when all the time...' He looked down over at her swollen stomach with renewed amazement. 'All the time you were pregnant. Pregnant! Carrying a *baby*.' The word came out on a breath of disbelief. 'How can this have happened, Bella?'

She met his accusing gaze and then she *did* flinch. 'Do you really want me to answer that?'

'No. You're right. I don't!' He sucked in a hot, angry breath. 'Don't you realise that your father is worried *sick* about you?'

'How can you know that?'

'Because he rang me yesterday from Brazil.'

'W-why should he ring *you*?' she stumbled in confusion.

'Think about it,' he grated. 'He asked me to come and see you, to find out what the problem is. Why your letters have been so vague, your phone-calls so infrequent.' He shook his head and the black eyes lanced through her with withering contempt. 'I certainly don't relish telling him the reason why.'

'So he still doesn't know?' she questioned urgently. 'About the baby?'

'It would seem not,' he answered coldly. 'Unless he's a very good actor indeed. His main anxiety seemed to stem from the fact that he could not understand why you had chosen to flunk university to become an au pair.'

'But he knew all that! I wrote to him—and told him that living in England was an education in itself!' she protested.

She'd kept her father supplied with regular and fairly chatty letters—though carefully omitting to mention her momentous piece of news. As far as he knew, she would probably go back and repeat her final year at college. She hadn't mentioned when she was going home and he hadn't asked. And she thought that she'd convinced him that she was sophisticated enough to want to see the world. 'I've been writing to him every single week!'

The chill did not leave his voice. 'So he said. But unfortunately letters sent from abroad are read and re-

read and scoured for hidden meanings. Your father suspected that you were not happy, though he couldn't put
his finger on why that was. He asked me to come to see
whether all was well.' Another cold, hollow laugh. 'And
here I am.'

'You needn't have bothered!'

'No, you're right. I needn't.' His mouth curved with
disdain as he gazed around the bland room, with its un-
adorned walls and rows of videos where there should
have been books. Littered on the thick, cream carpet
were empty chocolate wrappers. 'My, my, my—this is
certainly some *classy* hide-out you've chosen, Isabella!'
he drawled sarcastically.

His criticism was valid, but no less infuriating because
of that. She struggled to find something positive to say
about it. 'I like the boys,' she came up with finally. 'I've
grown very fond of them.'

'You mean the two hooligans who nearly rode their
skateboards straight into the path of my car?'

Isabella went white. 'But they aren't supposed to play
with them in the road!' How was she supposed to watch
them twenty-four hours a day? 'They *know* that!'

Paulo narrowed his eyes as he took a look at her pale,
thin face, which seemed so at odds with her bloated body
and felt adrenaline rush to fire his blood. He'd felt a
powerful sense of injustice once before in his life, when
his wife had died, but the feeling which enveloped him
now came a pretty close second.

And this time he was not powerless to act.

'Answer me one question,' he commanded.

Isabella shook her head. This one she'd been anticipating. 'I'm not telling you the name of the baby's father, if that's your question.'

'It's not.' He almost smiled. Almost. He had somehow

known that she would proudly deny him that. But he was glad. Knowledge could be a dangerous thing—and if he knew, then he might just be tempted to find the bastard responsible, and to…to… 'Is there anything special keeping you in this house, this particular area?'

'Not really. Just…the twins.'

Which told him more than she probably intended. That the father of her baby did not live locally. Nor live in this house. It wasn't probable—but it was possible. His mouth tightened. Thank God. 'Then go upstairs and get your things together,' he ordered curtly. 'We're going.'

It was one more bizarre experience in a long line of bizarre experiences. She stared at him blankly. 'Going where?'

'Anywhere,' he gritted. 'Just so long as it's out of here!'

Automatically, Isabella shook her head, as practical difficulties momentarily obscured the fact that he was being so high-handed with her. 'I can't leave—'

'Oh, yes, you can!'

'But the boys nccd me!'

'Maybe they do,' he agreed. 'But your baby needs you more. And right at this moment you look as if you could do with a decent meal and a good night's sleep!' He steadied his breath with difficulty. 'So just go and get your things together.'

'I'm not going anywhere!' she said, with a stubbornness which smacked of raging hormones.

Paulo gave a faint, regretful smile. He had hoped that it would not come to this, but he could be as ruthless as the next man when he believed in what he was fighting for. 'I'm afraid that you are,' he disagreed grimly.

Suddenly she wondered why she was tolerating that

clipped, flat command. She lifted her chin in a defiant thrust. 'You can't *make* me, Paulo!'

'I agree that it might not be wise to be seen carrying a heavily pregnant woman out to my car—though I am quite prepared to, if that's what it takes,' he told her, a soft threat underpinning his words. 'You can fight me every inch of the way if you want, Isabella, but I hope it won't come to that. Because whatever happens, I will win. I always do.'

'And if I refuse?'

Her eyes asked him a question, a question he had no desire to answer—but maybe it was the only way to make her see that he was deadly serious.

'Then I could threaten to tell your father the truth about why you left Brazil. But the truth might set in motion all kinds of repercussions which you may prefer not to have to deal with at the moment. Am I right?'

'You wouldn't do that?' she breathed.

'Oh, yes. Be assured that I would!'

She stared back at him with helpless rage. 'Bastard!' she hissed.

'Please do not use that particular term as an insult!' he snapped. 'It is entirely inappropriate, given your current condition.' His eyes flickered coldly over her bare fingers. 'Unless you have an undisclosed wedding to add to your list of secrets?' He read her answer in the proud tremble of her lips. 'No? Well, then my dear Isabella— that leaves you little option other than to come away with me, doesn't it?'

It was far too easy. Far too tempting. But what use would it serve? Could she bear to grow used to that cold judgement which had hardened his face so that he didn't look like Paulo any more, but some dark and disapproving stranger? 'I can't just leave without notice! What will the boys do?'

He refrained from telling her that her priorities were in shockingly bad order. 'They have their mother, don't they? And she will just have to look after them for a change. Does she work?'

Isabella shook her head. 'Not outside the home,' she answered automatically, as her employer had taught her to. In fact, Mrs Stafford had made leisure into an Olympic sport. She shopped. She had coffee. She lunched. And very occasionally she lay in bed all day, making telephone calls to her friends...

'Run upstairs—'

She turned on him then, moving her bulky body awkwardly as the emotion of having borne her secret alone for so long finally took its toll. She blinked back the tears which welled up saltily in her eyes. 'I can't run anywhere at the moment!' She swallowed.

He resisted the urge to draw her into his arms and to give her the physical comfort he suspected that she badly needed. It was not his place to give it. Not now and certainly not here. 'I know you can't—that's why I'm offering to help you. If you go and pack, I will deal with your employer for you.'

'Shouldn't I tell her myself?'

He thought how naive and innocent she could look and sound—despite the very physical evidence to the contrary. He shook his head impatiently. 'She's going to be angry, isn't she?'

Isabella pushed a dark strand of hair away from her face with the back of her hand. 'Furious.'

'Well, then—you can do without her fury. Let her take it out on me instead. Go on, *querida*. Go now.'

The familiar word made her heart clench and she had

to put her hand onto the back of a chair to steady herself.
She had not heard her mother-tongue spoken for months,
and it penetrated a chink in the protective armour she
had attempted to build around herself. She nodded, then
did as he asked, lumbering up to her room at the top of
the house with as much speed as she could manage.

She did not have many things to pack. She'd brought
few clothes with her to England, and what few she had
no longer fitted her. Instead, she'd bought garments
which were suitable for this cold, new climate and the
ungainly new shape of her body.

Big, sloppy jumpers, two dresses and a couple of pairs
of trousers with huge, elasticated waists which she was
currently stretching to just about as far as they could go.

She had been forced to buy new underwear, too—and
had felt like an outcast in the shop. As if everyone knew
she was all alone with her pregnancy. And that no man
would ever feast his eyes with love and pride on the
huge, pendulous breasts which strained against the func-
tional bra she'd been forced to purchase.

She swept the clothes and her few toiletries into the
suitcase and located her passport. On the windowsill
stood a wedding-day photo of her parents and, with a
heavy heart, she added it to the rest of her possessions.

And then, with a final glance round at the box-room
which had been her home for the last five months, she
quietly shut the door behind her.

At the foot of the stairs, a deputation was awaiting
her. Towering over the small group was Paulo, his hair
as black as ebony, when viewed from above. Next to
him stood Rosemary Stafford, her fury almost palpable
as she attempted to control the two boys.

'Will you keep *still*?' she was yelling, but they were
taking no notice of her.

Charlie and Richie were buzzing around the hallway like demented flies—whipped up by the unexpected excitement of what was happening, and yet looking vaguely uncertain. As if they could anticipate that changes would shortly be made to their young lives. And correctly guessing that they would not like those changes at all.

Isabella reached the bottom of the stairs and Paulo took the suitcase from her hand. 'I'll put this in the car for you.'

She felt like calling after him, Please don't leave me! but that *would* be weak and cowardly. Instead, she turned to Rosemary Stafford and forced herself to remember just how many times she had helped the older woman out. All the occasions when she had agreed to babysit with little more than a moment's notice. And never complained. Not once. 'I'm sorry to have to leave so suddenly—'

'Oh, spare me your lies!' hissed Rosemary Stafford venomously.

'But they're *not* lies!' Isabella protested. 'It isn't practical to carry on like this. Honestly. The truth is that I *have* been getting awfully tired—'

'Oh? And what about other, earlier so-called "truths"?' Rosemary Stafford's glossy pink lips gaped uglily. 'Like your assurance that the father of your baby wasn't going to turn up out of the blue and start creating havoc with my routine?'

Isabella was about to explain that Paulo was not the father of her baby—but what was the point? What could she say? The boys were standing there, wide-eyed and listening to every word. Trying to make two seven-year-old boys understand the reality of the whole bizarre sit-

uation was more than she felt prepared to take on right
then.

Instead, she reached out an unsteady hand and ruffled
Richie's blond hair. Of the two boys, he'd been the one
who had crept the furthest into her heart, and she didn't
want to hurt him. 'I'll write,' she began uncertainly.

'Take your hands away from him, and don't be so
stupid!' spat out Mrs Stafford. 'What will you write to
a seven-year-old boy about? The birth? Or the *conception*?'

Isabella shuddered, wondering how Mrs Stafford
could possibly say things like that in front of her children.

'It's time to leave, Isabella,' came a low voice from
behind them, and Isabella turned to see Paulo framed in
the neo-Georgian doorway. His face was shadowed, the
features so still that they might have been carved from
some rare, pitch-dark marble. Only the eyes glittered—
hard and black and icy-cold.

She wondered how long he had been standing there,
listening, whether he had heard Mrs Stafford's assumption that he was the father of her baby.

And her own refusal to deny it.

'Isabella,' prompted Paulo softly. 'Come.'

Impulsively she bent and briefly put her arms round
both boys. Richie was crying, and it took every bit of
Isabella's willpower not to join in with his tears, knowing that it would be self-indulgent to break down and
confuse them even more. Instead, she contented herself
with a swift and fierce kiss on the top of each sweet,
blond head.

'I *will* write!' she reaffirmed in an urgent whisper, as
Paulo took her elbow like an invalid, and guided her out
to the car.

CHAPTER THREE

As soon as the front door had shut behind them, Paulo let go of Isabella's elbow and she found herself missing its warmth and support immediately.

'The car is a little way up the street,' he said, still in that same flat tone which she'd never heard him use before.

He'd parked it there deliberately. Just in case. He had not known what he expected to find. Or who. He hadn't known if she would come willingly. And how he would've coped, had she refused. Because some instinct had told him even then, that he would not be leaving without her.

Isabella walked beside him towards the car, suspecting that he'd slowed his normal pace down in order for her to keep pace with him. She got out of breath so easily these days. 'Where are you taking me?'

'Taking implies force,' he corrected, looking down at her dark head, which only reached up to his shoulder. She seemed much too tiny to be bursting ripe with pregnancy. 'And you seem to be accompanying me willingly enough.'

What woman wouldn't? she thought, with another wistful pang. 'Where?' she repeated huskily.

A plane droned overhead, and he briefly lifted his face to stare at it. 'For now, you will have to come home with me—' He sent her a searing glance as if he anticipated her objection. 'Think about it before you say anything, Bella. It makes the most sense.'

If anything could be said to make sense at that precise moment, then yes, she supposed that it did. And hadn't that been her first choice? Before she'd seen him prowling half-naked around his own territory—like some sleek and beautiful cat? *Gato*. Before she'd seen the beautiful woman who'd frozen her out so effectively. Before she'd decided that she could not face him with her terrible secret.

'Doesn't it?'

Isabella nodded, wondering what Judy was going to say *this* time. 'I suppose so.'

'As to what happens after that...' A silky pause. 'There are a number of options open to you.'

'I'm not going back to Brazil!' she declared quietly. 'And you can't make me!'

He let that one go. For the moment. 'Here's my car.'

A midnight-blue sports car was parked with precision close to the kerb, and Isabella stared at the low, gleaming bodywork in dismay.

'What's the matter?'

She glanced up to find that the black eyes were fixed intently on her face. He must have noticed her hesitation. She gestured to her stomach, placing her hands on either side of her bump, to draw his attention to it. 'Look—'

'I'm looking,' he replied, taken aback by the sudden hurl of his heart as one of her hands strayed dangerously close to the heavy swell of her breast.

'I'm so big and so bulky, and your car is so streamlined.'

He held the door open for her. 'You think you won't fit?'

'Look away,' she said. 'It won't be a graceful sight.'

She began to ease her legs inside and his face grew grim as he turned back to look at the house they had just left—where two small boys forlornly watched them from an upstairs window. He did not know what lay ahead, beyond offering her temporary refuge, but already he suspected that his loyalties might be torn. How could they not be?

He'd known Isabella's father for years—ever since he was a boy himself. And for the last ten summers since his wife's death had accepted Luis's hospitality for both himself and his son.

Eddie had been just a baby when his mother had died so needlessly and so tragically in a hit-and-run accident that had produced national revulsion, but no conviction. The man—or woman—who had killed Elizabeth remained free to this day. In the lonely and insecure days following her death, it had seemed vital to Paulo that Eddie should know something of his South American roots.

As a father himself, Paulo felt duty-bound to inform Luis Fernandes what was happening to his daughter. But Isabella was not a child. Far from it. Would she expect him to collude with *her*? To keep quiet about the baby? And for how long?

He waited until they'd eased away from the kerb, before jerking his head back in the direction of the house.

'How long were you planning to stay there?'

'I don't know.' She stared at the road ahead. 'I just took it day by day. Mrs Stafford said that I could work the baby into my routine.'

Paulo's long fingers dug into the steering wheel. 'But you must have *some* idea, Isabella! Until the baby was…what…how old? Six months? A year? Would you then have returned to Brazil with a grandchild for your father to see? Or were you planning to keep it hidden from him forever?'

'I told you,' she answered tiredly, wishing that he wouldn't keep asking her these questions—though she noted that he'd refrained from asking the most fundamental question of all. 'I honestly *don't know*. And not because I hadn't thought about it, either. Believe me, I'd thought about it so much that the thoughts seemed to just go round and round inside my head, until sometimes I felt like I would burst—'

Paulo's mouth hardened. Hadn't he felt exactly like that after Elizabeth's death? When the world seemed to make no sense at all? He stole a glance at her strained, white face and felt an unwilling surge of compassion. 'But the more you thought about it, the more confused you got—so that you were still no closer to deciding what to do? Is that right?'

His perception disarmed her, just as the warmth and comfort of the car soothed her more than she'd expected to be soothed. Isabella felt her mouth begin to tremble, and she turned to look out of the window at the city speeding by, so that he wouldn't see. 'Yes. How could I be?' She kept her voice low. 'Because whatever decision I reach—is bound to hurt someone, somewhere.'

Her words were so quiet that he could barely hear, but Paulo could sense that she was close to tears. A deep vein of disquiet ran through him. Now was not the time to fire questions at her—not when she looked so little and pale and vulnerable.

He thought how spare the flesh looked on her bones— all her old voluptuousness gone. As if, despite the absurdly swollen bump of her pregnancy, a puff of wind could blow her away.

'You haven't been eating properly,' he accused.

'There isn't a lot of room for food these days.'

'Have you had supper?'

'Well, no,' she admitted. She'd been seeking refuge in her room: too tired to bother going downstairs to hunt through the junk food in the Staffords' fridge for something which looked vaguely nutritional.

'Your baby needs sustenance,' he growled. 'And so, for that matter, do you. I'm taking you for something to eat.'

Nausea welled up in her throat. She shook her head. 'I can't face the thought of food at the moment. Too much has happened—surely you can understand that?'

'You can try.' His mouth twisted into a mocking smile. 'For me.'

She knotted her fingers together in her lap. 'I suppose I'm not going to get any peace unless I agree?'

'No, you're not,' he agreed. 'Just console yourself with the thought that I'm doing it for your own good.'

'You're so kind, Paulo.'

He heard the tentative attempt at sarcasm and oddly enough it made him smile. At least her spirit hadn't been entirely extinguished. 'More practical than kind,' he murmured. 'We need to talk and you need to decide your future. And we can't do that in private at my house.'

'Because of Eduardo?'

'That's right.' He wondered how he could possibly explain away her pregnancy to the son who idolised the ground she walked on. 'He'll be curious to know why you're here—and we can't give him any answers if we don't know what they are ourselves. And it might just come as a shock for him to see you so—' the words tasted bitter on his lips '—so heavily pregnant.'

She remembered the cool, blonde beauty who had let herself in and forced herself to ask the question. 'What about Judy? Won't she mind me landing myself on you?'

'I shouldn't think so.'

There was an odd kind of pause and she turned her head to stare at the darkened profile.

'I'm not seeing her any more,' he said.

'Oh.' Isabella was unprepared for the sudden warm rush of relief, but she tried not to let it show in her voice. 'Oh, dear. What happened?'

Paulo compressed his lips, resisting the urge to tell her that it was none of her business. Because it was. Because somehow—unknowingly and unwittingly—Isabella had exposed him to doubts about his relationship with Judy which had led to its eventual demise.

He'd thought that shared interests and a mutually satisfactory sex-life were all that he needed from a relationship. But Isabella's visit had made him aware that there was no real *spark* between him and Judy. And something which he'd thought suited him suddenly seemed like an awful waste of time. 'We kind of drifted apart,' he said.

'But you're still friends?'

'I suppose so,' he answered reluctantly. Because that was what Judy had wanted. She'd settled for 'friendship' once she realised he'd meant it when he told her it was over. But he knew deep down that they could never be true friends—she still wanted him too badly for that. 'We're not supposed to be discussing *my* love-life, Isabella.'

'Well, I don't want to discuss mine,' she said quietly.

'Does that mean you aren't going to tell who who the father of your baby is?'

Isabella flinched. 'That's right.'

'Do I know him?'

'What makes you think I would tell you, if even you did?'

He found her misplaced loyalty both exasperating and admirable. 'And what if I made you tell me?' he challenged.

The streetlights flickered strange shadows over his face and Isabella felt suddenly uncertain. 'You couldn't.'

'Want to bet?'

'I n-never bet.'

'I'm not sure that I believe you,' he said softly. 'When you are living, walking proof that you took a *huge* gamble.' And lost, he thought—though he didn't say it. The look on her face told him he didn't have to. The car came to stop at some traffic lights and he shifted in his seat to get a better look at her.

And Isabella forgot the baby. Forgot everything. Through the dim light, all she could see in that moment were his eyes. Dark, like chocolate, and rich like chocolate, and sexy like chocolate. And chocolate was what Isabella had been craving for the past eight months. 'Paulo—'

But he'd turned his attention back to the road ahead. 'We're here,' he said grimly.

She heaved a sigh of relief as he pulled up outside an Italian pasta bar. Heaven only knew what she'd been about to blurt out when she had whispered his name like that. At least the activity of eating might distract him from his interrogation—and maybe she was hungrier than she had previously thought. It would certainly make a change to have a meal cooked for her.

The restaurant was small and lit by candles, and almost full—and Isabella was certain that they would be turned away. But no. It seemed that here they knew him well. Paulo asked for, and got, a table in one of the recesses of the room—well away from the other customers.

She glanced down at the menu she'd been given, at the meaningless swirl of words there. And when she looked up again, it was to find him studying her intently.

'Do you know what you want?'

She shook her head. 'No.'

He jabbed a finger halfway down his menu. 'Why don't you try some spinach lasagne?' he suggested. 'Lots of nutrients to build you up. And you, *querida*, could certainly do with some building up.'

She nodded obediently. 'All right.'

He wasn't used to such passivity—not from Isabella—and thought how wan her face looked as the waiter came over to their table. 'Drink some tomato juice,' he instructed, almost roughly. 'You like that, don't you?'

'Thanks. I will.' She shook out her napkin and smoothed it out carefully on her lap as he gave their order.

'So.' He traced a thoughtful finger on the crisp, white cloth and leaned across the table towards her. 'We—or rather *you*—have a few big decisions to make.'

'I'm not going home!

'No. So you said.' His mouth hardened. 'Anyway, your objection is academic, isn't it, Bella? No airline will allow you to fly in such an advanced stage of pregnancy.' He paused, his dark gaze on her belly, as if he could estimate the gestation just by looking. 'And you're…how many weeks?'

She hesitated. 'Thirty-seven.'

'Only three weeks to go,' he observed, his eyes burning into her. 'So when did you conceive?'

Isabella blushed. 'I don't have to answer that.'

'No, you don't,' he agreed. 'But I can work it out for myself in any case.' His eyes shuttered to dark slits as he did a few rapid sums in his head, then flickered open to stare at her with astonishment. 'That takes us back to just around Carnival time.'

'Paulo, *must* you?'

He ignored her objection, still frowning. 'That means you must have become pregnant just after I left.'

She supposed that there was no point in denying it. 'Yes.'

'Or maybe it was *during* my visit?' he suggested, unprepared for the lightning-bolt of jealousy.

'No!' she shot back.

He frowned again, not seeming to care that the waiter was depositing their food and wine before them. 'So who is it? I don't remember seeing you with anyone. No ardent lover hanging around the place. I don't remember you rushing off every minute to be with someone.'

Quite the opposite, in fact. She had been at *his* side most minutes of the day. Her father had even made a joke about it. *She has become your little shadow, Paulo,* the older man had laughed and Isabella had aimed a mock-punch at her father's stomach while Paulo had watched the movement of her lush breasts with hungry eyes and a guilty heart. And been very sure that if his host knew what was going on in his mind, then he would have kicked him off the ranch there and then.

'So who is it?' he asked again, only this time his voice sounded brittle.

Isabella mechanically ate a mouthful of pasta, forcing herself to meet his eyes. 'Is my coming to stay with you conditional on me telling you who the father is?'

'I don't need to know his name. I'm certainly not going to try to wring it out of you.' There was a long and dangerous pause. 'But if he turns up, demanding to see you—'

'He won't,' she put in hurriedly. 'It won't happen. I give you my word, Paulo.'

'You sound very sure,' he observed. He looked over the rim of his wineglass, fixing her with a dark gaze which was as intense as his next soft question. 'Does that mean that the affair is definitely over?'

The *affair*? If only he knew! 'Yes.' Isabella swallowed. She owed him the truth. Or as much of the truth as she dared give without earning making herself sound like the biggest fool who ever walked the earth. 'It's over. It never really got off the ground, if you must know.' Her eyes glittered with a defiant kind of pride as she stared at the man she had idolised for as long as she could remember.

'But I can't come to stay with you, not even for a minute—not if you despise me for what I've done, Paulo.'

'Despise you?' He looked across the table, saw the stubborn little tilt of her chin, and felt a wave of anger wash over him. What a way to have a first baby, he thought bitterly. It shouldn't be like this—not for any woman—but especially not for Isabella.

He remembered Eduardo's impending arrival, when Elizabeth had planned everything right down to the very last detail. Nothing had been left to chance, save chance itself. He had joked that her hospital bag had been packed almost from the moment of conception, and Elizabeth had laughed, too. His voice softened. 'Why on earth would I despise you?'

'Why do you think?' Isabella stared down at her plate with eyes which were suddenly bright. 'Because I'm going to have a baby. I'm going to be an unmarried mother! I've let my father down,' she husked. 'And myself!'

He leaned further across the table towards her, so that the flame of the candle was reflected in the black eyes. 'Now listen to me, Isabella Fernandes, and stop beating yourself up!' he whispered fiercely. 'We aren't living in the Dark Ages. You'll be bringing a baby up on your own—so what? A third of the population in England is *divorced*, for God's sake—and there are countless children who are the casualties of broken marriages. At least your child won't have to witness the deterioration of a relationship.'

'But I didn't *want* to have a baby like this!'

'I know you didn't.' He took her hand in his, staring down at it as it lay inertly in his palm. It felt small and cold and lifeless and he began to massage the palm with the pad of his thumb, stroking some kind of warmth back into it. He felt her trembling response and found himself filled with a sudden fierce need to comfort her. Protect her.

'There is no Merton Hotel, is there?' he asked suddenly.

She glanced up. 'How do you know that?'

His mouth twisted into a strange kind of smile. 'How do you think? I came looking for you.'

'*Did* you?'

'Sure I did.'

After she'd left his house so abruptly, he'd gone to the theatre with Judy. He had sat through the show feeling distracted and bored and had been forced to endure all kinds of intrusive questions afterwards at supper, when Judy had been determined to find out everything she could about Isabella.

Too much wine had made Judy tearful and very slightly hysterical as she'd accused him of concealing something about his relationship with the Brazilian girl.

She'd made accusations about Isabella which had appalled him nearly as much as they had aroused him...

Grim-faced, he'd driven her home and resisted all her attempts to seduce him. Afterwards, he had gone home and phoned Directory Enquiries for the number of the Merton Hotel, only to discover that no such place existed.

So Isabella had not wanted him to find her, he remembered thinking, with faint surprise, because women usually made it easy for him to contact them—not the opposite. But that, he had decided reluctantly, was her prerogative.

And now he knew why.

He stared at her. 'Just why *did* you come to see me that day, Bella?' he asked. 'Was it to ask for my help?'

She hesitated. 'I... Yes. Yes, it was.'

'But something changed your mind. I wonder what it was.' His eyes narrowed with interest. 'Why did you go away without telling me?'

'I couldn't go through with it. When it came down to it, I just couldn't face telling you.'

'And that's it?' he demanded.

Again, she hesitated, but she knew she couldn't admit that she'd been intimidated by his girlfriend. And by the very fact that he had one. 'That's it.' She turned her face up to his and stumbled out his name. 'Oh, Paulo!' she sighed. 'Whatever have I *done*?'

The choked little words stabbed at him, and he gave her hand one final squeeze. 'There's nothing you can do about it. You've been unlucky, that's all—'

'No, please don't say that.' She kept her voice low. 'This is a baby we're talking about! Not a piece of bad luck!'

'That's not what I meant. You took a risk—and

you've paid the ultimate price for that risk.' He gave a
bitter laugh. 'Didn't anyone ever tell you, Bella, that
there's no such thing as safe sex?'

But he found that his words produced unwanted images—images of Isabella being intimate with another
man, her dark hair spread in a shining fan across a
stranger's pillow and a bitter taste began to taint his
mouth. He put his napkin down on the table and threw
her a look of dark challenge. 'I just hope it was worth
it, *querida*.'

Worth it? Isabella stared down at her plate, but all she
could see was a blur of tears. If only he knew, she
thought. If only he knew.

CHAPTER FOUR

IT WAS getting on for nine o'clock when Paulo drew up in the quiet, tree-lined crescent. It was a cold, clear night and moonlight washed over the tall town houses, making them silvery-pale and ghost-like.

'Will Eduardo be asleep?' whispered Isabella, sleepy herself after the meal which she had surprised herself—and him—by almost finishing.

'You obviously have idealistic views on children's bedtime,' he answered drily as he put his key in the lock. 'He'll be playing on his computer, I imagine.' He opened the front door and ushered her inside, dumping Isabella's bag on the floor just inside the hall. 'Hello!' he called softly.

There was the sound of dishes being stacked some-where, and then a woman of about fifty appeared, wiping her damp hands down the sides of her trousers. She had short, curly red hair which was flecked with grey and a freckled face which was completely bare of make-up. Her navy trousers and navy polo-shirt were so neat and well-pressed that they looked like a uniform. She gave Isabella's suitcase a brief, curious look before smiling at Paulo.

'Ah, good! You're back just in time to read your son a story!'

'But he says he's too old for stories,' objected Paulo, with a smile.

'Yes, I know he does—unless his Papa is telling them. You're the exception who proves the rule, Paulo! As

50

always.' Her gaze moved back to Isabella and she gave her a friendly smile. 'Hello!'

'Jessie, I'd like you to meet Isabella Fernandes—who is a very old family friend.'

'Yes, I know—Eddie's talked about you a lot,' said Jessie, still smiling.

'And, Isabella—this is Jessie Taylor, who's so much more than a housekeeper! How would you describe yourself Jessie?'

'As your willing slave, Paulo, how else? Nice to meet you, Isabella.' Jessie held her hand out. 'Your father owns that amazing cattle ranch, doesn't he?'

'The very same.' Isabella nodded.

'Don't you miss Brazil terribly?'

'Only in the winter!' Isabella pulled her raincoat closer and gave a mock-shiver, grateful for Jessie's tact in not drawing attention to the baby.

'Isabella is going to be staying here with us for the time being,' said Paulo.

'Oh. Right.' Jessie nodded. 'That's in the spare room, is it?' she questioned delicately.

Paulo's eyes narrowed. Did Jessie honestly think that he'd brought a woman back here in the latter stages of her pregnancy for nights of mad, passionate sex?

He stared at Isabella's pink cheeks and guessed that she'd picked up on it, too.

'Yes, of course,' he said deliberately. 'In the spare room. Is the bed made up?'

'No,' said Jessie briskly. 'But I can do that now, before I go.'

'Oh, please don't worry,' said Isabella quickly. 'I'm not helpless—I can do it myself. Really!'

But Jessie shook her head. 'Good heavens, no—I

wouldn't dream of letting you! You look dead on your feet. Why don't you sit down, my dear?'

Isabella hesitated.

'Go on, sit down,' ordered Paulo softly. 'Make yourself at home.'

She was too tired to argue with him, thinking how easy and how pleasurable it was to have Paulo make the decisions.

She sank down onto one of the two vast sofas which dominated the room, and gingerly removed the shoes from her swollen feet. She glanced up to find him watching her, his brow criss-crossed with little lines of concern, and she produced a faint smile. 'You did tell me to make myself at home.'

'So I did. I guess I was just expecting you to argue back,' he observed drily. 'I had no idea you could be *quite* so stubborn.'

'And I had no idea you could be *quite* so domineering!'

'Didn't you?' he mocked softly and, when she didn't answer, he smiled. 'Stay there—I'm going in to say goodnight to Eddie.'

He found his son tucked up underneath the duvet, his eyes heavy with sleep.

'Hello, Papa,' Eddie yawned.

'Hello, son,' smiled Paulo softly. 'Did you get my note?'

'Uh-huh.' Eddie jammed a fist in his eye and rubbed it, giving another yawn. 'How's Bella?'

'She's…tired. And she's going to be staying with us.'

The child's face lit up. '*Is* she? That's fantastic! How long for?'

'I don't know yet.' Paulo paused as he tried to work out how to explain the complications of a very adult situation to a ten-year-old. But children dealt with simple truth best. 'She's going to have a baby, you see.'

Eddie removed the fist and blinked up at his father. 'Wow! When?'

Paulo smiled. 'Soon. Very soon.'

Eddie sat bolt upright in bed. 'And will the baby come and live here, too?'

'I doubt it,' said Paulo gently. 'They'll probably go back home to Brazil once it's been born.'

'Oh,' said Eddie disappointedly, and snuggled back down under the duvet. 'Judy rang.'

'Did she?' Paulo frowned. He had always been completely straight with the women in his life. From the start he told them that he wasn't looking for love, or a life-partner, or a substitute mother for his son. Judy had assured him that she could accept that—but time had proved otherwise and her behaviour over Isabella had only confirmed his suspicions. But Judy was tenacious and Paulo too much of a gentleman to curtail the occasional maudlin phone-call.

'Did she want anything in particular?' he asked carefully.

Eddie pulled a face. 'Just the usual thing. She wanted to know where you were and I told her. But she went all quiet when I mentioned Bella.'

'Oh, did she?' questioned Paulo evenly.

'Mmm.' Eddie yawned. 'Papa—do I have to go to school tomorrow?'

Paulo frowned. 'Of course you do. It's term-time.'

'Yes, I know, but…' Eddie bit his lip. 'But I want to see Bella—and she went rushing off last time.'

'She won't be rushing anywhere,' said Paulo, but he could see from the expression in his son's eyes that Eddie remained unconvinced. And then he thought,

What the hell? What was one day out if it helped a ten-year-old accommodate this brand-new and unusual situation? 'Maybe,' he said as he picked up the wizard book which was wedged down the side of the bunk-bed. 'I said *maybe*!' His eyes crinkled. 'Want me to finish reading this?'

'Yes, please!'

'Where had we got to?'

'The bit where he turns his father into a toad by mistake!'

'Wishful thinking is that, Eddie?' asked Paulo drily as he found the place in the book and began to read.

But Eddie was fast asleep by the end of the second page, and Paulo turned off the light and tiptoed out of the room to find Isabella in a similar state, stretched out on the sofa, fast asleep, her hands clasped with Madonna-like serenity over her swollen belly.

It was the first time he had seen the tension leave her face, and he stood looking down at her for a long moment, realising how much she must have had to endure in that soulless house—pregnant and frightened and very, very alone. Her hair spilled with gleaming abandon over the velvet cushion which was improvising as a pillow and her thick dark lashes fanned her cheeks. She'd loosened the top couple of buttons of her dress, so that her skin above her breasts looked unbelievably fine and translucent—as if it were made of marble instead of flesh and blood. He could see the line of a vein as it formed a faint blue tracery above her heart, could see the rapid beating of the pulse beneath.

He heard a sound and looked up to find Jessie standing on the other side of the room, her face very thoughtful as she watched him studying the pregnant woman.

She looked as though she was dying to fire at least one question at him, but her remark was innocuous enough.

'The spare room is all ready,' she said, and waited.

'Thanks.' He turned away from where Isabella slept, and walked into the dining room to pour himself a whisky while he pondered on what he should do.

Jessie had been working for him ever since Elizabeth had died. Sometimes he'd thought that she must have been sent to him by angels instead of an employment agency. She'd been widowed herself, and knew that practical help was better than all the weeping and wailing in the world. She was young enough to be good fun for Eddie, but not so young that she felt she was missing out on life by looking after a child who was not her own.

He also knew that she was expecting some kind of explanation now, and knew that he owed her one.

And yet he did not want to gossip about Isabella while she lay sleeping. He took a sip of his whisky and raised dark, troubled eyes to where Jessie stood.

'I'll be off now,' she said. 'There's a salad in the fridge, if you're hungry.'

'We ate on the way home.' He nodded at the tray of crystal bottles. 'Stay for a drink?'

Jessie shook her head. 'No, thanks—I've got a date.'

'A *date*?'

Her smile was faintly reproving. 'Don't sound so shocked, Paulo—I know I'm on the wrong side of forty, but I'm still capable of having a relationship!'

It occurred to him that Jessie might fall in love. Might even leave him. And, oddly enough, the idea alarmed him far less than he would have imagined. 'Is it…serious?'

'Not yet,' she said quietly. 'But I think it's getting there.'

'Whoa! And there was me thinking you were in love with your work!'

'In your dreams!'

He drew a breath and followed her out to the front door, where he helped her into her coat and handed her her gloves. 'Listen, Jessie—'

She turned to look up at him. 'I'm listening.'

'About Isabella—'

She shook her head firmly. 'No, honestly. You don't have to tell me anything—and I won't ask you anything.' She screwed her face up uncomfortably. 'Well, maybe just one thing—but then you probably know what that is, already.'

His gaze was nothing more than curious. 'What?'

'Are you the father?'

He very nearly spat his whisky out, and it took him several seconds before he was ready to answer. 'Jessie— that's so outrageous, it's almost funny! Almost,' he added warningly and his dark eyes glittered with indignant question. 'You don't honestly think that, do you? That I would suddenly produce a child-to-be? That I would have been having a relationship with Judy, when all the time I had made another woman pregnant?'

'No, of course I don't.' Jessie shrugged and sighed. 'When you put it like that, I suppose the very idea is crazy. But isn't that what everyone else is going to think?'

'Why would they think that?' he growled. 'She's only twenty!'

'And you're only just thirty!' Jessie retorted. 'It's not exactly the age-gap from hell!'

'And I've known her since she was a child,' he said stubbornly.

'Well, she's certainly no child now!' retorted Jessie.

After she'd gone, he walked back into the sitting room to stand over the sleeping woman on the sofa once more, mesmerised by the soft movement of her breathing. No, Jessie was right. Isabella was certainly no child.

She'd relaxed into her sleep even more. Her arms were stretched above her head and a smile played around her lips—the first really decent smile he'd seen all day. Though maybe that wasn't so surprising, in the circumstances. Maybe sleep offered her the only true refuge at the moment. And he realised with a pang just how much he had missed that easy, soft smile.

Overwhelmed by a sense of deep compassion, he leaned over her and put his hand on her shoulder and gave it a gentle shake.

'Isabella?' he said quietly.

She didn't respond—not verbally, anyway. She murmured something incomprehensible underneath her breath, and wriggled deeper into the sofa, and the movement made the fabric of her maternity dress cling to her thighs.

Paulo swallowed.

Pushing against the sheen of the material, the bump of the baby could be seen in its true magnitude. She should have looked ungainly, but she looked nothing of the sort—she looked quite lovely, and he felt his body battling with his conscience as he gently shook her shoulder again, but she continued to writhe softly.

He felt desire shoot through him like an arrow—all the more piercing for its unexpectedness and its inappropriateness. And he must have made a small sound, because her eyelids fluttered half-open to stare at him.

And in the unreal world between waking and sleeping, it seemed perfectly natural for Paulo's darkly implacable face to be bent so close to her that for a moment it seemed as though he might kiss her. It was a lifetime's fantasy come true and she stretched her arms above her head in unconscious invitation.

'Paulo?' she whispered dreamily. 'What is it?'

He shook his head, telling himself that she had aroused in him feelings of protectiveness, nothing more. Nature was cunning like that—it made a woman who was ripe with child look oddly beautiful so that men would *want* to protect her. 'It's bedtime,' he responded sternly, but the trusting tremble of her lashes stabbed him in the heart, and made him ache in the most unexpected of places. 'You look like you need it. If you want, I can carry you.'

'Heavens, no—I'll walk,' she protested, wide awake now. 'I'm much too heavy to carry.'

'No, you're not—I bet you're as light as a little bird. Want to test me it out?'

'No,' she lied, and struggled up into a sitting position.

He helped her to her feet and put his hand in the small of her back to support her, just the way he had once done with Elizabeth.

Except that Elizabeth had been almost as tall as him—while Isabella seemed such a tiny little thing beside him. Why, she barely came up to his shoulder. And yet looks could be deceptive—he knew how tough she could be. You only had to see her astride an excitable horse, expertly subduing it into submission, to realise how strong she could be. He had never imagined that she could look almost frail.

'Come on,' he said softly. 'Lean against me.'

Too sleepy to refuse, she allowed him to guide her

upstairs and into a bedroom, where there was a large bed with a duvet lying invitingly folded back.

'Get undressed now,' he whispered, as she flopped down on the mattress and sighed.

'Nnnng!' She pillowed her head on her hands, and closed her eyes.

'Isabella!' he said sternly. 'Get yourself ready for bed, unless you want me to do it for you!'

Her eyes snapped open. This was no dream. Paulo was here. Right here. And he was threatening to undress her! 'I can manage. Really.'

He gave her a narrow-eyed look of assessment, only really believing her when she unclipped her gold wristwatch and slid it down over the narrow wrist.

'Goodnight,' he said abruptly.

'Goodnight, Paulo.'

He left the door slightly ajar, so that the light from the corridor would penetrate the room if she woke. She would not flounder around frightened in the middle of the night in unfamiliar darkness.

But he was restless. Too restless for newspapers or the stack of paperwork he kept in the study, and which always needed attention. He drank some coffee and showered, and then slipped naked into bed, the cool sheets lying like silk against his bare skin while he lay and thought about the woman in the next room and who had made her pregnant. And how she could be persuaded to return to her own country—because surely that was the only rational option open to her.

He scowled up into the blackness, wondering why the idea of that should disturb him so.

In the end he gave up on sleep and decided that maybe he would tackle that paperwork after all. He pulled on a pair of jeans and shrugged a black T-shirt over his head, and on his way downstairs he paused briefly to look in on Isabella.

She was curled up on her side, facing the door, and from this angle the curve of her belly hardly showed at all. With the light from the corridor falling across the sculpted contours of her face and her lips slightly parted in sleep, it was easy to forget why she was here. Easy to imagine her being in a bed in his house for another reason entirely...

Paulo swiftly turned away and went downstairs.

He went through his papers on autopilot, gradually reducing the pile to a few sheets which his secretary could deal with tomorrow. He glanced down at his watch and yawned. *Today,* he should say. Better get to bed.

But he switched his computer on and began playing Solitaire.

He must have been dozing because he didn't hear the front door opening or clicking to a close. Nor did he hear soft footsteps approaching his study. In fact, the first indication that he had a visitor came from the sound of laboured breathing from just outside the door.

His eyes snapped open, his senses immediately on full alert, as he acknowledged that something had aroused him. He willed the aching fullness to subside.

'Bella?' he called softly. 'Is that you?'

'Sorry to disappoint you,' came an acid female reply. 'It's only me.'

He sat up straight as a tall, slim figure walked into the room and frowned at her in disbelief. *'Judy?'*

'Yes, Judy!' came the sarcastic reply. 'Why, did you think it was your little Brazilian firecracker?'

He reached out to click a further light on, his eyes briefly protesting against the bright glare as he stared at the woman standing uninvited before him.

The artificial light emphasised her pale-haired beauty—her long, willowy limbs and the pellucid blue eyes set in an alabaster skin. She wore jeans and an expensive-looking sheepskin jacket. And an expression he recognised instantly as a potent cocktail of lust and jealousy. He kept his face completely neutral.

'Hello, Judy,' he said softly, carefully. 'I wasn't expecting you.'

She raised her eyebrows and laughed. 'You made that obvious enough.'

He kept his voice steady. 'I didn't realise you still had a key.'

'That's what keeps life so interesting, isn't it, Paulo? These little surprises.'

He sighed. 'Judy, I don't want a scene.'

'No. It's pretty obvious from your greeting just what you *do* want!'

'Meaning?'

'Is that woman is staying here? She is, isn't she?'

'You mean Isabella?' he asked coldly.

Judy scowled, ignoring the warning note in his voice. 'You know damned well I do! You thought I was *her* when I came in, didn't you? "Bella"! Well, I'm so sorry to disappoint you, Paulo! How long is she planning on staying for?'

Paulo didn't react. The only movement in his face was the dark warning which glittered from his eyes. 'I don't think that this is a good time to have this conversation,' he said carefully. 'Apart from which, it's really none of your business.'

For a moment her face looked almost ugly as different emotions worked their way across it.

'She's the reason you dumped me, isn't she?' she demanded. 'You were never the same after she came here to see you. I could see it in your eyes that day. You were really *hot* for her, weren't you, Paulo? In a way you never were for me. Not once.'

His mouth hardened as he realised that she had no idea that Isabella was pregnant. And he had no intention of telling her. He carried on as though she hadn't spoken. 'I'm actually very tired, so if you don't mind…'

Judy stiffened as she read the rejection in his features. 'What's she got that I haven't, Paulo?' she pleaded. 'Just tell me that.'

He shook his head. 'Go home,' he whispered. 'Go home now, before it's too late.'

Her eyes lit up as she completely misinterpreted his words. 'For what? Too late to resist me, you mean? Well, maybe I don't want you to resist me. Maybe I want what you're trying to resist, just as badly as you do. What does it matter? I won't tell.' She moved towards the desk and the overpowering scent of her perfume invaded his senses and deadened them. 'Come on, Paulo—what do you say? For old times' sake.'

He shook his head, felt distaste whipping up his spine like a ragged fingernail. 'No.'

'No?' She flicked her pale hair back. 'Sure?'

This really was astonishing, thought Paulo. A beautiful blonde begging him for sex. It was most red-blooded men's ideal fantasy and yet all he could think of was that she was going to wake the pregnant woman who lay sleeping upstairs.

'Quite sure. Keep your voice down.' He flattened his voice as the needs of his body fought with the demands of his mind. 'And I think it's better if you go right now.'

'And what if I stay and do…this…?' Her hand swooped towards him and he knew immediately just where she intended to touch him.

'I don't want you to.' With razor-sharp reflexes, he snapped his fingers around her wrist to stop her. *'I don't want you to,'* he repeated deliberately. 'Ever again. Got that?'

She stared into his eyes, like a woman who had never encountered rejection before and snatched her hand back. 'Why not?' she sneered. 'You want to do it with *Bella*, I suppose?'

He didn't have to tell her to get out; the look in his eyes must have done that effectively enough. He just heard her running down the hallway and slamming the front door so loudly that it echoed through the house like gunfire.

He waited until the automatic response of his body had died away completely, and he felt an ugly kind of taste in his mouth. Quietly, he turned the computer off and went to find himself a drink.

Barefooted, he went silently along to the kitchen where he poured himself a glass of water and stood drinking it, looking out of the window into the night sky. Outside, silver-white stars pin-pricked the darkened night and he found himself picturing Isabella's father's ranch in Vitória da Conquista. Where the stars were as big as lollipops—so bright and so close that you felt you could lean out and pluck them from the sky.

He pressed the empty water glass to his hot cheek as he anticipated the fireworks to come. What the hell was Isabella's father going to say when he discovered that his beloved daughter was going to have a baby? By a man she was refusing to name! He was going to be *absolutely furious*.

He was just thinking about going back to bed when he turned to see Isabella standing in the doorway, silently watching him.

She had changed into a big, white nightshirt and a pair of bedsocks and had plaited her hair, so that two thick, dark ropes hung down either side of her face. She looked impossibly sweet and innocent, making the swollen belly seem indecent in comparison.

'Did I wake you?' he asked. He saw the way she grimaced, then tried to turn it into a smile and he pulled a face himself. 'Obviously, I did.'

'I heard…er…noises. Then the door slammed.'

'And did it startle you?'

'Only for as long as it took me to realise where I was. But I probably would have woken at some point, in any case. Indigestion,' she said, in answer to the query in his eyes. 'It's the bane of late pregnancy.'

'I suppose it is,' he said slowly. He stared again at her bulging stomach. 'Would a glass of milk help?'

'Yes, please.'

'Sit down, then, and I'll fetch it for you.'

She pulled a chair out from under the kitchen table and negotiated herself into it, wriggling her toes around inside the roomy bedsocks.

Paulo reached into the fridge and poured her a big, creamy tumblerful, then leaned against the draining board and watched while she drank it. He found himself fascinated by the white moustache she left behind, and by the tiny pink tongue-tip which snaked out to lick it away. Who would ever have thought that a heavily pregnant woman could look so damned sexy? he wondered.

His wife had been sick for a lot of her pregnancy. The doctors had told him she was 'delicate'. Like a piece of Dresden china that he dared not touch for fear of breaking her. And yet Isabella looked real and very, very touchable.

Isabella could feel him watching her, and she tried to drink her milk unselfconsciously, but it was difficult. And she could feel the baby moving around at the same time as her breasts began to sting uncomfortably in a way she was certain had nothing to do with the pregnancy. What conflicting and confusing messages her body was sending out!

She put the half-empty glass down on the table with a clunk. 'Did…did Elizabeth have an easy pregnancy?'

Paulo frowned. 'No, not really. It didn't agree with her. She was very sick for the first five months or more.'

Her expectant look didn't waver. Here in the quietness of the night, it was easier to ask questions which had always seemed inappropriate before. 'You must miss her.'

He didn't answer for a moment. 'I did. Terribly, at first. But it was such a long time ago,' he said slowly. 'That sometimes it seems to have happened to another person. We were together for two years, and Lizzie's been dead for ten.'

'Doesn't Eduardo ever ask?'

'Sometimes.'

Isabella studied him. 'And does he have any contact with his mother's family?'

'A little,' he began, then suddenly his temper flared. 'What is this, Isabella?' he demanded, suddenly impatient. 'Truth or dare?' Women did not ask him about his wife—in fact, they did the very opposite. Ignored the few photographs which existed of Elizabeth with her infant son. Never asked the child any questions about his mother, as though they could not bear to acknowledge that he had loved a woman and had a child by her.

'You want to squeeze every painful fact out of me?'

he grated. 'Yet obstinately refuse to disclose the identity of your baby's father?'

'That's different.'

'Why?' he snapped.

'Because there's no point in your knowing,' she said stiffly. 'I told you. It's over.'

'So why this sudden interrogation? Is this one rule for you and another for me? Is that it?'

She shook her head. 'If I thought that telling you would do any good, then I would.'

'But you don't trust me not to use the information?' he probed softly.

'No, I don't,' she admitted.

For some inexplicable reason, he smiled. 'Then you are wise, *querida*,' he murmured. 'Very wise indeed.'

He saw the way that one plait moved like a silken rope over her breast when she lifted her head to meet his gaze head-on like that. 'Now go to bed, Bella,' he said roughly. 'You need your sleep.' And I need my sanity.

She paused by the door. He had warned her off prying, but there were some things she really *did* need to know. And if Paulo was in the habit of having late-night visits... 'Did I hear you talking to someone earlier?'

'I had an...unexpected visitor.' He gave a grim kind of smile. And anyway, what was the big secret supposed to be? 'It was Judy.'

'But I thought you said that it was over?' She'd blurted the indignant words out before she could consider their impact. Or the fact that she had no right to say them.

He knew it was a loaded question. Knew it and was surprised by it. No, maybe not completely surprised. 'It is.' He gave her a brief, hard look. 'She won't be coming back again.'

'Oh.' She kept her voice as expressionless as possible and hoped that her face did the same. 'Was it serious between the two of you? I suppose it must have been if she had a key.'

He gave a faint frown, tempted to dodge the question, knowing instinctively that the truth would hurt her. 'I don't do "serious" any more, Bella,' he told her quietly.

She felt her heart plummet. 'No. Right. Well, I guess it's time I went back to bed.'

Paulo's eyes narrowed with interest as he watched the interplay of emotions on her face. Maybe Judy had been more astute than he had given her credit for.

'I guess it is,' he agreed blandly. 'Goodnight, Isabella.'

CHAPTER FIVE

ISABELLA was woken by a timid knocking on her bedroom door, and she yawned as she picked up her wristwatch from the bedside locker.

Sweet heaven—it was nearly ten o'clock! She stretched beneath the bedclothes after the best night's sleep she had had since arriving in England. How wonderful to have the luxury of lying in. By now in the Stafford house she would have been up and running for three hours. She would have cooked breakfast and loaded the washing-machine and be just about to pick up the vacuum cleaner.

The knocking on the door grew louder.

She sat up in bed and smoothed her hands over her dishevelled plaits. 'Come in!' she called.

A small, dark head poked itself round the door. It was Eduardo. And she could see wariness and excitement on his face.

'Hello, Eduardo.' She smiled. 'Come on in!'

'Hello,' he said cautiously.

'Or should I call you Eddie? That's what Jessie calls you, isn't it? Would you prefer that?'

'Only in England.' He nodded. 'When we're in Brazil, you can call me my real name.' He stood there rather awkwardly. 'Shall I draw the curtains back?'

She sensed his diffidence and widened her smile. 'Would you mind? That would be wonderful—then I can see what kind of view I have!'

The pale, sharp light of winter came flooding into the

room as the curtains swished back to reveal the green blur of the distant park. Eddie turned round and Isabella patted the edge of the bed. 'Come and sit down over here. Or do you have to go to school?' She frowned down at her gold wristwatch. 'Aren't you a little late?'

'Papa said I can have the day off—to welcome you,' he added shyly.

'I'm honoured,' she replied softly and patted the mattress again. 'Come and sit down.'

He hesitated for one shy moment, then came over and did as she asked, glancing at the huge bump rather cautiously. 'Papa said you were going to have a baby.'

'That's right.' She supposed he must have told Eddie the evening before, when he'd gone in to read a bedtime story and she had been lying dozing on the sofa. She wondered what he'd said to the child. How he'd explained away the lack of a father. Maybe he'd turned it into a lecture on morality. 'I am.'

'Does it hurt?' he asked.

Isabella smiled. 'No. Why should it?'

'You must have to grow more skin?'

She laughed, and the movement made the baby start to protest. 'I've never thought about that, to be honest. The most painful thing is when it kicks. Sometimes it gets you right—' she clutched at her ribs and screwed up her face in an expression of mock-anguish '—here!'

'Maybe that means he'll be a football player,' suggested Eddie hopefully.

'But what if it's a girl?'

He shrugged. 'Then she can watch!'

'Or be the star of an all-girls team?'

'Nah!' Eddie shook his head decisively. 'Girls don't play football! Not properly, anyway!'

Isabella laughed, enjoying the comfort of the bed and

the room, and the winter sunshine which streamed into the room and made bright puddles of light on the crisp blue and white bedlinen. It was very obviously a spare room—well-decorated and luxuriously appointed, but with little in the way of personality stamped on it. A vase of flowers might help, she thought. Or would that just look as though she was taking up permanent residence?

'Papa sent me in to ask whether you like tea or coffee in the morning?'

She made a face. 'Your father asked *that*? Tell him that I drink only coffee in the mornings—and then it must only be Brazilian coffee!'

'Ah! Then I must be a mind-reader,' came a murmured boast and Paulo appeared, carrying a tray of the most wonderful-smelling coffee.

He glanced over to the bed, to where she sat with strands of dark-bronze hair escaping from her plaits; Eddie was perched on the bed next to her and Paulo's breath caught like grit in his throat.

They looked such a *unit* sitting there together, that for a moment he found himself imagining what life might have been like if Elizabeth had not died, an indulgence he rarely surrendered to. There might have been brothers and sisters for Eddie, and Eddie might have sat on the bed with his pregnant mother, just like that. He felt a great wave of sadness for the hole in his son's life. 'OK if I come in?'

'Of course it is.' But Isabella had noticed the swift look of pain and wondered what had put it there.

'Papa—Bella says the baby's kicking!'

'Well, that's what babies tend to do.'

'Did *I*?'

'Sure you did.' Paulo nodded, and put the tray down.

He had not foreseen that having a pregnant woman around the place would open up a new channel of thought for his inquisitive son. 'Your mother used to say that you were sure to be a star footballer when you finally made an appearance!'

'But that's what Isabella just said about *her* baby!'

Glittering black eyes connected with hers. 'Oh, did you?' he asked softly, as he lifted up the coffee pot and began to pour.

Isabella found herself wishing that she had leapt straight out of bed and replaited her hair. Or something. Not, she reminded herself, that she was in any kind of condition to go leaping anywhere. And not that Paulo would even notice if she had done. She took the coffee he offered her. 'Thanks.'

He searched her face for shadows, real and imagined, but he could see none. 'Sleep all right?'

'Mmm.' Eventually. She'd heard him moving restlessly in the next room for a while after they had gone their separate ways, and then the milk had made her sleepy.

Eddie looked up at his father. 'Where are we going today, Daddy?'

'Well, Isabella needs to see a doctor—'

'No, I don't—'

'Oh, yes, you do,' he argued.

'But I saw one last week!' she protested.

'Not in London, you didn't,' he pointed out. 'And you need to meet the doctor who will be delivering you. A Brazilian friend of mine.' He stirred sugar into his coffee. 'Who happens to be one of the country's finest obstetricians! I've already spoken to him.' He saw her mutinous expression and turned to his son with a smile. 'Go and fetch Isabella some crackers, would you, Eddie? Pregnant women need to eat when they wake up.'

Isabella put her cup down as the child jumped off the bed and ran from the room and fixed Paulo with a determined look. 'I am not so provincial that I need to have a fellow countryman deliver me, you know!'

'No. But why not make life a little easy for yourself?' His mocking expression seemed to indicate that it wasn't too late to start. 'You can speak to him in Portuguese and he will understand you.'

'But I'm bilingual!' she replied.

His stare was very direct; the mischief in his eyes unmistakable. 'Yes, I know you are. But I won't feel happy until I've had you checked over properly.'

'You make me sound like a car! Whichever doctor I decide to see is my business, Paulo—not yours.'

'Ah.' He glittered her a look. 'But you've made it my business.'

'No, you did that all by yourself! My father just asked you to look me up,' she argued. 'That was all. *You* were the one who insisted on bringing me back to your home.'

'And by agreeing to come, I'm afraid that you put yourself under my domain. Don't fight it, Bella,' he murmured softly, his eyes gleaming as he deliberately made his statement as ambiguous as possible. 'I feel responsible for your mental and physical welfare—and that automatically gives me certain rights.'

'Rights?' She stared at him, and an odd kind of excitement began to unfurl in the pit of her stomach. 'What sort of rights?'

He gave a slow smile because her reaction hadn't gone unnoticed. 'Such as making sure you look after yourself—which you haven't been doing up until now. Simple things like eating properly, and getting enough rest and fresh air.' He looked up as his son came back into the room, and his eyes were still glittering. 'Oh, and a little gentle exercise wouldn't hurt.'

Isabella wondered if she was going insane. She must be. His words seemed to be laden with sexual overtones this morning—and the look in his eyes only seemed to confirm it. She put her empty cup down, reminding herself that she knew nothing of men—and even less about a man like Paulo Dantas—the man they called *gato*.

He sipped his coffee and watched her over the rim of his cup. 'Now, *querida*,' he said softly. 'On the subject of baby equipment.'

Isabella looked at him blankly. 'Baby equipment? What about it?'

'Exactly! You don't have any, do you? No crib. No pram. No nappies, even. And even little babies need toys and stimulation.'

She shook her head. 'No, babies need roots and they need wings,' she contradicted dreamily. 'Anything else is just extra.'

'Very idealistic, Bella,' he said drily. 'And it makes for a good opt-out clause if you don't happen to like shopping. But where are they supposed to sleep?'

'Babies can sleep in drawers, if they need to!'

'*Can* they?' asked Eddie, who came back in, carrying a plate of dry crackers.

'Sure they can!' Isabella took a biscuit. 'When people lived in caves, they didn't have bassinets, did they?'

'When people lived in caves, the man's word was law—sounds like good sense to me,' said Paulo coolly. 'And as the man of the house I suggest we go out today and buy everything you need.'

'And can we go to the toyshop, Papa?' Eddie demanded eagerly.

'Provided Isabella isn't too tired.' He frowned as he handed her a cup of coffee. 'And, just out of interest, how were you planning to manage at the other place? Were you really planning to put the baby in a drawer?'

'Of course I wasn't.' She waited while the baby completed its three hundred and sixty-degree turn in her belly before replying. 'Mrs Stafford said I could use the twins' old baby stuff.' Tired-looking pieces of equipment which had been stacked in a disused garage and covered with dust and cobwebs. 'She said they would clean up perfectly!'

'I'll bet she did,' said Paulo grimly. 'Well, why don't you get showered and dressed.' He glanced down at his watch. 'Your doctor's appointment is at midday.'

He was certainly showing a very bossy side to his nature, thought Isabella as she stood beneath the power-shower in her luxurious en-suite, which gushed as efficiently as a small waterfall. She savoured every moment of it, washing her hair without difficulty.

She lumbered back into the bedroom afterwards and slipped her other maternity dress on. She'd only bought a couple—unwilling and unable to invest money in clothes she would never wear again. But at least Paulo hadn't seen her in this one before, and its cheerful yellow colour warmed the pale olive of her skin and brought out the red highlights in her dark hair.

Everything took such a long time when you were this pregnant. She sat down heavily at the dressing-table and picked up her hairbrush, wondering if she had the energy to dry her wet hair, strand by laborious strand.

A movement at the open door attracted her attention and she glanced up to see Paulo reflected back at her— and it was with a sense of guilt that she noticed how the dark trousers moulded themselves so beautifully to the jut of his hips and the powerful line of his thighs. Surely she shouldn't be thinking about his *legs* at a time like this?

'Want me to do that for you?' he asked.

'Dry my hair?'

The eyes gleamed with the faintest hint of laughter. He had seen just where her gaze had focussed itself. 'That's what I meant.' He walked over to the mirror and plucked the silver-backed hairbrush from her hand. 'Relax,' he soothed, as he stroked the bristles down through the resisting locks. 'Come on. Relax.'

Relax? How could she possibly do that when his pelvis was on a level with her back, and the reflection of his black eyes was mocking her in the mirror?

But the soothing movement of the brush lulled her into a glorious state of peace and calm. Ironic, really, considering just how precarious her position was. She guessed that this was what they called false security, and let her gaze drift upwards to clash with the hard glitter of ebony once more.

'You know, I'm going to have to ring your father today, Bella. He'll be expecting me to get back to him and wondering why I haven't. And you'll need to speak to him yourself.'

She kept the tremor of nerves away. 'Not today.'

'When, then?'

'Tomorrow. When I feel...calmer.'

'You think twenty-four hours will make such a difference?' he demanded.

'I don't know. I just haven't made up my mind what to tell him.'

'How about the truth?' he suggested sardonically. 'Or is that something which is beyond you?'

'I haven't told him any lies!' she defended.

He gave a short laugh. 'You just ran away instead. Well, I'm afraid that it won't do, Bella!'

She stiffened. 'What do you mean, it won't do? It'll do if I say it will!'

'Not if I decide to tell him myself,' he said silkily.

'You wouldn't do that!'

'Oh, wouldn't I?' he questioned softly, but a note of steel had entered his voice. 'Believe me, I would do whatever I felt necessary to guarantee the well-being of you *and* your baby.'

'Even if it was contrary to what I wanted?'

'Your wants are of no particular concern to me!' he snapped. 'Your *needs* are far more relevant! Have you stopped to think about the things that could go wrong?'

Her golden eyes widened in alarm. 'Such as what?'

He drew in a deep breath. He didn't want to put the fear of God into her—but that did not mean she could bury her head in the sand, either. 'You're young and fit and healthy—but pregnancy carries its own risks. You're an intelligent woman, Bella—you know that. Your father needs to know about the baby.'

He did not want to spell it out, that if some calamity befell her during labour... He gripped the hairbrush so hard that his knuckles whitened. 'That doesn't mean you have to tell him who the father is,' he added gently. Not yet, anyway.

He hoped that she wasn't about to get a rude awakening and that her airy assurance that she would feel herself after the birth proved to be the case. He wondered how she would cope if she fell foul of the baby blues. Or how he would cope...

He picked up the hairdryer and blasted the thick, dark mass with warm air until her hair hung in a shimmering sheet all the way down to her waist. 'Let's see what the doctor says first,' he said evenly.

She met his eyes in alarm, realising that whatever she said he would blithely ignore it, if he thought that it was in her best interests to do so.

She thought about arguing with him, but instinct told her that it would be a waste of time. And besides, deep down she knew he was right. 'OK,' she sighed.

He carefully caught up the great weight of hair and tied it at the base of her neck with a saffron-coloured ribbon which matched her dress. 'I think I like it when you're acquiescent,' he murmured.

She met his eyes in the mirror. 'Don't hold your breath!'

The doctor's suite of rooms was in an upmarket patch of Knightsbridge, and Isabella wondered how much this was all costing. But when she tentatively broached the subject of cost with Paulo, she was silenced by an arrogant wave of his hand.

The doctor insisted on conducting the entire examination in Portuguese, despite all Isabella's protestations that her English was fluent.

'But it is the mother-tongue.' The doctor smiled sentimentally. 'And particularly appropriate for the mother-to-be. Do you want Paulo to stay with you?' he added.

Isabella shot Paulo a look of pure horror.

'No, I won't be staying,' answered Paulo smoothly, answering her furious query with an unconcerned smile. 'Isabella is by nature a traditionalist, aren't you, *querida*? She knows how easily men faint!'

She didn't trust herself to reply, just gave him a frozen smile before the nurse popped the thermometer into her mouth.

The doctor was ruthlessly thorough, making little

clicking noises as he listened to the baby's heartbeat with an old-fashioned trumpet, as well as the most high-tech equipment she had ever seen.

She dressed again and sat down in front of the doctor and Isabella didn't realise how nervous she was until he looked at her over the top of his spectacles and gave her a look which managed to be both reassuring and alarming.

'Everything is fine—but there is room for improve-ment! You have not been resting enough!' he announced sternly. 'And you are a little underweight. You must look after yourself, do you understand?'

'Yes, Doctor,' she answered meekly.

Paulo was ushered back into the room and the doctor spread out some shiny black and white ultrasound photos on the desk.

'See what a beautiful baby you have.' He smiled at them both.

Isabella swallowed as she looked down at the tiny limbs. So perfect. A lump rose in her throat and when she looked up it was to see Paulo's eyes on her—the dark gaze oddly soft and luminous.

'A very beautiful baby,' agreed Paulo softly, giving her such a blindingly brilliant smile that she felt quite dizzy—so dizzy in fact, that she couldn't make out a word the doctor was saying to him.

In fact, the nurse was busy chattering herself. She wanted to know everything. Which part of Brazil did Isabella come from?

'From Bahia.'

'Very beautiful,' the nurse replied. 'The Land of Happiness.' It seemed that she had taken holidays there as a child. She glanced down at one of the ultrasound photos Isabella was clutching, and smiled. How long had she known Paulo for?

'Oh, most of my life,' Isabella replied automatically.

'*That* long?' The nurse gave a dreamy sort of sigh.

'Mmm. Obviously, I was a child for a lot of that time.'

'Ah, of course! He is a handsome man—a *very* handsome man,' whispered the nurse, though Isabella wasn't sure whether this was at all professional. '*Gato,*' she finished huskily, with an admiring look at Paulo's hips.

'What was the nurse saying to you?' Paulo asked her, as they walked out of the clinic towards the car.

'Oh, nothing much,' replied Isabella vaguely. She certainly wasn't going to boost his ego by telling him that the nurse had unerringly hit on his Brazilian nickname. 'What was the doctor saying to *you*?' she asked him suspiciously.

He hesitated, and waited until she was safely strapped into the low, deep blue car before he told her.

'He said that between the two of us, we had created a fine Latino baby!'

She felt a pang of something approaching wistfulness. 'Oh, Paulo, he *didn't*!'

'Yes, *querida*—he did. I suppose it was a natural enough assumption to make under the circumstances.'

'So why didn't you explain that you weren't the father?'

'And what would you have me tell him instead?' he questioned, his voice chilly now. 'That you're refusing to say who the father is?'

'That *is* my prerogative.'

'Though maybe you don't even know yourself?' he challenged insultingly.

Isabella felt the blood rush to her face. Is that what

he thought of her? That any number of men could qualify for paternity? 'Of course I know who the father is!'

A look of triumph flared darkly in his eyes and she realised too late that she had walked into some kind of trap.

Paulo's voice was deceptively soft. 'But he doesn't know about the baby either, does he? You haven't told him, have you, Isabella?'

Her lips trembled, but she could not afford to break down. Not now, when she had nursed her secret so carefully and for so long. 'No, I haven't.' She found herself imprisoned in the searchlight of his keen, dark gaze.

'Why not?'

She had kept the identity of her baby's father secret from everyone. Because the moment she gave a name to either Paulo—or Papa—she could just imagine the outcome. Somehow they would track Roberto down, demand that he take an active role in her child's life. Isabella shuddered. Never! 'I don't have to answer that,' she said.

'No, of course you don't. But don't you think that he—as the father—has a right to know? And not just a right—a *responsibility* to share in the child's upbringing.'

'No! Because it's over! There's no *point* in telling him!'

But even as she spoke she felt guilt descend on her like a dark cloud. She wasn't being fair to Paulo—allowing him to pay for everything and allowing him to care for her, too. He had rescued her. Given her sanctuary. A sanctuary she hadn't realised she had needed, until it had been forced upon her. And maybe that gave *him* some rights.

Paulo turned the key in the ignition with an angry jerk,

wondering why he almost preferred to think that she *didn't* know who the father was. As if it was somehow more acceptable to imagine her having some regrettable one-night stand with far-reaching consequences, than the alternative. Had she loved the man responsible? Did she love him still?

Perhaps her statement that it was over was just a ruse. She could be using the baby as a way to lever herself back into the man's life. Planning to just turn up and present a child who crooned so sweetly in her arms. Some proud, dark lover, maybe, who would be swayed by the sudden production of his own flesh and blood. It wouldn't be the first time it had happened.

Isabella sneaked a look at the forbidding set of his jaw, and her heart sank even more. To Paulo, it must seem as though she was letting her child's father get off scot-free. Yet it was not quite as simple as that. The situation was bad enough—but if she tried imagining a future which involved Roberto—it made her feel quite ill. A man she didn't love and who didn't love *her*. What effect could he have on her life, other than disaster?

'Paulo?' she asked tentatively, but he smacked the flat of his hand down on the steering wheel in frustration.

'I never had you down for such a coward!' he stormed. 'What do you think is going to happen after the birth?'

'I don't know!' she answered back, and right then she didn't care—even that he had called her a coward—because a band of steel had tightened and stretched across her abdomen, and she felt her face distort with discomfort.

One look at her white face and Paulo's rage instantly evaporated. 'It's not the baby, is it?' he demanded.

She panted shallowly, the way she had been taught. 'No, I don't think so.'

He changed down a gear. 'Sure?'

She nodded. 'It's just one of these—' She struggled to remember the English for the unfamiliar medical term. 'Braxton-Hicks contractions—nature's rehearsal for the real thing.' She pressed her hot face onto the cool of the car window and gulped, hoping that Paulo wouldn't notice she was precariously close to tears.

But he did. He noticed most things. And as a way of bringing his interrogation to a close, her threatened tears proved extremely effective. He felt an impotent kind of rage and anger slowly unfurling in the pit of his stomach, and he was longing to take it out on someone. Or something.

If she hadn't been pregnant he might just have pulled into a layby and treated her to the kind of kiss he felt she deserved, and they both needed. He felt the first warm lick of desire and wondered grimly what masochistic tendency had pushed him towards *that* line of thinking.

If he had been on his own, he might have taken the car to the nearest motorway and driven it as fast as was safe. As it was, he didn't dare—one bump and her face might take on that white, strained look again. He slowed right down and negotiated the roads back to the house with exaggerated care.

Isabella had recovered her equilibrium by the time they got back to the house, but Paulo was busy treating her like an invalid. He made her eat an omelette and salad, then insisted that she lie down for a rest.

'But I'm not tired!'

'Really?' He cocked a disbelieving eyebrow at her.

'I'm fine,' she insisted, even while she allowed him

to crouch down by her feet to slip her shoes off. 'Honestly.'

'Well, you don't look fine.' He propelled her gently back against the stack of pillows. 'You look worn out.'

Isabella wriggled her head back against the pillow, and stared up into the glittering black eyes. 'Anyway, you promised Eduardo we could buy toys today—he was looking forward to it.'

'And we can. But only if you sleep first,' he ordered firmly. He brushed a damp lock of the bronze-black hair away from her cheek and carefully extracted the photos of the baby from where they lay clutched tightly between her fingers.

'That's bribery,' she objected muzzily.

'So what if it is?' came the soft rejoinder. 'Remember what the doctor told you.'

He glanced in on her more than once, telling himself that he was just making certain that the pains *had* been a false alarm.

But if he was being truthful he *enjoyed* watching her as she lay sleeping. And, if he examined his conscience, wasn't it erotic? The steady rise and fall of her breasts, so full and ripe and hard. The way the dark fringes of her eyelashes brushed over the flushed curve of her cheeks. The firm swell of the child as it grew within her. Look but don't touch. Of course it was erotic.

When Isabella awoke she felt much better. She slapped cold water on her face and brushed her teeth and went to find Paulo and his son sitting at the dining-room table, playing Scrabble.

Paulo looked up and gave her a long, searching stare, then nodded his head as if satisfied. 'That's better,' he murmured.

'Bella!' exclaimed Eddie, his face lighting up. 'Papa

said I wasn't to wake you! He said that you needed your sleep.'

'And he was right.' Her cheeks were flushed as she bit back a yawn. 'I did.'

'See how tolerant I can be, Bella,' Paulo said softly. 'When some people might find the urge to say, "I told you so"!'

'Very tolerant,' she agreed gravely, relieved that his black mood of earlier seemed to have subsided.

'And he says we can go and choose toys for the baby if you're well enough. Are you, Bella?'

Paulo was on his feet. 'Shush, Eddie,' he murmured. 'Bella has already had a trip to the doctor's this morning. We might have to put the toys on hold until another day.' Night-dark eyes captured her gaze. 'How do you feel?'

'Absolutely fine. I'm looking forward to it.'

'Very well. We will have a leisurely afternoon in the toy-shop.' He rose to his feet like some sleek, black panther. 'On the condition that you take it easy if I tell you to.'

She opened her mouth to point out that he wasn't her personal physician, but the warning gleam in his eyes made her change her mind. 'Very well,' she agreed demurely. 'I'll go and get ready.'

He chose one of the capital's biggest children's stores, where he seemed hell-bent on buying the place up and it was Isabella who had to restrain him.

Having rather distractedly looked round the place at baby paraphernalia which still seemed so *alien* to her, she placed her hand restrainingly on his arm. 'I just need a small pram that can double as a carry-cot, Paulo—nothing more for the time being.'

He stared down at the slim, ringless fingers as they

rested on the dark blue wool of his overcoat. 'What about a crib? And a high-chair?'

She shook her head before he could recite the entire contents of the shop to her. 'No, none of those. Not yet. They take up too much room and the baby can sleep in the pram until...' Her voice tailed off.

His eyes narrowed. 'Until you fly home to Brazil?'

She tried to imagine it, and couldn't. Tried to imagine staying here with Paulo—and that was even harder. 'I guess so. Oh, look—the assistant is coming over.'

His mouth flattened with irritation as the sales assistant fluttered to dance attention on his every word.

Isabella let him buy a baby-seat for the car, a drift of cashmere blankets and a tape of 'mood-music' to play to the baby.

She was caught between delight and protest. 'It isn't necessary,' she began, but the look of determination on his face made her give up.

At last they went to find Eduardo, who was totally engrossed in a train set in the toy department. He looked up as they approached, and his face fell. '*Oh!* Can't I stay here for a bit longer, Papa?'

'Sure you can,' grinned his father. 'Come on, Isabella—let's wander round and see what the fashionable baby is playing with these days!'

She'd planned to say yes to only the simplest and most inexpensive of the toys, deliberately telling herself that manufacturers were making a fortune out of bits of plastic. But, even so, they were surprisingly seductive and her attention was caught by a pyramid of stuffed animals in pale shades of pastel.

'And all colour co-ordinated—especially for the nursery,' said Paulo. He held up two teddy-bears, one pink and one blue, and waggled them like semaphores, managing to attract looks of interest from most of the women in the shop. 'So what are you hoping for, Bella—a boy or a girl?'

It was an innocent question which every mother-to-be in the world was asked. But no one had ever asked Bella before. Maybe they had been too embarrassed. Perhaps people thought that an unplanned pregnancy for a single girl meant that you didn't have the normal hopes and fears for your baby. But Paulo's words sparked some complex and primitive chain of emotions which included hope and despair and a terrible feeling of regret. As if they were a normal, expectant couple and Paulo really *was* her baby's father.

Oh, if only, she thought longingly as her field of vision dissolved into a helpless blur of longing. If only.

'Isabella?' His voice seemed to come from a long way off. She tried to say something, but her stilted words came out as nothing more than a jerky wobble. 'Isabella? What is this?'

'N-nothing.'

He saw the bright glare of tears which had turned her eyes into liquid gold. Her mouth began to tremble and he acted purely on instinct. They were standing beside a large red play-tent, and he simply flicked the flaps back and pulled her inside, where it was mercifully empty. Into their own private world, and into his arms where she burrowed through the warmth of his coat, letting her tears fall like raindrops onto his silk shirt.

He could feel her warm breath shuddering against his chest as she drooped her hands softly over his shoulders, and he felt an overpowering urge to tightly cradle her.

It was a surreal setting. They were bathed in a soft red light which made the inside of the tent almost womblike. 'W-we can't stay here,' she husked, a hint of quiet hysteria breaking through the blur of her tears.

'We can stay anywhere we damned well please!' he contradicted on a silken whisper. 'But quietly. Quietly, Bella. Do not excite yourself...or the baby.' Or me, he thought, with a sudden guilty realisation.

Her huge belly was pushing against him, so close that he could feel the baby as it moved inside her. But instead of acting as a natural deterent he found the action one of unbearable intimacy. It was comfort he intended to give her. Not this...this...powering of his heart so that it pounded hotly inside his head and his groin.

He deliberately made the gesture more avuncular, smoothing the flat of his hand down over her hair, fluidly stroking her head as if she were a Siamese cat, while the tears continued to soak through his shirt and onto his shoulder.

And it wasn't until the flow had abated and he had traced one last glimmering teardrop away with the tip of his finger, that he used that same finger to lift her chin, imprisoning her in the sweet, dark fire from his eyes.

'Want to talk about it?' he murmured.

What—and tell him that she wished he *was* the man who had caused life to spring within her? Little could terrify a man who didn't 'do' serious, more than that. She shook her head. 'I'm overwrought,' she said. 'It's a very—' and she gulped '—emotional time.'

'You're telling me,' he said grimly.

'Oh, Paulo!'

'I know.' He tightened his grip. She felt so warm and trembling and vulnerable in his arms. So small. Tiny, almost. What else could he do but carry on holding her like this? This was a hug she needed, he realised. That he seemed to need it too was what troubled him. 'What is it?' he asked her in her own language, feeling her breath warm his chest as she attempted to speak.

'I'm s-so s-sorry!'

He frowned, as he wiped a tear-soaked lock of hair away from her forehead. 'You've got nothing to be sorry for.'

'I got pr-pregnant, didn't I?'

His stare was laser-sharp. His need to know momentarily overrode his desire to be gentle with her. 'Deliberately?' he questioned. '*Was* it a gamble you took, Bella? As a way of keeping a man who perhaps didn't love you as much as you loved him?'

She gazed at him, shocked. 'No, of course not!' But by a man I didn't love. And she couldn't tell him that, could she? Because if she admitted that, then it would make the consequences of her act even harder to bear. At least love would have justified the whole wretched mess.

His eyes narrowed with alarming perception. 'Even if you *do* regret the act, Bella, you must learn to accept the consequences. Otherwise you will suffer, and so will the baby. Here.' And he smoothed away the last strand of hair, which had escaped from its confining bow. 'Come on, now—we're going home.'

He demanded that Eduardo make sure she stayed sitting on one of the carved wooden benches which adorned the shop's lavish entrance hall, while he brought the car round to the front of the building.

In her weakened state, she watched him. Watched his muscular grace and confident stride. He seemed quite oblivious to the fact that he could stop the traffic. Literally.

He arrogantly stepped in front of the traffic and no one dared not to obey him as he raised an imperious hand in command. But several cars had slowed down so much that they were almost stationary anyway—eager, no doubt to watch the spectacular-looking man with the brooding features as he helped the pale and pregnant woman into the car.

CHAPTER SIX

'BED!' Paulo insisted, just as soon as they arrived home.

'But—'

'Bed!' he repeated grimly. 'From now on we obey the doctor to the letter. He said you needed rest—and that's what I intend to make sure you get.'

One look at his expression told her that to put up a fight would be a waste of her time and energy, so she crept away to her room, where the bed was almost as welcoming as his embrace in the shop had been. The pillow felt soft against her cheek, and as sleep enfolded her, she remembered the way he had held her, with concern softening the brilliance of the dark eyes.

He brought her soup and toast and fruit for supper, and afterwards she slept on. As if her body was greedily sucking up every bit of relaxation it had been denied during her stay at the Staffords'.

She slept right through the night still tantalised by the memory of that hard, beautiful face and awoke to the sound of silence, which made her think that perhaps the flat was empty. But when she had showered and dressed, she found Paulo lying stretched out on the sofa in the sitting room.

He looked more relaxed than she had ever seen him, his dark hair all rumpled as it rested against a silken cushion. A newspaper was spread out over his bent knees and the jeans clung like syrup to his muscular thighs. Her heart crashed painfully against her ribs and the baby kicked against her, as if objecting. She took a deep, calming breath.

'Hello, Paulo.'

He glanced up from the newspaper, thinking how warm and soft she looked, all breathless and sparkly eyed. And how that innocent-looking white blouse provided the perfect backdrop for the thick, dark curls. He found himself wishing that he could reach out and untie the ribbon which confined them and let the whole damned lot tumble down and spill like satin around her shoulders.

'Well, good morning,' he said thickly, and put the paper down. 'Or should I say good afternoon?'

Her breath seemed to have caught somewhere in her throat. 'I overslept again.'

'That's good.'

'Have you eaten breakfast?'

'Not yet. I was waiting for you. Then I started reading and forgot about it.' He stretched his arms and stood up. 'I'll make it.'

'Where's Jessie?'

'She's gone shopping,' he replied, without missing a beat. He had sent the housekeeper out over an hour ago. There were a few things he was planning to say to Isabella today, and he wanted to do so in private. And if Jessie were there she would inhibit him. Because for the first time since Elizabeth's death, he had felt a tiny bit *crowded* by the woman who had worked for him for so long and so tirelessly. And he couldn't quite decide whether it was all tied up with Isabella's presence, or by the fact that Jessie now had a man.

Jessie's attitude had changed. And it wasn't so much the things she said—more the things she *didn't* say. The pursed lips. The raised eyebrows. The knowing smiles.

As if she knew some mysterious secret that she was keeping from him. And he was damned if he was going to ask her what the hell it was.

Isabella glanced at the newspaper headlines, but the drama of world news held little interest for her. She supposed it was the same for all women at this stage in their pregnancy—her world had telescoped right down into this baby inside her.

It was almost lunchtime by the time they sat down to eat, and Paulo waited until she had munched her way through a pastry before delivering the first part of the little lecture he intended to give, no matter how much she fluttered those big amber eyes at him.

'I want to talk to you about yesterday, Bella.'

Her coffee suddenly lost all its appeal. 'What about it?'

'You were in a virtual state of collapse in the shop,' he accused, looking at her as fiercely as if she had set out deliberately to do it!

'It won't happen again, I promise.'

'Damned right it won't! Because there will be no more all-day excursions, that's for sure! Dr Cardoso has agreed he will see you here at the house in future.' He pushed a dish of fruit across the table towards her and, to avoid a lecture on supplementing her diet with vitamins, she obediently took an orange.

'I should not have trailed you halfway around London the way I did,' he snapped.

Isabella slowly began to peel her orange, tempted to point out that he hadn't had to drag her screaming, but one look at his face told her not to bother. 'Finished?'

'No. Not yet.' He watched her pop a juicy segment in between her lips and swallowed down a sensation which came uncomfortably close to lust. 'In future, you will rest when I think you need to rest, and you will eat properly.'

She met his eyes with amusement. 'Oh, will I?'

'Yes, you will,' came the silky promise. 'You'd better make the most of this enforced leisure, Bella—God only knows it will be over soon enough!' His eyes were deadly serious now. 'Are you *listening* to me, Bella? Do you understand what I'm saying?'

'Of course I do.' She lifted up the jug. 'Coffee?'

'Please.' He hadn't finished yet, but he let her attempt to distract him.

She poured him a cup, thinking that this was what living with a man must be like. The small intimacies. The shared breakfasts. Her eyes strayed to the triangle of flesh at his neck which was exposed by an open button and she found herself wondering what it would be like to slowly unbutton that shirt, to lay bare the skin beneath and touch its silken surface with the tips of her fingers... And she wondered, too, whether it was madness or just depravity to yearn for someone while she carried another man's child. 'More toast?' she asked, her cheeks going pink with guilt.

'No, thanks,' he said, knowing that she was studying him, and *liking* it—even though he was uncomfortably aware of the irony of their situation. He wasn't in the habit of having breakfast with women. He had always insisted on eating the first meal of the day alone, or with his son, no matter who he had spent the night before with—or how wonderful it had been. It had been a strict rule, necessary to his son's well-being and security. His girlfriends hadn't liked it—but none of them had been willing to risk making a fight of it.

He found himself studying *her*, his gaze mesmerised by the full, tight swell of her breasts.

Sitting there, with her white cotton blouse straining across the bump of baby and without a scrap of make-up on her face, she looked the antithesis of the glamorous women who had passed through his life after the death of his wife. The cool, pale-blonde beauties with their enigmatic smiles.

And if anyone had suggested that he might find himself physically attracted to a woman who was pregnant with another man's child, he might have seriously questioned their sanity.

So how was it that he found he wanted to run the tip of his tongue all the way along that deep cleft which formed such an erotic shadow between her ripe, swollen breasts? He tried to quash the slow, sweet burn of desire as he met her expectant golden eyes but his mouth felt sandpaper-dry.

He glittered her a look of warning across the table. 'Today you *must* speak to your father—you can't put it off any longer. And the truth, Bella—because nothing else will do. He needs to know that you're going to have a baby and that in a couple of weeks time he will become a grandfather.'

A segment of orange slipped unnoticed from her hand. 'Paulo, I told you—I *can't!*' She couldn't bear the inevitable hurt—the disappointment which would surely follow. She loved her father and the bond between them was close. Or had been.

'You can't put it off any longer, I know that,' he said grimly. A combination of frustration and a sudden irrational fear that something might happen to her during the birth made Paulo's temper begin an inexorable simmer towards boiling point. 'Why can't you? What's stopping you? Are you frightened of his anger? Is he such a tyrant that you daren't tell him? What is the worst thing that could happen, Bella?'

'Let me spell out the stark facts for you,' she whispered. 'I am an only child. The only daughter. All my father's hopes and dreams rest with me—'

'I know all this.'

'Then surely you can understand that I can't just let him down?'

He hardened his heart against the misty blur of her eyes. 'It's a little late in the day for that, surely?'

'Your will is very formidable, Paulo,' she told him quietly. 'But even you can't impose it on me.'

He pushed his chair back and stood up. 'No, you're right—I can't,' he said coldly. 'But if you won't tell him today, then I *will*. I've told you what I think. End of subject.' He began to move towards the door.

She looked up in alarm. 'Where are you going?'

'Anywhere, just so long as it's out of here and away from the crazy thinking that masquerades as logic inside that head of yours!' he snapped. He saw her soft mouth pucker, irritated by the way the little movement stabbed at his conscience. 'Call me if you need me—I'll be working in my study. You know where the phone is!' With that he left the room, closing the door behind him with an exaggerated softness.

Left on her own, Isabella was restless. She cleared away their breakfast things and then wandered around aimlessly, putting off the inevitable moment. It was a huge, sprawling house and yet the walls closed in on her like a prison. She forced herself to curl up on the sofa and channel-hopped the TV stations for a while, but nothing grabbed her attention enough to draw her in. There just seemed to be inane game-shows and cookery programmes which didn't seem to teach you anything about cookery.

She found herself looking out of the window at the rain which lashed relentlessly against the pane and a deep, aching part of her knew that Paulo was right. That a baby was not a secret you could keep hidden for ever.

She *should* ring her father. Take all her courage and tell him.

Pity there were no books you could study to prepare for moments such as these. What should her opening line be? 'Papa, you know you always used to talk about becoming a grandfather—'

She shook her head and went back over to the sofa, glancing at her wristwatch. It would be lunchtime now at home, and her father would be tucking into a large plate of beans and rice and meat with vegetables. She dampened down a sudden pang of homesickness. Not a good time to ring. She would try later—after the siesta.

She must have drifted off to sleep herself, because she was woken up by the sound of a distant ringing, and then the click of a door opening, and when she opened her eyes it was to see Paulo standing looking down at her, his face tight and white and strained with an unbearable kind of tension.

She opened her eyes immediately. 'Paulo? What is it? What's happened?'

'I think you'd better come and speak to your father.'

She blinked at him, still befuddled. 'Did he phone?'

'Bella! This has gone on for long enough. You've got to start some kind of dialogue with him—and you can start *right now*!'

She levered herself up with difficulty.

'I'm waiting until after his siesta,' she yawned. 'I'll ring him then.'

He shook his head and his voice sounded odd. Quiet and controlled, but odd. 'I don't think you understand. You're too late. We've moved beyond the stage of being hypothetical. Your father is on the telephone, waiting to speak to you.'

'He can't be!'

'I can assure you that he is.'

The urgent pitch of his voice told her something else, too. 'He knows about the baby?' she asked him tonelessly.

'What do you think?'

She rose to her feet, putting her hand out onto the arm of the sofa to steady herself. 'You told him, didn't you?'

His gaze was steady. 'I had to.'

'Oh, no, you didn't!' she breathed in disbelief. 'You were just playing God, weren't you? You decided! You just went straight ahead and did exactly what you thought best—'

'Isabella.' He interrupted her with an icy clarity which stopped her in her tracks. 'Your father was worried sick—wondering why you hadn't got back to him. He asked me explicitly whether anything was wrong. So what did you want me to do? Compound what is going to happen anyway with a lie? How would that make me look?'

'That's all you care about, is it? How *you* look?'

He shook his head. 'Believe it or not, I care about you—I always have done. Why else would I have brought you back here?' he put in drily. 'But try putting yourself in my shoes and you'll realise you're not being fair. I owe it to your father, after all he has done for me, to tell him the *truth*! How could I look him in the eye if I had done otherwise? I am thinking only of your welfare, Bella, truly.'

He paused for a moment to let the impact sink in, aware that he was hurting her—maybe even frightening her—but even more aware that it was time she faced up to facts. 'You are acting like a child. It is time to face the music, *querida*.' He gentled his voice. 'Now, your father is waiting, impatient for the answers to his questions. I suggest you go along to my study and provide them for him. Go on.'

She knew then that she could not put this off any longer. She was beaten. And ashamed. She had let them both down—more than that—her stubbornness and her cowardice had made a difficult situation even worse.

She stared up into Paulo's eyes, searching for something…anything. Some sign that she was not all alone, and the faint black gleam of empathy there was the only thing which gave her courage to do as he said.

Walking tall and very straight, she went into his study, where the telephone receiver was lying amidst the heap of paperwork which littered his desk. She picked it up with a hand which was oddly steady.

'Papa?' she breathed.

It was her father as she had never heard him before, his voice distorted with a kind of dazed disbelief.

'Bella, please tell me this isn't true,' he began.

'Papa,' she swallowed, but that was all she could get out.

'So it's true!' There was a short, terse exclamation, as if her inability to speak had damned her. 'You're *pregnant*,' he accused in a low voice.

There was no place left to go. No hiding place. The steel door of the prison clanged shut behind her. 'Yes,' she whispered. 'Yes, Papa—I'm afraid I am.'

In the seconds it took to confirm his fears, his voice seemed to have aged by about ten years. *'Meu Deus,'* he said heavily. 'I should have realised that something was the matter! Your explanation why you wanted to leave college never really convinced me, not in my heart. You were doing so well. *I should have realised!*'

'Papa, I didn't think—'

'No!' He cut across her words with uncharacteristic impatience. 'It is *me* who didn't think—*me* who has let your poor, dear mother down and failed as a parent.'

This was worse than unbearable. 'That's not true and you know it! You've been the best father there ever could have been.' She sucked in a painful breath. 'Papa, I'm so sorry.'

There was a short, strained silence and she could almost hear her father struggling to gain control over his composure.

'*You're* sorry?' The voice changed. 'But you are not the only one who is to be held accountable, are you, Bella? What of the...father—' he bit the word out with difficulty ' of your baby?'

'What about him?' A shadow fell over the desk, and she looked up into a silent black stare and the hand which was holding the receiver began to shake. 'I don't want to talk about him.'

Her father ignored her. 'Well, I do.'

'Papa—'

'What does he say about all this?' he persisted. 'Has he offered to marry you yet?'

'No, he hasn't. And even if he had I wouldn't want to. Women don't have to do that these days if they don't want to.'

'Please don't tell me what women "want"!' he snapped. 'Maybe your own wishes should not be paramount—you have a baby to think of, in case you have forgotten!' There was a pause. 'Put Paulo on.'

'Paulo?'

'Is he there?'

'Yes, he's here.' Wordlessly, she handed the phone to the man who towered over her, but whose body language was so distant that he might as well have been a million miles away.

She stayed exactly where she was, because this wasn't what you could ever term a private conversation. She had every right to hear what they were saying about her.

'Luis?' Paulo kept his voice impassive, suspecting that Isabella's father would be angry at him for having kept her secret for so long.

'Paulo, how could you do this?'

'I'm sorry, Luis,' he said, genuinely contrite.

'A little late in the day for that, surely?' asked the older man, then sighed. 'I should have *realised* what was happening. Everyone else seemed to.' There was a moment's silence. 'Maybe it was inevitable—she always worshipped the ground you walked on—'

'Luis—' said Paulo, as alarm bells began to ring inside his head. But the older man sounded as if he was in therapy—talking through a problem in an effort to solve it.

'Maybe it was fate. I'm her father and even I thought you looked good together.' Another sigh, heavier this time. 'Still, these recriminations won't help now. These things happen in the old and the modern world. You're together now and that's all that matters. But I need a little time to get used to the idea. You understand. The last thing Bella needs at a time like this are harsh words. Tell her I'll call in a day or so, will you?'

'Sure,' said Paulo evenly.

'Goodbye, Paulo.'

'Goodbye, Luis.'

He replaced the receiver very slowly, and stood looking at it for a moment. And when he raised his head, his
eyes were filled with a cold fire which sent a tremor of
apprehension shivering its way down her spine.

'What is it?' she whispered.

'Sit down,' he said.

'Paulo?'

'Sit down,' he repeated.

She slid into the chair he was indicating, placing her
knees together like a schoolgirl in a class photo. Which
was a bit how she felt. 'OK. I'm sitting.' There was an
air of seriousness about him that she had never seen
there before and her heart picked up a beat. She braced
herself for the worst. 'What did he say?'

He stared at her. The way she had lifted her chin—
the slightly defiant gesture not quite hiding the very real
fear and confusion which lurked at the back of the amber
eyes. He guessed there was no easy way to tell her.

'Paulo—*what did he say*?'

He laughed, still reeling from the irony himself. 'That
I am the father of your baby.'

There was a moment of disbelief, followed by a
stunned silence. 'But that's crazy!' she said, shaking her
head in furious denial. 'Crazy! I've never heard anything
so—'

'Isabella,' he interrupted, seeming to choose his words
with enough care to bring them slamming home to her.
'Just think about it.' He slid into the chair opposite hers,
so that their knees were almost touching and even in the
midst of her jumbled thoughts, her body still registered
his proximity.

'I am thinking about it!' It was the most bizarre thing
she had ever heard. How could she be pregnant by a
man she had never even kissed? 'I mean, we haven't

even…even…' Her words faded away to an embarrassed whisper.

'Had sex?' he supplied brutally, quashing the guilty thought that indeed they had not…just in the fevered bed of his imagination and maybe it was about time he started turning fantasy into reality. 'No, we haven't. How very right you are, Bella,' he murmured. 'It's a sickener, isn't it—to be blamed for something you haven't actually done?'

'So how can he possibly believe it to be true?'

'He isn't the only one, is he?' he snapped. 'That Stafford woman thought I was responsible. So did the doctor. Even Jessie secretly believes it—no matter how much I deny it!'

'But why?'

'I believe it's called circumstantial evidence,' he clipped out. He moved his face closer to hers, his voice low and urgent. 'Point one—you have steadfastly refused to reveal the true father's identity.'

'But—'

'Point two,' he interrupted coldly. 'As soon as you found out you were pregnant, you left Brazil and came rushing straight to England—to *me*. Didn't you?'

'Well, what if I did?' she croaked. 'That on its own doesn't make *you* the most likely candidate, does it?'

His smile was forced. 'On its own, no—it doesn't. But add that to the fact that your father noticed a certain frisson between the two of us, back in February. A chemistry which was apparently remarked on by most of the people there at the time.' He paused, and frowned, because this was puzzling *him*. 'Which was almost *nine months ago*.'

The final damning piece of evidence fell into place and made the whole picture clearer—except that it was not the true picture at all, merely an illusion. 'Oh, my God!'

'Precisely,' he snapped, and his face grew hard. 'Now I'm not going to deny the attraction which fizzed up between us, because only a self-deluding fool would do that.' His mouth twisted in tandem with the convoluted line of his thoughts. 'But nothing more than wishful thinking happened on my part. I did not have sex with *anyone* during my trip to Brazil. I can't speak for you, of course.'

She couldn't look at him, her gaze falling miserably to her lap. She knew what his eyes would accuse her of. That she had lusted after him, but had fallen into the bed of someone else almost immediately. And when it boiled down to it—wasn't that the awful truth?

'Now, the facts may be stacked up against me, *querida*—but just in case your father comes after me with a shotgun in his hand I want you to tell me one thing.'

She knew what his question would be, even before his lips had started to coldly frame the words. A question she had evaded for so long now that evasion had become almost second nature.

'Just who *is* the father of your baby?'

CHAPTER SEVEN

ISABELLA swallowed. 'His name is R-Roberto.'

Paulo's eyes grew stony as he heard her voice tremble over the name. He shook his head. 'Not good enough. I need more than that.'

It didn't even occur to her to object to that snapped demand. She was in too deep now to deny him anything. 'His name is Roberto Bonino and he—'

'Who is he?'

This was the difficult bit. 'I knew him at university.' She swallowed.

Paulo's stiffened as he recognised evasion on a mega-scale. 'Another student, you mean?'

She felt her neck grow hot. 'No.'

'Tell me, Bella.'

Something in his voice compelled her to look up at him and she knew that her pink, guilty cheeks gave her away at once. 'He...he was one of the lecturers, actually.'

There was a long, dangerous pause. 'One of the *lecturers*?'

'Y-yes.'

Somehow he had been expecting the worst, but the truth was no less devasting in its delivery. He felt the cold, dead taste of disappointment in his mouth. And the slow burn of anger. 'But that's a complete abuse of power!' he snarled.

'He was only temporary—'

'And you think that makes what he did acceptable?'

She shook her head, its weight pressing down like a heavy rock on her neck. 'No. Of course I don't.'

The anger inside him gathered and grew into bitter accusation. 'So was it love, Bella? True love? The kind that fairy-tales are made of? Eyes across a crowded room and wham-bam—' his black eyes glittered '—you're in so deep you can't think straight?'

She heard the cynicism which stained his words, and shook her head. There had only ever been one man who had had that effect on her and he was sitting within touching distance. 'No.'

He wanted to grab hold of her and lever her up into his arms, but he forced himself to stay sitting. 'What, then? What exactly *was* the relationship between you? Tell me what happened!'

Still she couldn't look him in the eye—unable to face his condemnation and scorn when she told him what lay behind her ugly seduction. That it had been Paulo who had set her senses on fire. Paulo who had set in place a fevered longing that meant she hadn't been able to think straight. It had been Paulo who had planted the rampant seeds of desire—but had left just before the inevitable harvest...

'I used to go to his psychology lectures,' she explained painfully.

'Psychology? Oh, *great*!' He felt like punching his fist through the wall. 'Do you think he'd ever thought about studying his *own* behaviour?'

She carried on as if he hadn't interrupted, a slight desperation touching her words now. 'He was more a friend than anything. At least—that's what I thought. We used to go out in a big group sometimes—'

'Didn't he have any friends his own age?' he asked sarcastically.

'Actually, he wasn't much older than most of the people he used to teach, so he fitted in.'

'Yeah, he sure did,' he agreed pointedly, then found her answering blush too painful to contemplate. 'And?' he prompted, but the harsh note of accusation had all but gone.

Isabella looked at him—at the carved perfection of his face with its intriguing blend of light and shade. A proud, beautiful face which now wore an icy-cold mask of disapproval. 'I guess I was all mixed up.' That much was true. She had been longing for Paulo—obsessed by his memory.

'And randy?' he questioned cruelly. 'Surely you're not forgetting that?'

She swallowed down a lump of distaste. 'Let's just say I wasn't completely indifferent—' She saw him jerk his head back as if she had struck him, and tried to be as honest with him as possible. 'We'd both had a few drinks and...' Her voice tailed off, too embarrassed to continue.

Paulo seethed with a terrible kind of rage. He bit the words out as if they were bitter poison while his fist itched to connect with her tutor's pretty, young face. 'You mean he got you *drunk*?'

'No, of course he didn't!' She nearly asked him what he took her for, but she didn't dare. He might just tell her. 'I had a couple of glasses of wine on an empty stomach and I'm not used to alcohol.' She looked him straight in the eye then, challenging him to condemn her. 'So go on, Paulo—call me a tramp! Call me whatever names you want, if it makes you feel better.'

Impossibly, and appallingly, he thought of what *would* make him feel better—and it had something to do with covering the soft, rosy tremble of her mouth with his.

Covering it so that the memory of Roberto's kiss would be as stale as ashes in her mind. He shook his head. 'You're no tramp, Bella,' he said softly. She had told him most of what he needed to know—so why the defensive tightening of her shoulders? 'But there's still something you're not telling me, isn't there?'

She bit her lip and looked away. 'There's quite a lot, actually. But I didn't think you'd want to know.'

His mouth hardened, unprepared for the sudden blitz of bitterness. 'I don't mean every sordid detail of your night with this...this...' He stopped himself from spitting out the only word which was halfway suitable, and one which he would never use in front of a woman. Especially about the man who had fathered her child.

'Were you a virgin?' he asked suddenly, though deep-down he knew what her answer would be.

'I... Yes.' She hung her head as he made a sound as though she had hit him. 'Yes, I was.'

Swallowing down the taste of bitter jealousy, he let his hand reach out to cup her face, his dark eyes luminous with a kind of poignant sadness.

'It should have been me,' he said softly.

Meeting his gaze, she was already close to tears, but she held them at bay for long enough to whisper, 'Wh-what should?'

He let his hand fall, so that it was on a level with her belly and then, intimately, shockingly—he reached out a finger and drew it meticulously down over the drum-tight swell of the baby and Bella gasped aloud as he touched her.

'This. This baby of yours. It could have been me, couldn't it?' he questioned huskily, beginning to stroke a tiny circle around her navel. *'This.'* And his finger undulated over her belly as the baby moved beneath it. 'Mine.'

'Yours? How could it possibly be yours?'

'How do you think? By the *traditional* method of fathering children, of course. I should have made love to you,' he whispered, but he saw that beneath the fine olive complexion, her face looked almost bloodless in response. He let the anger go for a moment and let regret take its place—a bitter, lasting regret that he hadn't felt since his wife had died.

He could barely bring himself to acknowledge the precious gift he had refused—only to have someone else step in and steal it in his place. 'If only I hadn't listened to my crazy, *stupid* conscience!' he groaned aloud.

She stared at him in confusion. 'What are you talking about?'

'Oh, Bella—you know what I'm talking about!' His words sounded urgent and bitter, but his hand felt unbelievably gentle and she let him leave it right where it was, splayed almost possessively over the bump of the baby. 'You wanted me as much as I wanted you, didn't you?' he questioned softly.

She couldn't escape the question burning from his black eyes, even if she had wanted to. And she was through with evasion and half-truths. She would not tell him a lie. She couldn't. Not now, not after everything he had done for her. Was doing for her. Even now. 'Yes,' she said quietly.

'So subdued,' he murmured. 'So unlike the Bella I know.'

She wondered if the Bella he knew existed any more, but by then the moment for sensible debate had vanished and the unbelievable was happening instead. Paulo was pulling her to her to her feet and into the warm circle of his arms and the thoughtful look on his face gave her the courage to ask, 'So why didn't you?'

It was almost scary that he knew exactly what she meant. 'Make love to you?' He stroked her thickened waist reflectively. 'How many reasons would you like? Because you were only twenty and I suspected that you were innocent, as well as being the daughter of my host?' Or because he recognised the danger she represented, as well as the excitement? A danger to his well-ordered life and its carefully compartmentalised emotions.

'Of course,' and he paused—a slow, dangerous beat. 'None of those obstacles have any relevance any more, do they?'

With a thundering heart Isabella stared at the darkening of his eyes and the deepening colour which highlighted the broad sweep of his cheekbones. And just for that moment it was easy to pretend that he really *was* her lover.

'Paulo!' she gasped, because the baby chose just that moment to kick her very hard beneath her heart, or maybe that was just the effect he had on her.

'What is it, *querida*?' His voice was gentle but he didn't wait for an answer, just bent his head and began to kiss her. And all sane thoughts dissolved as Isabella was left with the sensation of a long-awaited dream being fulfilled.

This had been too long in coming, Paulo thought with an edge of desperation as he lowered his mouth onto hers. He could not recall a hunger of such keen, bright intensity. Nor kissing a woman so heavily pregnant with such raw passion before. For a brief, heady moment he allowed himself the sensation of melting, of their mouths moulding together as though they had always been joined with such perfect chemistry.

But this was *Bella* he was kissing. Sweet, stubborn Bella. And a very pregnant Bella, too. He reached his hand out—supposedly to push her away—but the hand somehow connected with enchanting accuracy over the heavy swell of her breast. And he gave into temptation. Cupped it. Kneaded it. Fondled it until he felt it peak like iron against his fingertips and he heard her half-moaned response.

Bella felt her knees threaten to give way. Her heart was fluttering and so was the baby—while all the time she could feel the heavy pulsing of desire as it began its slow inexorable throb. She clung onto his broad shoulders and kissed him back as though her life depended on it. And maybe it did.

He dragged his mouth away from hers with an effort and gazed down into her flushed, dazed face. He could barely speak, he was so aroused—so much for his reputation as the cool, controlled lover! 'We have to stop this right now, Bella,' he told her huskily. 'Jessie will be back soon.' And so, he remembered in horror, so would his son.

'And Eddie!' She echoed his thoughts as she frantically smoothed the palms of her hands over her hot cheeks, aware that her hair must be mussed up, her lips stained dark by the pressure of his mouth. 'I'd better go and…tidy myself up,' she gulped.

She made to move away, but he caught hold of her hand, his eyes boring into her as he understood one more reason why she had borne her secret for so long. 'That's why you couldn't bring yourself to tell your father about the baby, isn't it? Because this man—Roberto—abused his position.'

She nodded, causing even more disarray to her hair. 'That's how Papa would see it, yes. He would create a big scene. Can you imagine? He might even attempt to prosecute, and then it would be in all the papers. Can't you understand why I ran to England, Paulo?'

'Yes, I can.' He nodded his head slowly. 'But you've compromised me now, haven't you, *querida*? Your father is convinced that I have sired your baby. And to tell him otherwise would risk the kind of commotion you're so anxious to avoid—even if you were willing to do so.'

'So what do I do?'

His eyes glittered as he considered her question, the memory of her kiss still sweet on his mouth. 'You stay here. With me. And Eduardo. And after the baby is born, well, then...' He shrugged as he gave his rare and sexy smile—thinking that she could work *that* one out for herself.

The arrogance and complacency of that smile brought Isabella crashing back into the real world. 'Then what?' she questioned slowly. 'What exactly are you suggesting?'

'Why, then we could enjoy our mutual passion, Bella,' he purred, seeing the darkening in her eyes and feeling his body's answering leap in response. 'After all, why should I take all of the responsibility of impending paternity, but with none of the corresponding pleasure? Live here. With me. And we will become lovers.'

Lovers.

There was silence in the room, save for the ominous ticking of a clock she had never noticed before. And, while he must know how much she wanted him, something held her back.

Because she'd already made one big mistake in her life—she certainly did not intend making another. And if she allowed herself to fall eagerly into his bed on the strength of that coolly impassive suggestion, then how would he ever have any other image of her than that of a passive sensualist, all vulnerable and needy where men were concerned?

'And just how long did you have in mind?' she questioned acidly. 'Until you've taken your fill of me, I suppose?'

He stared deep into the amber eyes, respecting the guts it must have taken to ask that question. A trace of the old Isabella, he thought—her spirit remarkably uncrushed, despite what fate had thrown at her.

'Who can say, *querida*? Until it is spent. All burned out. Until you decide where you want to settle with your baby. Who knows for how long? I certainly can't tell you.' He paused, watching carefully for her reaction. 'But of course there are alternatives open to you if the idea doesn't appeal.'

She opened her mouth to speak, but the ringing of the front doorbell shattered the spell and he moved away from her. Her eyes followed him as he moved across the room.

He was wearing only a simple sweater with a pair of faded denims. The washed-out green of the sweater only drew attention to the spectacular darkness of his Latin American colouring, while the jeans were moulded to buttocks and thighs so powerful that... She found herself imagining seeing him, every bit of him, naked and warm in the act of loving.

'Oh, yes.' He nodded, his voice deepening as he observed her flushed reaction and her darkening eyes. 'I can see that it *does* appeal.'

Pride made her tilt her chin to stare at him, but pride also made her speak from the heart. 'I can't deny the attraction between us either,' she said slowly. 'But soon I'll have a baby to think about, as well as myself. I can't just leap into an affair with you. I might feel differently after the birth.'

'You might not,' he objected.

Her eyes mocked him. 'Well, you'll just have to wait and see, won't you, Paulo?'

It was not what he had wanted to hear. Nor expected to hear. Isabella could tell that much from the frozen look of disbelief which briefly hardened his outrageously gorgeous face.

But she kept watching him, waiting for the inevitable thaw—and when it came the frustration had been replaced by an emotion he used to swamp her with, but one which had been absent just lately.

It was called respect.

CHAPTER EIGHT

'WHAT'S the matter?' Paulo flicked off the television programme he had been half-heartedly trying to watch and stared instead at Isabella, who'd been shifting her position rather distractedly on the sofa, distracting him in the bargain, despite all his good intentions.

She'd told him that he would have to wait and see and he was going to abide by her decision. Even if the effort half-killed him.

Isabella stifled a yawn as she met the soft question in his eyes, aware that he'd been sitting watching her for the best part of an hour while pretending to watch TV. She'd spent the early part of the evening having Eddie teach her a computer game and now she was paying the price for having sat upright in front of a small screen for over an hour. She shifted around on the sofa again. 'Nothing.'

'Something,' he contradicted, thinking how pale her face looked and wondering if her nights had been as short of sleep as his had. Probably not. She probably slept smug and sound in her bed, knowing that she had him right where she wanted him—dangling on the end of a string.

He sighed, realising that he'd forgotten the last time a woman had said no to him, and the last person he'd ever imagined it would be was Isabella—not after the way she'd come to such swift, passionate life in his arms. 'Come on, Bella,' he urged softly. 'I can tell you're uncomfortable.'

'Her back hurts,' explained Eddie, who chose that moment to wander into the room in his pyjamas to say goodnight. 'It always does at this time of the night, doesn't it, Bella? 'Specially if she sits still.'

'Oh, really?' Paulo shot her a look which bordered on the accusing before rising to his feet to take his son to bed to read him a story. And when he came back he found that she had changed position on the sofa, but still with that same faint frown creasing her brow.

He sat down beside her, registering the way her body tensed as his weight sank onto the sofa beside her and he slowly and deliberately stretched his long legs in front of him, smug himself now to realise she wasn't entirely immune to him. 'So how come my son knows more about your current state of health than I do?'

She shrugged her shoulders uncomfortably, aware of the arrogantly muscular thrust of his thighs. Was he lying in that provocative position on *purpose*? she wondered agitatedly. 'He heard me telling Jessie that I get backache.'

Paulo frowned, badly wanting to reach out and trace the sweet, curving outline of her lips. 'And is that unusual?' he asked huskily.

'No, it's perfectly normal. They told us to expect it.'

'Who are ''they''?' he asked softly.

'The childbirth classes I went to when I was au pairing. And the books say so, too.'

'Maybe I should read them, too,' he mused, before asking. 'Is there any known cure?'

Not for the ache in her heart, no. Backache was an altogether simpler matter. A smile hovered on her mouth in spite of the fact that her whole world seemed to be a maelstrom of swirling emotions. 'Massage,' she told him stolidly. 'It helps but it doesn't cure.'

'Hmm.' He shifted in his seat. 'Turn around, then.'

Oh, sure—having Paulo caressing her skin was exactly what she *didn't* need. 'No, honestly—'

'Turn around,' he repeated quietly. Because at least if she turned away she wouldn't be able to read the hunger in his eyes.

With difficulty she did as he said, wondering if he had noticed the slow flush of colour which had risen in her cheeks.

He moved his thumbs into the hollow at the base of the spine and heard her expel a soft breath as he began to press away some of the tension.

It was crazy—more than crazy—but this innocent act of kneading her flesh felt like the most indecent act he had ever performed. 'Is that—' his voice deepened '—good?'

Any minute now and her thundering heart would burst right out of her chest. 'It's…fine,' she managed.

Paulo's nerves were stretched to the breaking point in an exquisite state of frustration. He wondered what she would do if he slid his hands round to cup her breasts, then sighed. Because he was essentially a man of honour. And that, he thought, would be taking advantage. Definitely.

'Better?' he murmured.

'Mmm. A hundred times.' She was torn between longing for him to continue and yearning for him to stop.

'Get yourself to bed then, and I'll bring you something warm to drink.'

She shook her head. 'I'm not thirsty.'

'It's a very expensive, very delicious chocolatey drink which I went out of my way to buy you when I was coming back from work,' he coaxed, and injected a stern note into his voice. 'Because chocolate is what you told me you'd been craving, Miss Fernandes—and because I notice you just pushed your supper around your plate this evening.'

'Does nothing escape your notice?' she teased.

Very little, he thought as he steadied her on his arm. And nothing whatsoever to do with her. She looked like a different woman since coming to live with him. Pregnancy had made her hair shine like mahogany and her skin gleam with radiant, glowing health.

In her bedroom, Isabella struggled out of her clothes and into the nightshirt which made her look like a vast, white tent, and was sitting up in bed when Paulo brought her a cup of chocolate.

He sat leaning moodily on the window-ledge while he looked around the room—noticing that she must have been out into the garden and picked a selection of berried twigs and brightly coloured pieces of foliage and placed them in a tall, silver vase. Jessie never did that kind of stuff. And he liked it, he realised... He liked it a lot.

In the corner of the room stood her bag, all packed for hospital, and beside it a small pile of Babygros as well as a yellow teddy-bear which he had picked up personally after they had had to cut short their visit to the toy-shop.

'You're all ready, then?' he asked.

She followed the direction of his gaze and nodded, not missing the warm approval in his voice. 'More than I was before.'

'You were heavily into denial,' he observed slowly, remembering how she hadn't brought a single baby thing back with her that day he had picked her up at the Staffords'. 'So what changed all that?'

'Telling my father, I guess.' She sighed, and knew

that once again she owed him her gratitude. Did being indebted to the man mean she could never be his equal? she wondered. 'You were right to push me into it, Paulo. I feel such a fool now for not having the courage to do so in the first place.'

'We're all allowed to be cowards sometimes, Bella,' he said softly, thinking that if she had done that then she would never have arrived here, seeking his help. Would never have slotted into his life like this—disrupting it, yes, undoubtedly, but making it seem more *alive* than it had done for a long time. And he realised too, that her life had not been easy since she had found out about the baby. Not easy at all.

He kept his voice casual. 'How would you like to catch a taxi into the city, and meet me after work tomorrow night? I could show you my office—we could maybe grab a bite to eat.'

She looked down at her bump, horrified. 'Like *this*?'

He smiled and shrugged. 'Why not?'

'What will your colleagues think?'

He gave the smile of a man who had never pandered to other people's opinions. 'Who cares what they think?' He raised his dark brows. 'So, would you?'

'Well, I would,' she admitted, almost shyly.

In the end, she took Eddie along with her because having Paulo's son accompany her seemed to legitimise her presence. She met most of Paulo's frankly curious colleagues, seeing from their expressions just what deductions they were making about her role in their director's life.

While Eddie was busy changing the screensaver on his father's computer, she took Paulo aside and hissed into his ear, 'You do *know* what everyone's thinking?'

'That I'm such a super-stud?' he mocked.

Her eyes widened and she met the look in his eyes and started to giggle. Well, if Paulo didn't care, then she certainly wasn't going to waste her time worrying about what was, in fact, her private fantasy!

So she settled back and allowed herself to be steered through the building with all the exaggerated courtesy which would naturally be afforded to a rich man's pregnant mistress.

They toured the impressive glass-fronted skyscraper, and then the three of them got a cab to Covent Garden for hamburgers and milkshakes—or rather Paulo and Eddie ate the hamburgers while Isabella indulged herself with a very thick strawberry milkshake.

On the way home, Paulo turned to her in the taxi. 'Tired?'

She shook her head. 'Not a bit.'

'Back hurting?'

She smiled. 'My back is fine.'

He tapped the connecting glass and asked the driver to drive down around by the Houses of Parliament so that they could see the historic buildings lit up by night.

Eddie turned to Isabella. 'What an amazing night!' he exclaimed. 'It's just like being on holiday!'

Yes, it was. But holidays always came to an end, she reminded herself.

The following evening—just by way of saying thank you—she had a martini waiting for Paulo when he arrived back from work, and if he was unsettled by the distinctly *wifely* gesture, he didn't say so.

He sipped it with pleasure and regarded her with thoughtful eyes. 'Oh, by the way, a letter arrived for you from Brazil this morning,' he said, putting his drink

down on the table and fishing a flimsy blue air-mail envelope from the breast pocket of his suit jacket.

Isabella stared at it. 'It's from my father.'

'I know it is. Why don't you e-mail each other? Eddie
says he gave you a crash-course the other day.'

'I told you. Papa hates technology. He'd use pigeon-
post if it was reliable enough.'

He smiled. 'Oh.'

She held it in her hand for a moment. She had had
several conversations with her father since the one when
he had slammed the paternity accusation at Paulo. She
had been expecting his anger to be ongoing, but there
had been none. More a kind of quiet resignation. Most
unlike her father, she thought.

'Well, go on, then—open it.'

He watched while she ripped the envelope open with
suddenly nervous fingers and quickly scanned the page,
relief lightening her face as her eyes skated over the
main portion.

'Good news?' he queried.

'*Kind* of,' she answered cautiously, but then she began
to study it in more detail and her colour heightened.

Paulo was watching her closely. 'Want to read it out
loud?'

'Not really.'

'Bella,' he said warningly. 'I thought we were through
with secrets?'

She made one last helpless attempt at evasion. Or was
it pride? 'A woman should always keep a little something back—didn't you know?'

He held his hand out for the letter. 'Please.'

She handed it over.

Paulo scanned the sheet for the source of what had

obviously made her react like that and it didn't take him long to find it.

Obviously, I would have preferred for this to happen in a more conventional manner, but I cannot pretend that I am displeased. Paulo is a fine man and a fine father. I could not have wished for a better husband for you, Bella—so cherish him well.

Paulo looked up to find her attention firmly fixed on the glass of mango juice she had poured herself.

'Bella? Look at me!'

'I don't want to discuss it,' she said fiercely, but she raised her head to meet the accusation sparking from his eyes.

'Well, I *do*! Perhaps you've already booked the church and arranged the venue?'

'I have not!'

'But we're getting married—apparently—so don't you think the prospective groom should be informed?'

'Do you honestly think I told my father we were getting married?'

'How should I know?' he questioned arrogantly, thinking that he would like to untie that velvet ribbon in her hair and have it tumble all the way down her back. Her naked back. '*Now* where are you going?'

She jerked the chair back from the table, her breath coming in short little gasps. 'As far away from you as possible!'

He was on his feet in seconds, standing in front of her and forming a very effective barrier. 'Stop it and calm down.'

'I do not *feel* like calming down!' she told him distractedly. 'I feel like…like… Ow, ow, *ouch*!'

'Is it the baby?' he demanded immediately.

It felt like someone tightening a piece of string around her middle and then tightening it again. Her hands reached up and she clutched onto his shoulders, her nails digging into him. 'I don't *think* so!'

'I'm going to call the doctor—'

'No! No. Wait a minute!' She panted and paused. 'No, that's OK. I think it's gone.'

He dipped his head so that their eyes were on a level. 'Sure?'

Her heart seemed to suspend its beating. She was still, she realised, gripping tightly onto his shoulders. And through the thin shirt she could feel the silken yield of his flesh to the hard bone beneath. 'Qu-quite sure.'

She let her hands fall away, and Paulo forced himself not to grab them back. She was about to have a baby, for God's sake—and here he was wanting to feel her in his arms again.

'Maybe I'd better call the doctor?'

She shook her head. 'To say what?'

'That you had a pain—'

'Paulo, it was more of a twinge than a pain. And it's gone now.'

'Sure?' he demanded.

'Positive.'

'I just don't want to take any chances.'

'Who's taking any chances? The pain has gone.' She spread her arms out as if to demonstrate. 'See? All gone. I don't want to be one of those neurotic women who calls out the doctor ten times—and every time it's a false alarm. Now go away. Don't you have any work to do?'

Paulo shrugged unenthusiastically. He wanted to stay. He wanted to kiss her. He wanted to do a lot more besides. Maybe it was better if he *did* clear off. 'I've always got work to do.'

'Then go away and do it,' she shooed.

'And what will you do?'

'I'm not planning on going far. You don't have to worry.'

'I'm not worrying.' But that was a lie, he thought, as he headed off to his study. He was—and, oddly enough, his worries were not the ones he would have imagined at all. It didn't bother him one iota that most of the world imagined that he was the father of her unborn child. In fact, wasn't that a supposition he had deliberately *flaunted* by inviting her into his office last night?

No. He found himself wondering what on earth would happen when the baby arrived. He had told Bella that she had a home for as long as she wanted one and now it suddenly occurred to him that she might not want a home at all. Or to be his lover.

As she had said herself, she might feel differently after the birth. Because now that her father knew and seemed to be coming round to the idea—and bearing in mind that she could usually twist him round her little finger—then what was to stop her going back to Brazil as an unmarried mother?

He imagined her leaving with her baby, and instead of a sense of reprieve he was aware of a great yawning idea of emptiness.

When Elizabeth had died he had decided to live his life in the best way he could for their son, completely forgetting that life never remained static. That life *was* change. He frowned as he switched on the computer.

Isabella prowled the house like a thief, restless without knowing why and looking for something to do. She sat down and wrote a long and chatty letter to Charlie and Richie, as promised—and hoped that Mrs Stafford would be adult enough to pass the letter on to her two young sons.

When she had stamped the envelope, she found a feather duster and wandered from room to room, polishing flecks of dust from all the mirrors. Next she cleaned the two sinks in the downstairs cloakroom, even though they were spotless and gleaming. After she had rearranged all the spices in the store-cupboard, she rang the local Portuguese delicatessen and placed an order for a delivery.

'I'd like rib and shoulder and breast of pork, please. Sausage. Linguica. Green cabbage. Oh, and beans.'

'And when would you like this delivered, madam?'

She frowned at herself in the mirror, thinking that she looked especially enormous today. 'Any chance of tomorrow morning?'

There was no hesitation whatsoever—probably because of the delivery address, Isabella decided.

'That shouldn't be a problem, madam.'

When Eddie got in from school the next day, he came straight into the kitchen as he always did, to find Isabella up to her elbows in cooking utensils. He strolled over to the work-surface, where she was chopping onion as if her life depended on it.

'What are you doing?' he asked with interest.

'Jessie isn't here, so I'm making feijoada for our supper.' She smiled.

'What's that?'

'Come on, Eddie,' she chided. 'You remember? It's Brazil's national dish. With lots of meats and different sausages—'

Eddie looked down at all the different pots which

were cluttering the work-surface. 'Looks difficult to make.'

'Not difficult. Fiddly. Lots of different things all added to one big pot at different times. See?'

'Can I help?'

'Of course you can help. Wash your hands first and then you can prepare this garlic for me. See this clever little machine? Now—' she leaned over his shoulder '—put each bulb in here—and it will crush it up for you.'

That was where Paulo discovered them when he arrived home from work. Unknotting his tie, he wandered into the kitchen to find Isabella removing a large piece of meat from the pot with Eddie standing glued to her side.

Paulo smiled—as much at the sight of their obvious companionship as the warm, homely smell which triggered off snatches of boyhood memories. 'Mmm. Feijoada.' He sniffed, as he walked into the kitchen. 'What's brought all this on?'

'You don't like it?' she asked him anxiously.

He smiled conspiratorially at his son. 'Show me the man who doesn't like feijoada—and I'll show you a man who doesn't deserve to eat! No, I was just thinking that it's a pretty adventurous thing to cook, if you're feeling tired.'

'But I'm not feeling in the least bit tired!' She energetically threw a handful of bay leaves in the pot, as if to demonstrate.

Jet eyes lanced through her. 'So I see,' he agreed slowly. 'And wasn't that polish I could smell in the hall-way?'

'Oh, it's Jessie's day off and I was just waving a duster in the air,' she explained airily. 'More for something to do than anything else.'

He nodded. 'Eddie—want to go and get changed out of your school uniform, now?'

'Sure, Papa.'

He stood looking at the image she made once Eddie had gone. Her stomach was so big that she should have looked ungainly as she moved towards the cooker—but she didn't at all. She just seemed perfectly ripe and extremely beautiful—even though her cheeks were all flushed from bending over a hot pan.

'You're nesting,' he said suddenly.

She turned round, wooden spoon in hand. 'Mmm?'

'It's called nesting. That's why you're doing all this.' He waved a hand around. 'Cleaning and polishing and chopping and cooking. You're getting ready to have your baby.'

'You can't know that.'

'Yes, I can. Elizabeth did it, too—it's nature telling you to make your home ready for the new arrival.'

She searched his face for signs of sadness. 'Does having me here like this bring it all back?' she asked softly.

He didn't look away. 'A little.' He saw the look of contrition on her face and shook his head. 'It's not a problem, Bella—I came to terms with what happened to Elizabeth a long time ago. I had to—for Eddie's sake. But—' and he narrowed his eyes into a searchlight stare as he saw her face grow pale '—it does give me the upper hand when it comes to knowing what I'm talking about. And that was another one, wasn't it?'

'Another what?'

'Contraction,' he elaborated roughly.

Suddenly an intimation of what was about to happen to her whispered fingertips of fear over her skin. She shook her head and gave the beans a stir. 'It can't be,' she said, a slight edge of desperation in her voice. 'The baby isn't due until next week.'

'And babies never come when they're supposed to.'

'Oh, really?'

'Yes, really,' he agreed calmly, when he saw her attempt to turn a grimace into a smile. 'And for goodness' sake, will you stop pretending that you're not getting contractions, when it's pretty obvious to me that you are?' he exploded.

So she wasn't fooling him at all! At least his words gave her licence to drop the wooden spoon with a clutter and to bend over and clutch at her abdomen as she had been dying to do for ages.

And it took a moment or two for her to realise that he was standing in front of her, his face a shifting complex of shadows looking for all the world like some dark guardian angel sent to protect her. Her eyes were big and fearful as she stared up at him. 'Ow,' she moaned softly. *'Ow!'*

'What is it?' he demanded, his hands spanning her expanded waist and feeling her tense beneath his touch. 'Another contraction?'

She nodded her head. His hands felt strong and real and supportive, but wasn't all that an illusion? In fact, wasn't everything just an illusion compared to the razor-sharp lash of pain she had just experienced? You spent nine months imagining that something couldn't possibly be happening, and then all of a sudden, it was. And there wasn't a thing you could do to stop it. 'Paulo—I'm scared.'

He lifted one hand from her waist to soothe softly at her head, the shiny curls clinging like vines to his fingers. 'I know you are, *querida*, but you've just got to take it easy, remember? Slow and easy. This is what you've been preparing for, Bella. You know what to do. Remember your breathing. And the relaxation—all that stuff you did in your childbirth classes—I know it too, don't forget. I've done it before. I'll be there to help you.' He paused. 'If you want me there.'

A few minutes later, she choked out a gasp at a new, sharper pain. 'Another one!'

Paulo glanced down at his watch. 'That's ten minutes,' he observed, as calmly as possible.

'Is that OK?' she whispered, because everything she had been taught seemed to have flown clean out of her head.

He frowned. This all seemed to be happening far more rapidly than it was supposed to. 'I'd better ring Jessie and get her in to come and look after Eddie,' he said, watching her body tense up again. 'I think it's time I took you to hospital.'

This time the contraction almost swamped her, and the sweat ran down in rivulets from her forehead. And if this was just a taste of things to come...

Isabella gripped Paulo's hand, not feeling the sticky moistness from where her nails dug into and broke the skin to make him bleed.

'Don't leave me, Paulo,' she moaned softly. 'Please don't leave me.'

That vulnerable little plea smashed its way right through his defences, and he was filled with an over-whelming need to protect her.

'I won't leave you,' he promised, as he reached for the telephone.

CHAPTER NINE

THE whirling blue light of the ambulance cast strange neon flashes over both their faces and the sound of the siren screamed in their ears as they sped towards the hospital.

Through a daze, Isabella gripped onto Paulo's hand, squirming around to try and get comfortable—but no position seemed to help.

Paulo was trying to stay calm, but it was harder than he had anticipated. He had tried paging Dr Cordosa, but the obstetrician had been sailing and was currently making his way back up the motorway. Paulo glanced down at Isabella, thinking that if her labour continued at this alarmingly fast rate, then Dr Cordosa would miss it anyway.

'How are you feeling?' he asked.

'Hot!' Sweat beaded her forehead. 'Will Eddie be OK?'

'Stop worrying about Eddie—he'll be fine. Jessie is there with him.'

'What about the feijoada? It's only half-cooked!'

'Bella!' he said warningly.

At the hospital they were rushed straight into the Emergency Department, where Bella was put, protesting, onto one of the trolleys. Paulo held her hand all the way up to the labour ward and when the midwife arrived to examine her she continued to grip onto it as tightly as a drowning woman.

The midwife gently pushed him aside, speaking to him as if he was a child himself.

'Can we have the father on the other side of the bed, please?'

He was about to say that he wasn't sure that he'd be around for the main part of the action, when he felt Bella's fingernails digging into the palm of his hand again. He looked down at her, the question in his eyes being answered by the beseeching look in hers. His heart pounded. When she had begged him not to leave her, she had meant it, he realised with something approaching shock.

'Sure,' he said, but he delicately kept his eyes on her face while the midwife conducted her intimate examination, and for the first time in his life he actually felt *shy*.

What Paulo wanted for Isabella more than anything was a straightforward birth, but he knew the instant that the midwife raised an expressive eyebrow at her runner across the delivery room and the runner hurriedly left the room that maybe this birth was not going to be straightforward at all.

He could tell that the team was trying to play any drama down, but he knew when two other doctors entered the room that things weren't going according to plan. He quickly read their name badges. One was an obstetrician and the other was a paediatrician. So didn't that mean that both mother *and* baby were in danger?

His heart made a painful acceleration, and he found himself praying for the first time in years. Dear God— he had already lost one woman in his life—surely fate would not be so merciless as to take the other one?

But he must not let his fear communicate itself to Bella. Not when she was being so brave. He watched the look of grim determination on her face as she conquered the rising tide of each contraction and he was reminded of her fundamental fearlessness. He gritted his teeth, frustrated at his inability to help her when she most needed him.

For Isabella nothing existed, save the powerful demands of her body—everything else faded into complete insignificance. She refused the drugs they offered her, but gulped down the gas and air, which helped. And so did Paulo, just by being there. She gripped onto his hand when the contractions grew so strong that she did not think she could bear to go through another one. Whenever she unclenched her eyes, his face swam into her line of vision and she could read the encouragement there.

And something else, too—a kind of pride and admiration which filled her with a powerful new energy.

People had started telling her to push, but she didn't need them to tell her anything, because by then the urge to get her baby into the outside world had become too strong to resist.

'Here's your baby!' called someone.

'Come and see your baby being born, Paulo,' urged one of the midwives.

Paulo couldn't have refused the midwife's request, even if he had wanted to. And he didn't. He knew that it was important for Bella to have someone witness an event which was as miraculous for her as for any other woman—even if the circumstances surrounding it *were* unconventional.

He let go of her hand and walked down the room to see the dark, downy head beginning to emerge and his heart gathered speed as a shoulder quickly followed. He was aware of furious activity executed with an unnatural calm, and then the baby slithered out, but made no sound as precious seconds ticked by. There was more activity, and then, quietly and dramatically, the first tenuous wail of life which hit him like a punch to the guts.

'It's a girl!' said the paediatrician, bending over the baby and cleaning the tiny nose and mouth.

Paulo walked over to Isabella and looked down at her pale face and the hair which was matted to her brow and cheeks. He bent down and brushed a damp curl away, so tempted to kiss her. 'Congratulations, *querida*,' he whispered instead. 'You have a beautiful daughter.'

A great wave of relief washed over her, leaving her shaky and exhausted in its wake. 'Can I hold her?'

'Just for a moment,' said the paediatrician, as he carefully placed the tiny bundle in her arms. 'Her heartbeat was a little low during the delivery and she was a little slow to breathe—so we're going to take her off to Special Care for her first night, just to keep an eye on her. Does she have a name yet?'

Bella stared down at the impossibly small head. The peep of dark curls through the swaddled blanket. And all the dark, frightened thoughts which had driven her half-crazy at the time she'd become pregnant—dissolved like magic. Because this baby *was* magic. A sense of love flooded her. 'She's called Estella,' she said, the overwhelming emotion making her breath catch in her throat. 'It means "star".'

'No, you're the star,' said Paulo softly, but he spoke in Portuguese, so that only Bella understood.

She looked up into his face and saw that his eyes were bright—the warmth and care in them surely too strong to be imagined? As proud as if he really *were* the father. Her lips began to tremble and she looked down and kissed her baby's head.

*   *   *

Bella opened her eyes in the middle of the night and wondered what was different. She sat bolt upright and looked around her. After the delivery she had submerged herself in the most delicious bath and had then fallen asleep, with Paulo sitting like some dark, beautiful guard beside her.

But now Paulo had gone and the crib by the bed remained empty. Fear clutched erratically at her heart as she reached out and rang the bell by her side and the nurse came hurrying into the room.

'Yes, dear—what is it?'

'Where's my baby, please?'

'She's still in Special Care—but not for very much longer. I spoke to them a little while ago, and she's doing just fine.'

'I want to see her.'

'And you can. But why don't you rest for the time being, and wait until the morning?'

'I want to see her,' said Bella with a stubborn new resolve in her voice she didn't recognise.

The nurse insisted on taking her up to the Special Care Unit in a wheelchair and as they drew up in front of the cubicle, Bella felt tears of relief pricking the back of her eyes as she watched the tableau being played out in front of them.

Behind the bright glass screen stood Paulo, and he was cradling the tiny baby in his arms, his lips moving as he spoke softly to her.

And Bella made a broken little sound. A primitive sound which seemed to be torn from some place deep within her.

The nurse looked down at her. 'Are you all right?'

Bella nodded. *I love him. I've always loved him.*

The nurse beamed. 'You new mothers! Of course you love him—you've just had his baby, haven't you?'

Isabella hadn't even realised that she had spoken the words out loud, but suddenly she didn't care. And maybe Paulo realised that he was being watched or spoken about, because he suddenly looked up, and his brilliant smile told her that the baby was going to be fine.

'I'm going in,' she said to the nurse.

'Let me wheel you—'

'No. I want to walk. Honestly.'

Paulo stood and watched while she climbed carefully out of the wheelchair, watched the proud way she refused the nurse's arm and held herself erect, before walking stiffly into the cubicle and over to where he held Estella.

She looked into the black brilliance dancing in his eyes—eyes as dark as Estella's—thinking that he could easily be mistaken for her baby's father. But he wasn't. And he never would be. 'You've got my baby,' she whispered.

'I know. Can't resist her. Do you want her back? I thought so. Here—' And he held her out to Bella with a soft smile. 'Go to Mummy.'

Very gently, he placed Estella into her arms. The baby instinctively began rooting for her mother's breast and Isabella felt a tug of love so powerful that she stared down at the shivering little head with an indescribable sense of wonder.

And Paulo stood outside the magic circle, watched the first tentative explorings between mother and child, appalled by the dark feelings of exclusion which ran through him.

He wanted her, he realised. Just hours after she'd had

another man's baby and he wanted her so badly that it hurt. Now what kind of person had he become?

He glanced up at the ward clock which was ticking the seconds away. It was four in the morning. 'I'd better get back home. I want to be there for Eddie waking up. I'll bring him to visit tomorrow. Goodbye, Isabella—sweet dreams.'

Suddenly he was gone, and Isabella and the nurse stared after his dark figure as he strode off down the hospital corridor without once looking back.

The nurse turned to Isabella and gave her a confused kind of smile. 'Why, the naughty man didn't even kiss you goodbye!' she clucked.

Isabella dropped a tired kiss on the top of Estella's head. 'I think the excitement of the delivery must have got to him,' she said. Far better to think that than to imagine that he hadn't kissed her because he simply hadn't wanted to...

CHAPTER TEN

THE following morning, Paulo arrived on the ward before the night-staff had gone home, bearing a bottle of champagne tied with a pink ribbon.

Three staff midwives looked up as he appeared at the office door and their mouths collectively fell open at the sight of the tall, dark-haired vision in a deep blue suit and an amber tie of pure silk.

'I know I'm early.' He smiled. 'But I wanted to see Bella before I went to work.'

The trio all sprang to their feet, smoothing down crisp white aprons. 'Let me show you where she is,' they said in unison.

Paulo's black eyes crinkled with amusement. 'I know where she is,' he said softly. 'I asked one of the nursing assistants. And I'd like to surprise her, if I may.'

Bella was busy feeding Estella, the baby nestled into the crook of Bella's arm while she tugged enthusiastically at her mother's breast. It was the strangest and most amazing sensation, Bella decided, her mouth curving into a slow smile of satisfaction.

Paulo stood outside her cubicle and watched her, marvelling at how easily and how naturally she had taken to feeding her child.

Breast-feeding had not been quite so popular when Eddie had been born and, in any case, Elizabeth's postnatal blues had meant that he had been able to take on most of the bottle-feeding so that she could rest.

He thought how the bearing of Isabella's breast,

though intimate, was not especially erotic. Then he saw her remove one elongated and rosy nipple and wondered just who he had been trying to kid.

Bella looked up to find herself caught in the intense dazzle of his black eyes and she felt the tremble of her lips as she gazed across the room at him.

And any idea that she might feel differently after the birth or that her words of love yesterday had been the hormone-fuelled fantasies of a post-partum woman were instantly banished. Because just the sight of his dear, handsome face was enough to engulf her with an unbearable sense of yearning.

He came in and put the champagne down on the locker. 'Hi,' he murmured.

'Hi,' she said back, feeling almost shy—but maybe that wasn't so very surprising. He had seen her at her most exposed—body and emotions stripped bare as she had brought new life into the world.

'I thought I'd pop in on my way in to work.'

And play havoc with her blood pressure in that beautifully cut dark suit. She smiled. 'I'm glad you did.'

He looked down at the baby who had now flopped into an instant, contented sleep. Had Eddie ever been that tiny? he wondered in bemusement. 'How is she?'

'Beautiful.'

Like her mother, he thought. 'Can I take her—or would that disturb her?'

She shook her head. 'Take away,' she said huskily.

He bent to pluck the swaddled bundle from her arms, surprised at the pleasure it gave him to hold Estella again. She smelt of milk—and of Bella—and he felt compelled by a powerful need to drop a kiss on top of the tiny head.

Isabella watched while he cradled and kissed Estella,

and in that moment she loved him even more for his warmth and his generosity. I wish he would hold *me* like that, she thought with fierce longing.

'I phoned your father,' he said.

Her heart thudded a little. 'And?'

'He's puffed up with pride—I never imagined that he could go a full minute without saying anything!'

No need to tell her that he had then uncomfortably submitted to Luis's congratulations and endured the inevitable questions about who the child most resembled—Paulo or Bella. 'It's difficult to say,' he had replied smoothly, without stopping to question why the evasion had slipped so easily from his lips.

'How's Eddie?' she asked.

He stroked the downy head with the tip of his nose. 'Excited. More than excited—even the computer doesn't have an edge on this baby. I'll bring him in with me tonight.'

Paulo visited her morning and evening until she and the baby were discharged a week later, and he had an air of anticipation about him as he led her outside to where a large and shining family car awaited them.

With her arms full of blanket-swathed baby, Isabella blinked at the gleaming motor in surprise. 'What's this— a new car?'

'That's right.' He opened the door for her. 'Like it?''

'It's lovely, but what happened to the old one?'

'Nothing. It's in the garage—this is an extra. We need a bigger car now that there's four of us.'

He doesn't mean it the way it sounded, she told herself fiercely, as she bent to strap Estella into the newly installed car-seat.

Eddie was standing on the doorstep waiting to greet

them, and he was hopping up and down with excitement. His father had taken him most days to visit them in hospital, leaving Paulo and Isabella feeling distinctly invisible! All Eddie's attention had been fixed on the tiny infant who clung so tightly to his finger with one little fist.

Paulo had found the experience strangely moving, noticing the interaction between his son and the new baby with something approaching remorse. He had always been so certain that Eddie should be the exclusive child in his life—always steeling himself against committing to a relationship again and the possibility of more children. Not that it had ever been a hardship. No woman had remotely tempted him to do otherwise.

But it was sobering to see how his son behaved with the baby—as if someone had just turned a light on inside him. As baby paraphernalia began to be delivered to the house, Paulo found himself wondering whether an immaculate house with a working father and a housekeeper was not vastly inferior to the noise and mess and love which this new addition seemed to have brought with her.

Isabella brought the baby into the house, walking with exaggerated care and still feeling slightly disorientated. She had only been away for a few days and yet she was returning as a different person. As a mother. With all the responsibilities which went with that role. Yet the sense of unreality which had descended on her since the birth had not completely left her, even though Estella was real and beautiful enough.

It was hard to believe now that Paulo had actually held her hand throughout. He had seen her stripped of all dignity—moaning and writhing with pain. He had wiped her brow just before she pushed the baby out and he had even watched her do *that*. But he had not touched her, nor kissed her and somehow she had thought—no, hoped—that he would. Maybe *he* was the one who had changed his mind.

But her troubled thoughts disappeared the moment she looked around her. The hallway was festooned with balloons and a lavish arrangement of scented pink flowers was standing next to the telephone. From the direction of the kitchen drifted a sweet, familiar smell.

'It's the feijoada,' explained Paulo as he saw her sniff the air and frown. 'We froze the meal you were making when you went into labour. Eddie said it would be perfect as a welcome-home feast.'

'Eddie's right—it's the very best,' said Isabella, looking at a silver and pink balloon saying 'It's a Girl!', which was floating up the stairs. 'And this all looks wonderful, too.' Her voice softened. 'You must have worked very hard.'

Jessie came out of the kitchen, a wide smile of welcome on her face. 'Welcome home!' she said, and hugged her.

'Thank you, Jessie!'

'Can I have a little peep?'

Isabella pulled the cashmere blanket away from the miniature face and sighed. 'Isn't she beautiful?''

Paulo found himself looking at the mother instead of the baby. There was no doubt that she looked absolutely breathtaking—her figure seemed to have gone from bulk to newly slender almost overnight. The nurse had said that because she was so young and fit her body had just sprung back into shape straight away.

She was wearing a pair of saffron-yellow jeans and a scarlet shirt stretched tight over her milk-full breasts. The abundance of copper-brown curls were tied back from her face with a black ribbon and her unmade-up face looked dewy and radiant.

So what was the matter with her?

She seemed so distant, he thought. Detached. Her movements jerky and self-conscious—her only true warmth appearing when she was relating to the baby. Or to Eddie. But certainly not to him.

'Come upstairs and see what we've done for Estella,' he said softly.

'Can I hold the baby for a bit?' said Jessie eagerly. 'Give you a bit of a break?'

'Of course you can!' smiled Isabella but, with the infant out of her arms, she felt curiously bereft.

'Let me see her too, Jessie!' said Eddie.

Isabella's heart was in her mouth as Paulo followed her up the stairs. 'Where exactly are we going?' she asked him.

'The room right next door to yours,' he said, a faint frown appearing as he heard the unmistakable note of wariness in her voice.

But Isabella's nerves were temporarily forgotten when she opened the door and looked inside and saw what a lot of effort he must have gone to. 'Oh, my goodness,' she sighed. 'How on earth have you managed to do all this?'

It was the cutest baby's room imaginable.

One wall was dominated by a mural of Alice in Wonderland—complete with white rabbit and grinning Cheshire cat—while the rest of the walls were the exact colour of cherryade. An old-fashioned crib stood next to the wall, with flounces of lace nestling delicately amidst the pink gingham, while a rag-doll sat with several of her sisters on the gleaming, newly painted window ledge.

She found herself thinking that he had gone to an awful lot of trouble for a stay which might only be temporary and her heart gave a sudden great lurch of hope.

'Like it?' he asked.

She turned to him. '*Like* it? Oh, Paulo—who in their right mind could not help loving it?'

'And are you in your right mind?' he asked her softly.

Something in his tone made the hope die an uncertain death. 'I…think so. Why do you ask?'

He smiled, but there was a cold edge to his voice. 'You are wearing the kind of expression which I imagine the early Christians might have adopted just before being fed to the lions,' he said drily. 'What's the matter, Isabella—did you think I was planning to drag you up here to make love to you already?'

From the look on his face, the idea clearly appalled him. 'I didn't say that,' she said woodenly. She trusted him not to hurt her, to respect her and not to leap on her before she was ready—yet he was hurting her far more by standing on the opposite side of the room like some dark, remote stranger.

He frowned at the reproachful look in her amber eyes. 'Bella, you're tired. And you've just had a baby. What kind of a monster do you think I am?'

'You're not a monster at all,' she said. 'I'm just grateful for all the trouble you've gone to—'

Damn it—he didn't want her *gratitude*, just some sign, some indication that she still wanted him. 'Don't mention it,' he put in coolly.

Rather desperately, she said, 'But it must have cost a lot of money?'

The light went out in his eyes. 'Please don't mention it again, Bella. Let's just call it a small repayment for the kindness shown to me by your father all these years.'

And wasn't that a bit like saying that the debt was now repaid? She wondered?

She wanted to touch him, to run her fingertips along the hard, proud outline of his jaw, but inside she was scared.

She *had* just had a baby and she also had a poor track record where men were concerned. If she started a relationship with Paulo, she had to be very sure that she was doing the right thing. And while in her heart there wasn't a single doubt, she needed him to know that she wasn't acting on a whim when they made love.

If he still wanted *her*—and she needed to be sure of that, too.

Paulo saw the discomfiture on her face and wondered if she felt compromised. 'Of course, you mustn't feel that just because I've had the room decorated you have to stay.' His eyes were full of question. 'You may have already made your mind up that you want to leave.'

She wondered if she was keeping her horror carefully concealed. 'Leave?'

He forced himself to continue, even though the words nearly choked him. She had to have a let-out clause, he decided grimly.

'You might want to go home,' he suggested softly. 'To Brazil. You could take Estella and show her to her father.'

She met the dark challenge in his eyes without flinching. 'But Roberto doesn't want me; I told you that. And I don't want him! It's over—it never really began.' Because he had only ever been a shadowy lover—an unwitting replacement for the only man she had ever really wanted.

'But he might feel differently once he knows about the baby.'

'He isn't going to *know* about the baby!'

'And don't you think he has a right?'

'I think I have a right to choose whether or not to tell him,' she told him softly.

'But your feelings towards him may change,' he argued, wondering what contrary demon was making him put forward a case which was detrimental to what *he* wanted. 'What if Estella grows to resemble her real father more and more—what then? You might find the biological tie irresistible—you might even want him back again.'

She didn't react—would not let him see how much his callous words had hurt her. He'd sounded as though that was what he *wanted* her to do. Maybe, as a father himself, he was now becoming indignant on Roberto's behalf.

She heard the sound of Estella's cry floating up the stairs towards her and in an instant she had stilled, lifting her head to listen. 'Is that Estella?'

'Yeah. Saved by the baby!' He noticed that there were two small, damp circles of milk on her shirt and gave a wry smile, which did little to ease the ache in his groin. 'But mightn't it be best if you change your shirt before you go down?'

She looked down her damp and rocky nipples and when she lifted her head to meet his eyes, she saw the unmistakable spark of desire. And laughter. 'Just go, Paulo!' she said huskily.

Downstairs he found Eddie sitting on one of the vast, overstuffed sofas, cradling the baby expertly in his arms.

'Are you OK holding her?' Paulo asked gently, and the look his son gave him cut him to the marrow.

'Of course I'm OK! Oh, Dad, look! She's so cute! Loads of the other boys in my class have got baby brothers or sisters—I wish Estella could be *my* little sister! Why can't you marry Isabella, and then she can?'

'Because real life isn't like that,' he said gently.

'Well, real life sucks!'

'Eddie!' Paulo opened his mouth to issue a short but terse lecture on the unattractiveness of swearing, but something in his son's haunted expression drew him up short.

He had lost his mother so young that he had no real memory of her, Paulo remembered painfully. Maybe it wasn't so surprising that Eddie had already forged a bond with this fatherless little infant, Paulo thought, and felt a lump catch in his throat.

The sense of loss had been with him for a long time— long after the pain of bereavement had gone. The random cruelty of life had made him wary of committing to anyone again—but now he was beginning to realise that you couldn't live your life thinking 'what if?'. He had once accused Isabella of cowardice, but hadn't he been guilty of emotional cowardice himself?

'Can I take her for a minute, son?' he said gently.

When Isabella came back downstairs, with her hair flowing loose around her shoulders, it was to find father and son being extremely territorial with *her* baby! She looked over at the two males sitting up close on the sofa, their dark heads bent over the sleeping bundle. To an outsider, she realised wistfully, they would look exactly like a normal family.

'Can I use the phone, Paulo?'

'You don't have to ask every time,' he growled.

'Thank you.' She gave him a serene smile. 'It's just that I'd better ring my father and tell him I'm safely out of hospital.'

'And neither do you have to tell me the name of everybody you're calling.'

'I'll remember that,' she said gravely.

Paulo paced up and down with Estella locked against his neck, desperately trying not to succumb to the temptation of eavesdropping into her conversation.

Maybe their conversation of earlier had been closer to the mark than he had imagined. Maybe even now she was talking to her father about the possibility of returning to Brazil... He had brought the subject up and she had grown quiet long enough to suggest that she had given it some serious thought. And why *shouldn't* she feel differently now? That was what babies tended to do to you.

'Paulo?'

He looked up to see those delicious curls falling almost to her waist and his lips tingled with the need to kiss her.

'You got through OK?' he asked thickly.

She nodded, thinking how tiny the baby looked in his arms. And how right. 'He said to thank you for the photos, and asked how the hell did you get them over to him so quickly?'

'There isn't much point me having access to all the latest technology—' he shrugged, with a smile '—unless I'm actually going to use it. What else did he say?'

'He's desperately excited. Buying up every pink article in Salvador. And...'

He narrowed his eyes. 'And what?'

Isabella hesitated, glancing over at Eddie and Paulo guessed that she wanted to speak to him in private.

He followed her out into the hallway. 'What is it?' he demanded softly.

She met his eyes with embarrassment. 'Well, since we haven't issued a denial—' she paused again.

'Go on,' he prompted.

She shrugged awkwardly. 'He still seems to be labouring under the illusion that we're getting married.'

'Oh, does he?' asked Paulo slowly.

'I really should tell him that we aren't, but...'

He looked up, trying to work out what emotion was colouring her voice. 'But what?'

She sighed. Paulo did not need to know that her father thought he was the most wonderful thing since sliced bread. And that the prospect of his only daughter making such a glorious marriage seemed to have erased the memory of her unconventional pregnancy. 'Oh, I don't know,' she hedged. 'It seems to be keeping him happy.'

'Then why don't we keep it that way?' he suggested thoughtfully.

CHAPTER ELEVEN

ISABELLA turned Estella's night-light on and went quietly downstairs to the dining room where Paulo was waiting for her.

He looked up as she came in, his dark face thoughtful as she did up the final button of her bodice, and he sighed. How in God's name had he ever been stupid enough to think that breast-feeding a baby wasn't erotic?

'Is she asleep?' he asked.

'Out for the count.' She slid into her seat and watched while he heaped a pile of glossy black grapes into the centre of the cheeseboard, thinking that Saturday night dinner in the Dantas household was an experience not to be missed.

Because, despite the undeniable masculinity of his appearance, she had discovered that Paulo was no slouch when it came to finding his way round a kitchen. And that, as well as a hundred different ways with pasta, he cooked a mean steak. But then, as he had told her, Jessie might have been around to do the bulk of the housekeeping duties—but she certainly wasn't on call twenty-four hours a day, seven days a week!

He was sitting staring at her now, the black eyes softly luminous. 'So what did the midwife say?'

Isabella swirled red wine around the globe of her glass and pretended to study it. She certainly wasn't going to repeat the midwife's brisk question word for word! 'Sex-life back to normal by now, I expect?' And Isabella had nodded her head vigorously, because how—*how*—could

148

she possibly tell the nurse the truth? That she had never, ever been made love to by Paulo Dantas. But that oh, she wanted to.

'Hmm, Bella?' he prompted on a murmur.

'Oh, just that Estella was the most beautiful, bouncing baby—'

'Uh-huh. Anything else?'

'And that we're doing everything right.' She heard the word 'we' slip off her tongue and silently cursed it. Just because she continued to play happy families inside her head, that didn't mean the rest of the world had to join in. Even though Paulo seemed to be doing a masterly job of playing happy families himself.

'That's all?'

Isabella put her glass down on the table. 'Paulo, just what are you trying to say?'

He suspected that she knew damned well. 'Nothing.'

'Look, why don't you come right out and ask me?'

'It would shock you, pretty lady.' He gave a gritty smile, thinking that lately she didn't look just pretty— she looked absolutely knock-out beautiful. Like tonight, for instance—in that silky red thing which covered her from neck to knee and yet left absolutely nothing to the imagination. He wondered whether it had been designed for the sole purpose of having a man itching to tear the damned thing off.

'I told you.' She sipped her wine and smiled encouragingly at him. 'I'm unshockable, these days.'

Paulo pushed his untouched plate of cheese aside and stared at her, thinking that much more of this and he was going to go out of his mind. Because, even though he and Bella and Eddie and Estella had been living the kind of lifestyle which usually featured in the glossy supplements of Sunday newspapers, deep down, the undercur-

rent of tension between the two of them had been unbearable.

There had been all the frustration of having her so
close—but not close enough. Of nights laced with hot,
erotic dreams which left him waking up, sweat-sheened
and frustrated—despite the inevitable conclusion to
those dreams. Of knowing—or hoping—that she was lying there tossing and turning, just the same as he was.
Aching with the need to touch her, to lay his hands on
a body which was driving him slowly insane. So that
going to work each morning had become a welcome
kind of escape from the unwitting spell she was casting
over him.

She moved with such unconscious grace that he found
he had never enjoyed watching a woman quite as much
as he did Isabella. There was nothing of the flirt or the
tease about her. She was as uncomplicated in her young,
strong beauty as any of the thoroughbreds he had seen
her ride on her father's ranch.

But a deal was a deal and he forced himself to remember the stark facts. He was older—and far more
experienced. He knew just what to do and exactly which
buttons to press if he wanted to get Bella into his bed.
But the decision had to be hers, and hers alone. And,
whilst before the baby had been born he had deliberately
flirted with her, he no longer trusted himself to do that.

A distended stomach meant that you couldn't exactly
throw a woman to the floor and make love to her like
there was no tomorrow. Which was what he had felt like
doing earlier when Isabella decided that she was going
to dress up for dinner. He swallowed down a mouthful
of wine without really tasting it.

Isabella stared at him through the candles, willing him
to say something—*anything*—which would bring the

subject round to the question of them becoming lovers without her having to actually blurt it out.

'Paulo?' she whispered huskily, her eyes full of question.

'Yes, *querida*?' He kept his voice neutral and his smile bland.

She stared at him in frozen disbelief. Because when push came to shove she needed a little more in the way of wooing. She knew he had promised her nothing other than an affair which would 'burn itself out', and she could accept that. She wasn't asking him to sign the register and produce a band of gold—just give her some sign that he really, really *wanted* her—because she was damned if she was going to beg!

She slammed her napkin down onto the table before jumping to her feet. 'Oh! Paulo Dantas!' she cried frustratedly. 'You are so...so...'

'So?' he goaded, his black eyes laughing even while his body sprang into aching life.

'*Stupid!*'

And she pushed her chair back and walked straight out of the dining room, resisting the urge to slam the door behind her—because Eddie was in bed, fast asleep, and so was Estella.

She got as far as the top landing before she heard the sound of soft footfalls behind her, and for some reason the idea that he was silently chasing her through the house was unbearably exciting. She speeded up until she was almost past his bedroom door, when a hand appeared from behind to grab her wrist and to twist her round to face him and she nearly fainted with pleasure when she saw the hunger written darkly in his eyes.

'Stupid, you say?' he drawled softly.

Her heart pumped erratically. 'D-did I?'

'Stupid?' He gave a low, exultant laugh. 'Let's see, shall we, *querida*?' And he pulled her into his bedroom and softly kicked the door shut behind them.

Isabella felt the instant shimmer of arousal as his arms locked tightly around her waist and he stared down at her, his eyes devouring her with a hot, dark fire.

'Oh, *querida*,' he said, on a low groan of submission before giving in to the temptation which had been eating away at him for too long now. 'Bella, *querida*.' He felt like a man who had strayed into paradise unawares as he crushed his mouth down on hers, feeling the rose-petal softness of her lips. He kissed her until he had no breath left and then he raised his head. 'Do you want me?' he asked dazedly.

I've always wanted you. 'Yes,' came her throaty response as she wrapped her arms around his neck and clung onto him like she was drowning and Paulo represented safe harbour. Her gorgeous, beautiful Paulo. 'Yes, yes, yes.'

Paulo couldn't remember a kiss this hot or this intense and he knew that if she continued to generously press her body against him like that, that he would end up taking her against the wall. And he didn't want to just ruck her dress up and push aside her panties, ending up with his trousers round his ankles while he thrust long and hard and deep into her. He groaned.

Well, he did—of course he did. But she deserved more than that.

'Come here,' he said breathlessly. 'Come to bed.'

She was barely aware of the sumptuous fittings. Or the vast bed with its cover of rich, earthy colours. All she could see was the intense black light shining from his eyes as he sat her down, and began to unbutton the bodice of her dress.

'I want to touch you,' he said shakily. 'I need to touch you. Every bit of you. Inside and out.'

Bella shivered, unable to look away, feeling the buds of her breasts begin to tighten and the honey rush of desire as it soaked through her panties. She wondered if he could see the love which must surely be blazing from her eyes, but maybe she had better keep them closed. Love wasn't part of the deal, was it?

Paulo's fingers faltered for a moment as he caught an unmistakable scent of her sex, but he forced himself to continue unbuttoning, even though he would have willingly bought her twenty replacements if only he could rip it off. Her fingers had started to flutter over the silk of his shirt, skittering downwards in a way that made him shake his head.

'No,' he whispered.

'No?' She wanted to be good for him. She wanted to give him pleasure and she had read that all men liked to be touched *there*.

'*Querida*,' he said, speaking with difficulty because he felt seconds away from exploding. 'I've been wanting this for too long.' Because if she touched him there...

He peeled away the dress and a moan of rapture was torn from his lips. Her breasts were as full as they had been during her pregnancy, and very, very beautiful. He dipped his head reverentially towards one, and flicked the tip of his tongue towards one hardened nipple which pushed pinkly through the gossamer-fine black lace.

It was like being injected with some earth-shattering drug and Isabella fell helplessly back against the mattress, her hips moving in synchrony with her disbelieving gasp of pleasure. 'Please, Paulo,' she whispered, though she had no real idea what she was asking him for.

The husky plea and erotic action threatened to end everything before it had started and Paulo groaned again. He forced his head away from its sensual plundering of her lips, staring down into amber eyes which now looked black as raisins.

'Easy,' he breathed raggedly. 'For God's sake, Bella—take…it…easy.'

She wondered how she was supposed to do that. Especially now that his hand was slithering up her skirt, and then he gave a disbelieving little moan.

'Wh-what is it?' she stumbled.

'Stockings.' He swallowed. 'You're wearing *stockings*.'

Isabella heard the deepening of his voice and smiled. She might just be a girl from a ranch in the middle of nowhere, but there were some things that every woman over the world should know.

'Doesn't *every* woman wear stockings?' she asked him innocently.

'They should.' He groaned again. 'They should.'

But then his fingertips had moved beyond her suspenders to the cool, pale flesh of her thighs. And beyond. Oh! 'Paulo!' she breathed. *'Gato. Querido gato.'*

'You are making this bloody difficult for me,' he groaned as her head fell back and she moved distractedly again. Unable to resist, he briefly touched the warm, damp silk of her panties until he remembered that he was trying to undress her. His fingers skated away and she mouthed a silent prayer of protest, so that one finger in particular came skimming back again.

He could feel her fullness and her wetness and tightness, heard the broken words which escaped from her lips and which made no sense to him. She spoke in a mixture of English and Portuguese, her voice heavy with longing and thick with need.

He gave up and began to touch her with rhythm and purpose, thinking that this wasn't how it was supposed to happen.

Well, maybe part of it was. Hadn't he dreamed of seeing her like this, her body stretched out with abandon on his bed? Writhing with need and with desire and no thought of anything other than pleasure—the wild tumble of her hair painting his pillow with such dark curls.

He gave a small smile as he rubbed his finger against her and she nearly leapt off the bed. He had expected passion, yes. And response, yes—that, too. But this...

He dipped his head down and took the blunt tip of her nipple into his mouth, while his finger continued to tease and play against her.

Isabella felt like she had entered another world—a world dominated by sensation. By pleasure. By Paulo. And he seemed to know exactly what to do to make it get better all the time...

With something approaching astonishment, he felt her begin to tighten with an incredible tension, which could only mean one thing and he stared down into her face. Saw the mindless seeking of rapture which made her oblivious to everything except what was just about to happen in her own body. He speeded up the rhythm and spoke to her in her own language, sweet, erotic words he had never used before, words which made her melt enchantingly against his finger.

'Paulo!' she called out, and the slurred pleasure in her voice was tinged with surprise.

He smiled as he saw the sudden, frantic arching of her back, the incredulous little gasp she made as she reached that elusive, perfect place and then began the slow, shuddering journey back to sanity.

He watched the gradual stilling of her body, the flush which crept and bloomed like a flower on her neck. The way her lips parted in a helpless little sigh. The slumberous and lanquid stretch, like an indolent cat in front of a fire. And then the thick fluttering of her lashes as her slitted eyes gazed up at him.

'*Oh,*' she breathed uninhibitedly. 'What was *that*?'

He had suspected. No, deep down he had known. But her question—with all its implications—filled him with such a heady sense of his own power that it was as much as he could do not to throw his dark head back and give a loud, exultant laugh.

So. Roberto had given her a baby, yes. But no pleasure.

'*That*, *querida* of mine,' he purred, 'was the pleasure you deserve. The pleasure I intend to give you...over and over and over again.'

'*Again?*' She swallowed, with a greedy gulp.

He smiled. 'As many times as you like. But for God's sake let's get these clothes off.' His smile became rueful. He really *was* going to have to take control here, or he would never manage to get her—or himself—into bed!

And he wanted to. Needed to. Needed to feel close to her, skin on skin. Limb on limb.

He found the side fastening of her dress and slid the zip down—sliding the silky garment down over the curve of her hips with a hand which shook like a schoolboy's. And it was a long time since he had undressed a woman like this.

Those who had been in his bed since Elizabeth's death had all been icons of experience. So eager. So orderly. Neatly disappearing into the bathroom before returning to bed, all washed and toothbrushed and douched, smelling of perfume and soap and chemicals.

While Bella... She smelt like a real woman. He bent his head to unclip a stocking and again caught the raw perfume of her sex as it drifted towards him, and he resisted the urge to bury his head in the dark blur of curls which was lying with tantalising temptation above the creamy flesh of her thighs.

Later, he thought. They could do all that and more—but later. He dropped the dress onto the floor, and the stockings and garter belt followed, until she was just lying there in her bra and panties.

Her breasts were swollen, pushing against the black lace of the bra she wore and he found himself praying that she wouldn't have to go and feed the baby. But then he remembered that she had slipped away at the end of dinner, and he gave a great shuddering sigh of relief. Now, how selfish is *that*? he asked himself, as he tugged the lace panties down over her knees, trying hard not to touch her—anywhere—because he was holding onto his self-control only by the thinnest possible thread.

'Get into bed,' he said urgently.

'Touch me again,' she begged him, but he shook his head.

It had been too long. He had wanted her for too long. 'If I touch you again, I'll explode,' he husked, and the expression in his eyes made her draw in a shivering breath of excitement. 'Get into bed while I get undressed.'

She watched him take his clothes off. His face was shadowed in the unlit room as first the white T-shirt was removed to reveal the quietly-gleaming olive of his muscular torso. The black jeans followed, sliding them down over the powerful shaft of his thighs until he stood in just a pair of dark silk boxer shorts. His movements were naturally slinky and sensual as he peeled off the final piece of clothing.

Isabella's eyes widened. *'Gato,'* she murmured out loud, without thinking, and his smile was one of pure brilliance.

He paused only to tear open a condom and to carefully sheath himself with it and Isabella wondered if it was normal for a man to be that aroused, that quickly.

He drew back the cover and climbed into bed with her, pulling her into his arms, and smoothing the rampant curls away from her face. 'I don't know very much,' she admitted huskily.

'I'll teach you everything I know,' he promised and felt her shiver with anticipation in his arms. Her eyes were as bright as stars and the flush on her neck was beginning to fade. He bent and kissed the tip of her nose, just for the hell of it. And then her lips. A soft, sweet, drugging kiss that went on and on until he could wait no longer.

He pushed her back against the pillow and lay over her, his elbows taking all his weight, while the creamy swell of her breasts pushed alluringly towards him.

'Scared?' he asked.

She opened her eyes very wide. 'Why should I be scared?'

'It's your first time since having a baby. I'll be very—' he swallowed, feeling unbearably moved by the look of trust in her eyes '—gentle.'

Her faith in him was implicit. She felt the moist tip of him pushing against her and she gave an experimental little thrust of her hips, so that he nudged gently inside, filling her completely. And if she shuddered, then so did he. 'Be what you want to be, Paulo.'

He gave up. The questions could come later. Right now, it was her turn. And his. His.

He made one long, slow, hard stroke. And then another. Dipping his head to kiss her, his tongue copying the same, slick and erotic rhythm. Increasing the tempo as her control began to leave her. Watching the opening of her lips in a frozen exclamation as it started happening to her all over again.

And he could no longer wait. Nothing in the world could have stopped him. Nothing. He tensed and steeled himself, aware that this was going to feel like nothing had ever felt before.

And it did.

Oh, it did.

CHAPTER TWELVE

PAULO opened his eyes to find his head resting on the glorious cushion of Isabella's breasts. And that she was trying to slip out from underneath him. He tightened his arms around her. 'Oh, no,' he objected sleepily. 'You're not going anywhere.'

'Paulo,' she whispered. 'I must. I hear Estella and I need to go and feed her.'

He rolled onto his side, and snapped the light on, blinking at the sudden intrusion, but just in time to watch her climbing out of bed, beautifully and unashamedly naked.

'You'll come back?' he asked.

Isabella pulled the red dress over her head, not bothering with underwear. The front fastening of the dress meant that she would easily be able to feed the baby, and then she had better take a shower and...

She shook her head. 'I'd better not—it's two in the morning.'

He propped himself up on his elbow, and the black eyes glittered by the lamplight as he watched her. 'So?'

'By the time I've fed her, and changed her and settled her back down for what's left of the night—there won't really be time for me to come back in here.'

If he had learnt one thing and one thing only during that exquisite interlude, it was that she liked him to talk dirty.

'But I haven't finished with you yet,' he said quite deliberately.

Isabella swallowed as she heard the dark resolve in his voice, but knew that she had other responsibilities than being his lover. She was a parent, too. And so was he.

She bent to pick her disgarded panties and bra from the carpet and looked him straight in the eye. 'I don't think I should be here when Eddie wakes up.'

'You won't be! His room is right along the corridor and he's the world's heaviest sleeper—you know that,' he objected. 'Besides, I always wake first.'

'What if for once he doesn't?'

'He always knocks first.'

'But *we* might oversleep,' she told him softly, thinking that if they carried on the way they had been doing up until half an hour ago they might risk oversleeping for a week!

'Then I'll set the alarm.'

'Paulo!'

'OK, OK.' He sat up in bed and raked his hand back through the thick, dark hair, knowing deep down that she was right, damn her—and yet oddly irritated by her determination. Because at that moment he wanted her so badly that he felt like he would have shifted heaven and earth to have her back here in his bed.

Isabella smoothed her hair down and blew him a kiss. 'Bye.'

'Come over here and kiss me properly.'

'Or?'

He laughed, but the laugh was tinged with sexual danger. 'Guess?'

Her heart thundered in response as she walked over to the bed and bent down over him and he was given a tantalising glimpse of the shadowed cleft between her breasts. Her face and then her mouth hovered into his line of vision and she pressed a sweet, swift kiss on his lips, before going back to the door.

He very nearly said, When will I see you?

Until he remembered that he could see her whenever he wanted. Mmm. He sighed and smiled and snuggled into the pillow and was asleep in seconds.

Feeling hot and sticky and more than a little uncomfortable, Isabella fed Estella, changed her and then sang gently to her for a little while.

In her arms the baby snuffled, oblivious to the ever changing play of emotions on her mother's face. Isabella put her down in the beautiful gingham crib, tucked her in and stood looking down at her for a long moment. She thought about the years to come—God willing—when she would gaze down at her daughter like this.

She jammed her fist in her mouth and turned away, tears burning at her eyes as she realised just how irrevocable the sexual act could be. Out of her desperate attempt to put Paulo out of her mind had come this tiny baby.

And tonight. Irrevocable for a different reason—though there would be no baby. Paulo had made sure of that.

She thought about his tenderness and his passion. The way it had really seemed to be *her* that he wanted in his bed. Not just because she was a body, and any body would do.

Tonight had been irrevocable because it had sealed the truth in her heart once and for all. That she loved this man Paulo Dantas. Would love him forever. And that made her more than vulnerable where he was concerned.

He had been totally honest with her. He had told her she could stay with him for as long as... What had he said? 'Until it is spent. All burnt out.' Just as he had told her that they should indulge their mutual passion.

Well, now they had. So what came next?

One thing was for sure, she decided, peeling off the scarlet dress and dropping it into the laundry basket. She needed to keep some vestige of independence—if only to prove to herself that she didn't need him around every minute of every day. Because if that happened she would be lost.

The last thing she wanted was to become totally dependent on Paulo—to become addicted to his beautiful, strong body and his quick, clever mind.

Because everyone knew how difficult addictions were to kick. It was better to never get started in the first place.

Isabella woke for Estella's early-morning feed and then took a long, long shower, arriving in the dining room for breakfast at the same time as Eddie.

'Hi, sweetheart,' she smiled.

'Hi, Bella. Where's Estella?'

'Guess?'

'Sleeping!' he grinned.

'You've got it in one! You can go in and say goodbye to her before you go to school, if you want.' She saw the warmth on his young face. 'Tell you what—when you get home tonight, you can help me to bath her. Would you like that?'

'Oh, Bella—*can* I?'

'Can you what?' asked a deep, sleepy voice, and Isabella's mouth dried as Paulo walked into the dining-room.

'Hi, Papa! Isabella said I can help bath Estella tonight!'

'That's nice,' said Paulo blandly and, sitting down opposite her, poured himself a glass of juice and raised it up to her in a silent, sexy toast.

Isabella struggled to hold onto her self-possession, but it wasn't easy. What did he think he was playing at? Usually he presented himself for his morning bread and fruit already dressed for work. Wearing an immaculate suit, a pristine shirt and a silk tie which made him look like a walking advertisement for executive-hunk.

So *why* was he barefoot and unshaven, wearing a faded old T-shirt—having just thrown on *the same pair of jeans that he had worn last night*? And now a bare foot had moved underneath the table and was inching its way suggestively up her leg!

She snatched it away as if it had been contaminated and thought about pouring herself a cup of coffee, except that her hand was shaking so much she didn't think she would be able to make the cup connect with her mouth.

She met the glittering jet of his gaze. 'Won't you be late, Paulo?' she asked him pointedly.

'Late?' he enquired sunnily. 'I'm a director of the bank, *querida*. I can stroll in late once in a while if I feel like it.'

'But Dad.' Eddie frowned. 'You told me that if you're a director you must always set an example—and that you should only ever be late if you've got a genuine reason to be. Like that time when I didn't want to go in because we had a maths test, but you made me.'

'He does have a point, Paulo.'

'Oh, *does* he?' He glared dangerously, and then, drawing in a breath, managed to smile. 'Anyway,' he said casually, 'I thought I'd work from home today.'

Isabella knew exactly what he was playing at—and she wasn't going to let him do this. It was vital to her sanity not to let him invade every waking moment of her day as well as her night.

'Oh, what a pity I won't be here.' She smiled.

The glower deepened. 'What do you mean, you won't be here?'

'Just that I'm taking Estella to see the doctor.'

He stared at her. 'What's the matter with her?'

'Nothing.' Her mouth softened. 'It's just a regular check-up.'

'Well, he can come here—I thought we agreed that!'

'No, we did not!' she said quietly. 'That was before—when I was pregnant and exhausted. I *need* to get out, Paulo—and Estella needs the fresh air, too, because it's good for little babies. Right?'

The black stare iced through her. 'Right,' he said coldly.

She only toyed with a croissant and, in the end, gave up and went to the utility room to find a clean sheet. She was just tucking it into the base of the pram when she heard Paulo come up behind her. She was prepared for him to touch her, but he didn't—what she was not prepared for was the irritation which was sending dangerous jet sparks glittering from his eyes when she turned to face him.

'What's the matter, *querida*?' he purred, thinking that he had never been so expertly turned down by a woman before. And that as a method of increasing desire it was proving achingly effective. 'Been having second thoughts this morning?'

'No, of course not.'

'Then why are you so intent on keeping me at arm's length?'

Isabella looked over his shoulder to check that no one

else was around. '*Jessie's* here!' she hissed. 'What do you expect?'

He shrugged. 'So I'll give her the day off.'

'No!'

'Yes—'

'What, so *you* take the day off and then give Jessie the day off—and you and I spend the rest of it in bed together, I suppose?'

He grinned. 'Sounds pretty good to me.'

'Well, I don't think it's a good idea—in fact, I think it's the worst idea I've ever heard!' Well, maybe that was overstating her case a little, but she needed to make him understand how she felt.

There was a long, dangerous pause. 'Would you care to explain why?'

Isabella sighed, because this wasn't easy. She wanted him—she wanted him too much, that was the problem. 'Paulo, I desperately need to maintain some sort of routine with my baby, not launch headlong into a sizzling new love-affair with you.'

'Surely the two aren't mutually exclusive?'

'No, of course they're not… But I think it's important that I'm there for Estella. If she were *our* baby we'd both be gazing at her non-stop, not each other—'

'But she's not *our* baby,' he pointed out, unprepared for a sudden great lurch of sadness.

'No, she's not. That's why I need to get to *know* her—we need to bond—and if I'm in your bed all the time, then we won't.' She looked at him with appeal darkening the huge, amber eyes. 'You know we won't.'

Paulo sighed. The irony was that he wouldn't have it any other way. If she'd ignored the baby while playing all kinds of erotic sex-games with him, then he would have found it a complete turn-off.

'No, I guess you're right.' He sighed again. 'But night-times...and I mean *every* night-time...those are our times.' He gave her a look of dark, shivering intent. 'Got that?'

'Oh, yes.' She swallowed, and reached out her hand to touch his face, but he stopped the movement instantly, handcuffing her wrist between his thumb and forefinger while he shook his head.

'Oh, no, Bella,' he said softly. 'You can't have it every which way. You can't just love me and leave me, then kiss me goodbye and leave me aching all day.' And he swiftly covered her mouth with a sweet, hard kiss which sent *her* senses reeling, before giving a devastating and glittering smile as she gazed up at him in dismay. 'See? It hurts, doesn't it, sweet *querida*?'

But, before her befuddled brain could begin to think of an answer, he had turned on his heel and left.

By the evening Paulo had calmed down a little, though he conceded that his buoyant mood might have had something to do with his anticipation of the night to come.

On the way home from the bank, he stopped off at the florist and bought an extravagant display of white, scented flowers—'nothing too *obvious*', he had told the florist, who had taken one look at him and suggested red roses—plus chocolates and a video for Eddie.

He arrived home to find the house strangely silent. Eddie was sitting in the study, laboriously doing his homework, and Isabella was sitting by the fire in the smaller sitting room, breastfeeding the baby.

She hadn't heard him come in and carried on, blissfully unaware of his presence by the door, murmuring sweet nothings to the child who suckled her, and he felt a sudden great urge to kiss her.

Instead he said softly, 'Hi!'

She looked up and her heart leapt with the sheer pleasure of seeing him. 'Hi.'

'Good day?'

'Sort of.' She hesitated. 'Paulo—about this morning—'

'I'm sorry—'

'No, I'm sorry—'

'I said it first,' he teased softly, and produced the lavish bunch of flowers from behind his back like a magician magicking a rabbit out of a hat.

'For me?'

'Well, who else?'

She buried her nose in the blooms and breathed their scent in. 'Jessie?'

'No, seriously.'

'Paulo, I *am* being serious. She's—'

'Where is she?' He sniffed the air. Yes, *that* was the odd thing. Normally when he arrived home from work, Jessie was crashing around in the kitchen, cooking something for supper. But tonight there were no tempting aromas to signal the arrival of an imminent supper. 'Where is she?' he repeated.

'She's gone out to buy champagne.'

He frowned. 'But we've got plenty of champagne in the house.'

'I know we have. But she wanted it to be *her* champagne. *Her* treat.'

'*Querida*, you aren't making much sense.'

'Paulo—' She drew a deep breath. 'Jessie's gone and got herself engaged!'

'Jessie has?' He shook his head. 'I don't believe it!'

'Well, you'd better. It's true. In fact, that sounds like the door—so why don't you ask her yourself?'

In the distance, the front door slammed and Jessie came breathlessly into the room, carrying a brown paper bag with a foil-topped bottle in it, smiling so much that her face looked fit to burst.

'Jessie, is this true?' he asked, mock-sternly. 'Are you about to take the plunge and get married?'

'Yes,' Jessie beamed. 'It's true! Isn't it wonderful?'

'I guess it is,' he said slowly. 'It's just come as a bit of a shock, that's all.'

'It was a shock to *me* when Simon proposed,' confessed Jessie. 'I mean, we haven't *really* known each other for that long, and…' She gave a self-conscious and slightly apologetic shrug. 'He wants me to stop work as soon as you'll let me. You won't be needing me for much longer, anyway, will you?'

Paulo started, wondering what was happening to the smooth and well-oiled machinery of his life. 'You're not *leaving*?' he demanded, aghast.

Jessie frowned at him. 'Well, of course I'm leaving,' she told him softly. 'I can't keep coming in twice a day to cook your meals when I have a husband of my own to care for, can I? And besides—' she shot a quick smile at Isabella '—I sort of got the idea that I was becoming supernumerary around here anyway. You won't miss *me*, Paulo—not any more. You've got Isabella and the baby here now.'

Paulo opened his mouth to say something, but thought better of it. Now was not the time to selfishly think about his own needs and Jessie had been indispensable to him. She had helped and supported him through all these years—so now he must be genuinely happy for her.

'Congratulations, Jessie,' he smiled. He held out his arms to her and gave her an emotional bear-hug.

Over the top of her head, he tried to catch Isabella's eyes, but all her attention seemed to be concentrated fiercely on the baby in her arms. 'We'd better get that champagne opened and order in some pizza,' he observed thoughtfully. 'Let's make it a party!'

Supper was served amidst much excitement and some chaos in the dining room, where Simon was telephoned by Jessie and summoned in to join them. The tall librarian was clearly nuts about his future bride, and Isabella felt a pang of emotion which felt appallingly close to jealousy. But she fixed a bright smile onto her lips as they all raised their glasses in a toast, even Eddie.

It was late by the time that the newly engaged pair left, giggling like a couple of teenagers, while Eddie was yawning again and again.

'Come on, son,' said Paulo softly, as he shut the front door. 'Bed.'

'G'night, Isabella,' yawned Eddie.

'Goodnight, sweetheart.'

She felt oddly nervous as she busied herself throwing away the half-chewed slices of pizza and tipping the dregs of champagne down the sink, especially when she turned to find Paulo standing watching her.

'Leave that,' he said tersely.

'But—'

'*Leave* it, I said.' His voice roughened. 'And for God's sake just come over here and kiss me, before I go out of my mind.'

She didn't need to be asked twice. She went straight into his arms and raised her face tremulously to his, before he blotted out everything but pleasure with the pressure of his lips.

He raised her face to look at him, his brows criss-crossing as he took in the faint blue shadows beneath her eyes. 'You're tired,' he accused softly.

'Are you surprised?' She smiled.

He shook his head, feeling the instant spring of arousal as he thought about what had happened. 'No. I was pretty rampant with you last night—I couldn't keep my hands off you.'

'I noticed,' she murmured. 'Did you hear me complaining?'

'Nope.' He lifted her hand to his mouth and began to gently suck at each fingertip in turn, enjoying the way her eyes darkened in response and the impatient little shake of her shoulder as she squirmed for more. 'Tonight, though, you sleep.'

She blinked up at him in alarm. She had planned to ration her time with him, yes. That was why she had sent him to work this morning. But she had saved the nights exclusively for him. Only maybe he didn't want that any more. Maybe once had been enough to slake his thirst. 'Alone, you mean?'

He gave a short laugh, as if she just suggested something obscene. 'No, with me. In my arms. But definitely no sex.' He told himself that he had resisted women in the past—women far more experienced at seduction than Bella was.

Then wondered just who he was trying to fool.

CHAPTER THIRTEEN

'ISABELLA—there's a fax just coming in for you from Paulo!'

'Coming!' Isabella tucked the blanket around Estella and switched on the musical mobile above her head. 'Thanks, Jessie,' she said, walking into the study to see Paulo's fax machine spilling out paper. 'What does it say?'

Jessie looked affronted. 'I haven't read it! It might be…personal.'

Isabella didn't reply as she leaned forward to rip the finished message off. Jessie wasn't stupid. These days, it was an open—though unacknowledged—secret that she was sharing Paulo's bed at night. A fact brought pointedly home to her when her lost necklace was produced from down the back of the mattress in his room. But at least Jessie had had the tact not to ask any questions when she had handed it back to Isabella. In fact, these days Jessie was more interested in holding her hand up to the light to study her brand-new engagement ring.

Isabella smiled at the housekeeper before reading it. 'Only a few days to go now. Paulo's going to miss you.'

Jessie shook her head. 'I don't think so. He doesn't need me any more, not really. It's time for him to move on as much as me.'

But Isabella wasn't really listening; she was too busy reading the fax. It was a copy of a newspaper cutting, written in Portuguese, and it was a birth announcement

172

taken from one of Brazil's biggest nationals. She frowned at the date. A week ago. It said:

To Isabella Fernandes and Paulo Dantas—a girl. Luis Jorge Fernandes is delighted to announce the birth of a beautiful granddaughter—Estella Maria—in London, England.

Isabella quickly crushed the paper in her hand and walked out into the hallway when the phone started ringing. She snatched it up, knowing that it would be Paulo.

It was.

'You got my fax?'

'Yes.' She chewed on her lip. People *thinking* that he was the father was one thing, but actually seeing it in print... 'I don't what to say, Paulo—my father had no right to do that. I don't know what possessed him!'

'Don't you?' came the dry response. 'I've got a pretty good idea. He's obviously trying to shame us into getting married!'

It occurred to her that he couldn't possibly have picked a more loaded or offensive word to use. '*Shame* us?'

'You know what I mean. That's how he'll see it.'

'Well, I'd better telephone him right away,' she said stiffly. 'Just to set the record straight.'

There was a pause. 'Unless you want to, of course.'

Isabella stared at the hand which was tightly gripping the receiver. 'Want to what?'

'Get married.'

As a proposal it left a lot to be desired. Even if he *did* mean it—and she couldn't be certain that this wasn't just another example of Paulo's mocking, deadpan humour. Imagine if it was, and she started gushing, yes please—forcing him to hastily back-track and tell her he'd been joking. 'I won't be blackmailed into anything,' she told him fiercely.

Another pause. 'OK, Bella. But don't ring your father until we've discussed it.'

'Paulo—'

'Not now, Bella. I'm in the office and I'm busy. It's Friday, remember? We'll talk about it when I get home.'

She put the phone down, feeling as mixed up as she'd ever been. How *dared* her father? How *dared* he? And Paulo wasn't much better, either. Idily drawling a proposal of marriage down the phone as if he were asking her whether there was any bread in the freezer, when marriage was a serious undertaking which should not be undertaken lightly! How *could* he?

She felt glad that it was the weekend, and that Eddie had gone to stay the night with a schoolfriend. The last thing she felt like doing was eating, but Jessie had made a casserole and Paulo would be hungry, so she put a low flame underneath it.

Paulo walked into the kitchen to find her stirring at the pot, thinking that she managed to look a very sexy hausfrau indeed, and was just about to tell her so, when he saw the tell-tale glitter of anger sparking from the amber eyes, and merely remarked, 'Hmm. No point asking for a kiss, then.'

Her anger was threatening to spill over like some horrible corrosive liquid, but she forced it under control. 'Correct.'

He pulled a cork from a bottle of wine, and poured himself a glass. 'Like some?'

'No, thanks,' she said tightly.

He sipped the wine, looking at her defensive body language through the thick forest of his lashes, and sighed. 'OK, Bella—just who are you angry with? Me, or your father?'

'Both of you! And I don't need any patronising proposals of marriage from *you*, Paulo Dantas! Just because Jessie is leaving and you think you'll be left in the lurch! Well, it's probably cheaper in the long run to employ another housekeeper instead of bothering to get married. It will certainly be less trouble!'

'How very right you are,' he agreed coolly, and walked out of the kitchen, leaving Isabella staring after him, feeling...feeling...well, *cheated*. She had wanted a passionate defence of his offer to marry her—not that rather bland indifference, which confirmed her worst fears that he hadn't meant it at all.

She heard him slamming out of the house without bothering to say goodbye or tell her where he was going and, for the first time since they had become lovers, Isabella slept in her own room that night. She lay wide awake, and thought she heard Paulo's door close long after midnight.

And in the long, grey hours before dawn she was able to realise with an aching certainty, just how much she missed him. She missed him lying next to her. And not just Paulo as her lover—even though he was the most perfect lover imaginable. She missed the way he held her during the night. The bits that came *after* the sex. A lazy arm locked possessively around her waist. A thigh resting indolently on hers. He made her feel warm and comfortable and very safe.

She must have dozed fitfully because, when Estella woke at six the following morning, Isabella felt more exhausted even than when she had first brought the baby home from hospital. And there seemed little point in going back to bed.

She wasted time in the shower and spent even longer getting dressed, forcing herself to make coffee and toast and thinking that the sound of movement might bring Paulo out of his bedroom. But it didn't. And she couldn't just barge in there and wake him. Could she? Even if she was sure that he would have wanted her to.

So she wrapped the baby up warmly and took her outside in the pram. The park was almost deserted and it was a bitterly cold day. The trees were all bare now, and the leaves had been neatly brushed up and taken away, leaving a stark winter landscape behind.

But Isabella didn't even register the plummeting temperature. She was trying to tell herself that maybe it was a good thing that her father had brought matters to a head. She was going to *have* to come to some kind of decision about her future. Because she knew in her heart that she couldn't just stay on indefinitely, playing pretend families with Paulo and his son.

And didn't Eddie risk getting hurt too, the more she hung around slipping irresistibly into the role of mother-substitute? What would happen to him when the relationship finally petered out?

Beneath the snug protection of bonnet and blankets, Estella began to stir and when Isabella looked at her watch she was amazed to discover that she had been out walking for almost two hours.

She went back to the house with all the enthusiasm of someone who was just about to sit an exam, and she had just bumped the pram through the front door when she heard the low sound of men's voices coming from the sitting room.

She left Estella asleep in the pram and walked into the room. Paulo stood by the golden flicker of the fire, his face as she had never seen it before. Dark and cold and frighteningly aloof. And then the identity of the other man froze itself onto her disbelieving brain.

The man stood with his back to her, his hair untidily spilling over the collar of an old denim jacket. But she recognised him in one sickening instant.

It had been almost eleven months since she'd last seen him, unshaven and loudly snoring off a hangover. She'd crept from his bed in the middle of the night, feeling that she couldn't have sunk any lower if someone had tied a heavy stone to her ankles and thrown her into the river.

But as a result of that night had come her baby—and although with hindsight she would never have chosen to behave in the way she did she could no more imagine a world without Estella than she could a world without...

'Paulo?' she whispered.

'You have a visitor,' he bit out. 'Aren't you going to say hello, Isabella?'

'Hello, Roberto,' she said flatly, but she kept her face expressionless, because some instinct told her that she was in some kind of inexplicable danger here.

Roberto turned around, and Isabella was unprepared for the revulsion which iced her skin, but still she kept her face free of emotion. She recognised now that she'd been a different woman when she had fallen for his practised seduction. That his smile was weak, not careless. And that he'd taken advantage of her vulnerability and her status as one of his students.

'What are you doing here?' she asked him quietly.

'Why don't I leave you both in peace?' put in Paulo silkily, but Isabella barely registered his words or even the fact that he had slipped silently from the room.

Because she could scarcely believe that Roberto was *here*, standing in front of her, his very presence tainting the place she had come to think of as home. 'How did you find me, Roberto?'

He shrugged. 'It wasn't difficult—thanks to your father's birth announcement. Paulo Dantas is one of Brazil's better-known bankers. And England's, too, it would seem,' he added jealously, as his eyes flickered around the room. And then it was *her* turn to be sized up, and he gave her a sly smile. 'You know, you're looking pretty good for a woman who has just had a baby—'

'Why are you here?' she asked, in a frozen voice.

'Why do you think?' He looked around him. 'Where is she, Isabella?'

Her heart pounded in her chest. 'Who?' she croaked.

'Please don't insult my intelligence.'

She opened her mouth to tell him that he flattered himself, but shut it again. Making him angry wasn't a clever idea.

'Where is she?' he repeated. 'My daughter. Estella.'

At the sound of Estella's name on *his* lips, Isabella grew rigid with terror, but she did her best to hide her reaction, instinctively knowing that she must appear strong. She must. 'You've only just arrived, Roberto,' she said softly. 'And have had nothing to drink. Let me offer you a little something.'

She saw him hesitate, and saw greed win out over the question of paternity—despite the earliness of the hour.

'Yeah, a drink would be good. Dantas could barely bring himself to speak to me without spitting.' His eyes glistened as they watched the uneven rise and fall of her breasts. 'But I guess I know why.'

'I'll go and get you that drink,' she breathed, and she just about made it to the kitchen before crumpling into a chair, her fingers jammed between her teeth to prevent herself from crying out in real terror.

And that was how Paulo found her. He didn't say a word until she raised her head to look at him, and what he read in her eyes caused him to flinch.

But he needed to hear it from her.

'Do you want him?' he asked flatly.

She swallowed down the nausea. 'How can you even ask?'

He forced the words out. 'Because he's the father of your baby.'

'Oh, Paulo,' she pleaded. 'Please. *Help* me.'

It was the lifeless quality to her voice which blasted into his consciousness and made him decide to act. Because through everything that had happened up until now she'd kept her spirit and her courage intact. Even her tears before the baby had been oddly defiant, brave tears. And for Isabella to look the way she was looking at him right now...helplessly...hopelessly...

'Come back into the sitting room with me.'

'He wants a drink—'

'*Damn* his drink!' Paulo contradicted in a voice of pure venom.

Roberto looked up as he heard them approach. 'No drink, I see. But you've brought lover-boy with you instead.' His eyes narrowed with malicious calculation. 'Though maybe you haven't told him how *close* we were, Isabella?'

'You've come a long way, Bonino,' Paulo observed, almost pleasantly. 'Surely not just to draw attention to your inadequacies in bed?'

Roberto flushed. 'A very long way,' he agreed. 'But I figured it was worth it.'

'So what have you come for? Money?'

Roberto tensed and a shrewd look entered his eyes. 'Actually, I came to discuss access to my daughter—'

Isabella sucked in a breath of outraged horror.

'She is not,' interrupted Paulo calmly, '*your* daughter.'

The two men stared at one another.

'She's mine,' said Paulo quietly.

Only the welfare of her baby gave Isabella the strength not to react, but her legs felt unsteady. She glanced anxiously over at Roberto.

'You're lying,' he accused.

Paulo shook his head and snaked out a hand to draw Isabella snugly against the jut of his hip, fingertips curving with arrogant ownership around her waist. 'We're lovers,' he said deeply and, compelled by something she couldn't resist in that deep, rich voice, Isabella raised her face to his. 'We've always been lovers, haven't we, *querida*?'

And in one sense she supposed they had. There had certainly never been any other man who had taken up residence heart, body and soul, the way Paulo had. She nodded her head, too dazed to speak.

'I d-don't believe you,' spluttered Roberto.

'Then prove it,' said Paulo in a cold and deadly voice. 'Go ahead—apply to the British courts. You can start the whole lengthy and exceedingly expensive legal proceedings *and you'll lose*,' he threatened.

Roberto swallowed. 'And if I won?'

Paulo appeared to consider the feeble question, then shrugged. 'Well, it's all academic—because you won't. But you certainly wouldn't get any co-operation from us if you were expecting to take Estella out of the country. Even if you could afford the return ticket—which I doubt, not on a lecturer's salary. A salary you may not have for much longer.'

His eyes glittered like black diamonds. 'If you take this any further, I shall hire the very best lawyers in the land to prove that you are an unfit father. And I don't think I'd have much trouble doing that, do you—in view of your rather *unconventional* attitude to student relationships?'

Roberto licked his lips. 'I think I will have that drink, after all; then I'll go.'

Paulo ignored the request. 'Are you still working?' he asked, still in that same calm, almost pleasant voice.

Roberto swallowed. 'Sure.'

Paulo smiled, but it was a hard, cruel smile. 'How do you think that your superiors would feel about you abusing your position by seducing students? They might get mad at that, mightn't they? So might the other students. And their parents—now they would be *really* mad, wouldn't they? You see, Roberto, even in the most liberal circles, people don't take kindly to a fundamental position of trust being abused.'

Roberto had started to shake. He licked his lips like a cornered animal. 'What are you planning to do?' he whimpered.

Letting Isabella go, Paulo took a deliberate and intimidating step forward. 'What I would like to do,' he said icily, 'is to beat your face into an unrecognisable pulp before extracting a full and frank confession which I would then take to the university authorities to deal with. I would like to see you jailed and to make sure that you never worked in a responsible position again. That is what I would *like* to do—'

'Paulo—'

'Not now, Bella,' he instructed softly, before turning

his attention back to the man who seemed to have shrunk in stature since Isabella had first entered the room. 'But I don't trust myself to lay a finger on you, you worthless piece of slime. So instead I am telling you to get out of Isabella's life once and for all. And to stay out. And that any mention of your fleeting—' his mouth hardened on the next word '—involvement with her will be rigorously denied and followed up with an exposé you will live to regret. Believe me.' His eyes glittered. 'Oh, and if word ever reaches me that you are forming unsuitable relationships with any of your students again...' He allowed himself a grim smile and shook his head. 'Just don't go there, Bonino,' he warned softly. 'And now get out of my house before I change my mind and hit you.'

Roberto opened his mouth like a stranded fish. He turned to Isabella with a question in his eyes, but something in her face made the question die on his lips, unasked. He swallowed and shrugged, then turned and walked out of the room without another word.

The echoing of the front door closing behind him was the only sound which could be heard for several long, tense moments.

'How can I ever thank you?' she whispered, lifting tentative fingertips to touch the dark rasp of his chin but he shook his head, and she let her hand fall.

'Keeping a creep like that out of Estella's life is thanks enough,' he answered coolly. 'You don't have to make love to me to close the deal, Bella.'

'Close...the...deal?' She screwed up her eyes in disbelief. 'But yesterday you were asking me to marry you.'

'And we both know what your reply was.'

'I thought it was a joke.'

'A *joke*?' He stared at her incredulously. 'Why would I joke about something like that?'

She met his eyes defiantly. 'Because you don't "do" serious, remember?'

'OK,' he conceded. 'That *was* a pretty arrogant statement to make—but it was true at the time I said it.'

'And you made asking me to marry you sound so casual,' she accused. 'Like you didn't really care one way or the other.'

'Bella,' he said patiently, 'our relationship has hardly been the model of conventional behaviour up until now, has it? But if a diamond ring and a bended knee are what you want—'

'They aren't!' she said furiously. 'But maybe you could try convincing me that our relationship isn't going to "burn itself out" the way you predicted! What's the point of getting married, if that's the case?'

He frowned. 'That's not what I said—'

'It is!'

He shook his head. 'No,' he contradicted flatly. 'You asked me how long we would be lovers, and I said that I didn't know—*until it burned itself out*. But it isn't going to, is it, Bella?' he questioned softly. 'We both know that.' He saw the way that her lips trembled, and gave a slow, lazy smile. 'We like and respect one another in a way that goes bone-deep. We click in a way that's so easy. I feel fantastic when I'm with you—and this kind of feeling doesn't come along in most people's lifetime. Believe me, *querida*.'

'Then why did you say it?'

'Why?' He stroked her hair thoughtfully. 'Because I was hurt and frustrated—furious that someone else had been your lover and furious with myself for not having prevented it. And yet, I had this overpowering urge to protect you and look after you. I wanted to ask you to marry me then, but the last thing you needed was *more* emotional pressure being heaped on you. That's why I was prepared to wait—and I thought that once we really *did* become lovers rather than just fantasising about it, then…'

'What?' she asked him tremulously.

'That by then you would know how much I loved you.' His eyes softened as he looked down at her. 'And I was certain that my behaviour since would have convinced you that I've fallen completely under your spell.' He gave a very sexy grin. 'Bella—do you think I'm like that in bed with *every* woman I've ever slept with?'

'Never, ever mention them again!' she warned him fiercely.

He smiled. 'I love you.' He turned and looked down at her upturned face, at the golden light dazzling from her huge, amber eyes. 'Don't ask me how or when or where it happened. It just did.'

She reached up to stroke the dark rasp of his chin. 'I've always loved you, Paulo,' she told him honestly. 'From childhood devotion to adult emotion. But when I got pregnant I felt so bad about myself that I didn't think anyone would love me…'

'But now you do?' he probed softly.

'Oh, yes. Yes! I love you, Paulo!' And she went straight into his waiting arms.

'Cue violins,' murmured Paulo, as he gathered her close and bent his head to kiss her.

CHAPTER FOURTEEN

ISABELLA turned around, the silk-satin of her gown making a slithery rustle as she moved away from the mirror. 'Do I look OK?' she asked uncertainly.

It was a moment or so before Paulo could speak. 'You look...enchanting, *querida*. So enchanting, in fact, that I would like to remove the dress that you have just spent so long getting into—and make love to you for the rest of the afternoon. But unfortunately,' he finished dramatically as he fastened a pure-gold cuff-link, 'I have a wedding to attend.'

'But wedding dresses are not supposed to look sexy,' said Isabella worriedly. 'That wasn't why I chose it.'

'I know—but I suspect,' said Paulo drily, 'that you could cover yourself from head to toe in sacking and I would still be overcome by desire for you.'

'Well, that's good,' she said contentedly. 'Do you think we ought to give Papa a knock? The cars will be here soon and we don't want to be late.'

'I just did. He's dressed in his morning suit, and is entertaining *both* our children. Eddie loves him.'

'So does Stella.'

Her father had flown over for the wedding, and it had been an emotional reunion. Isabella hadn't seen him for over a year and a year was a long time for a man of his age. He looked older, a little more stooped and certainly greyer, but his brilliant smile on seeing his brand-new granddaughter for the first time had made him seem positively boyish.

And once Luis had been convinced of his daughter's happiness he had been more than charmed by the comfortable life she shared in London with Paulo and their children.

'No homesickness?' he had questioned sternly.

And Bella had glanced across at Paulo. 'My home is here,' she'd said simply.

Luis had mentioned casually that he was leaving the running of the ranch in the hands of his manager and was in the process of buying a small flat in Salvador.

And that night in bed Paulo had told Bella that he suspected her father might have a romance brewing.

'Do you think so?'

'He mentioned something about it in the car when I picked him up at the airport,' he'd admitted, then studied her face in the moonlight. 'Someone he's known for a long time—but he was waiting until you were settled. Would you mind?'

'Mind?' she'd asked, with a grin. 'Why would I? I'm far too smug and happy to do anything other than shout the advantages of living in a loving relationship from the rooftops!'

'Good,' Paulo had whispered before he'd bent to lick her nipple.

She had also told her father that she would probably complete her university degree. 'One day,' she'd added, but there was no trace of wistfulness in her voice. No sense of dreams unfulfilled—not when she'd everything she had ever wanted right here.

'She's young enough to do anything she wants to do,' Paulo had said, sizzling her a narrow-eyed look of adoration.

'That's provided he doesn't give you any more

babies,' Luis had teased, as he'd bent to ruffle the dark curls of his granddaughter.

Paulo's and Bella's eyes had met across the room in a moment of perfect understanding. As far as Luis was concerned, Paulo really *was* the father of her baby—but they felt exactly the same. He was—in every single way that counted.

She watched him now as he slotted a scarlet rose into his button-hole, and thought that she had never seen her husband-to-be look more gorgeous. *Gato.*

With a hand that sparkled from the light thrown off by the enormous diamond which Paulo had insisted on buying her—'conventional enough for you?' he'd growled—Isabella picked up her bouquet.

'I guess we'd better go.'

'In a minute,' he murmured. 'But we have something very important to do first.'

Isabella straightened his button-hole and looked up at him in bemusement. 'What have I forgotten?'

He smiled. 'Why, this, of course.'

And he kissed her.

THE HOUSEKEEPER'S
AWAKENING

With special thanks to George Tilbury and Erika Ring, for teaching me how bodies heal.

Also, for invaluable insights into the world of motor racing, thank you to Keith Roberts and team-owner Roland Dane. Roland, in particular, helped breathe life into Luis Martinez!

And to Peter Crone for his invaluable help with wind-farms (although they appear in Murat's book—SEDUCED BY THE SULTAN!)

CHAPTER ONE

CARLY'S FINGERS STILLED as the angry voice echoed through the house like a low rumble of thunder.

'Carly!'

She stared at the cornstarch which had lodged itself under her fingernails.

Now what?

She supposed she could try ignoring him but what would be the point? When her fractious, brilliant, mercurial boss wanted something he wanted it ten minutes ago; preferably sooner. He was driven, committed and single-minded—even when operating at fifty per cent of his usual capacity. It was just that fifty per cent of Luis Martinez's capacity would be full throttle for most men.

She pulled a face. Hadn't he already disrupted the peace enough times over the last few weeks with his incessant orders and his bad temper? She supposed that he'd had a pretty good reason to be more demanding than usual, but even so… She had lost count of the times she'd been forced to bite her tongue, when he'd snapped out yet another arrogant command. Maybe that quicksilver mind of his would focus on something else if she pretended she hadn't heard him. Maybe if she wished hard enough, he might just go away and leave her alone.

Preferably for ever.

'Carly!'

Maybe not. The shout had grown even more impatient now, so she took off her apron and shook her ponytail free. Quickly washing her hands, she set off towards the gym complex at the back of the house, where Luis Enrique Gabriel Martinez was currently undergoing another rehabilitation session with his physiotherapist.

Or rather, rehabilitation was what he was *supposed* to be doing, following the car crash which everyone said he'd been lucky to survive. Lately, Carly had wondered if the daily sessions had slipped over the boundary from the professional to the personal. Which might explain why the previously cool physiotherapist had started adding significant amounts of make-up before her visits, and spraying herself with a cloud of gingery-lemon scent just before she rang the doorbell. But that was par for the course, wasn't it? Luis had something special when it came to women. Something to do with those rugged South American looks and an unquenchable appetite for life which frequently courted danger.

Luis came, saw and conquered—though not necessarily in that order. He had an unerring ability to turn women into puddles of meek surrender, even if he happened to be lying stricken on a hospital bed at the time. Hadn't half the nurses who had treated him turned up here after he'd discharged himself? They had trooped through the door, bearing nervous smiles and sad little bunches of grapes—along with some pretty flimsy excuses about why they were visiting. But Carly had known exactly why they were visiting. A bed-bound and very sexy billionaire was an irresistible target, though to her surprise he'd given them all short shrift—even the platinum blonde with the legs which seemed to go all the way up to her armpits.

Carly was just grateful to be one of the few women immune to the Argentinian's careless charm, even if the truth of it was that he'd never actually *tried* to charm her. Maybe that was one of the advantages of being known as a dedicated 'plain Jane'—that your sex god of a boss would inevitably look through you as if you were part of the wallpaper. Which left her free to do her job and work towards a brighter future. And to remind herself of Luis's many negative qualities: his selfishness, restlessness and disregard for his own safety—as well as his annoying habit of leaving tiny espresso cups all around the house, which she was always finding in the most unexpected places.

She reached the gym complex and hesitated for a moment, wondering if it might be better to wait until he had finished his massage.

'Carly!'

Had he heard her approaching, even though in these old sneakers her footsteps were practically silent? She knew it was said of Luis Martinez that his senses were as finely tuned as his cars and one of the reasons why he had dominated the racing scene for so long.

Still she hesitated.

'Carly, will you stop skulking around outside the door and get yourself in here!'

His raised tone was arrogant and peremptory and she guessed that some people would have found it offensive to be spoken to in such a way, but Carly was

used to Luis Martinez by now. She knew what his entourage said about him. That his bark was worse than
his bite. Though she wasn't sure if that bit was strictly
true. His last but one girlfriend had seemed rather *fond*
of his bite. Why else would she have kept appearing
at breakfast during her brief tenure as his lover sport-
ing bruises on her neck with a kind of joyful pride, as
if she'd spent the night with some obliging vampire?

Knowing that she couldn't put it off any longer,
Carly opened the gym door and walked into the room
where her famous employer was lying on his back on
the narrow massage table. His dark head was pillowed
on his clasped hands and his golden-olive body was
outlined against the white sheet. His gaze alighted on
her and his black eyes narrowed with something which
looked like relief.

Which was weird. She thought that they tolerated
each other pretty well, but there wasn't what you'd call
any real *affection* between them.

Or maybe it was not so weird after all. Quickly,
she became aware of the tension in the room and of
two things which couldn't go unnoticed. That Mary
Houghton, the physiotherapist, was standing on the far
side of the room breathing rather heavily as she stared
fixedly down at her shoes. And that Luis was completely naked, save for the trio of small white towels
which were strategically placed at his groin.

A wave of colour swept into Carly's face and suddenly she felt angry. Wouldn't it have been polite for
him to have covered up before she arrived? Surely he
must have known that it simply wasn't done to greet
a member of your staff in such a way. That she might
find it...*embarrassing* to see that rippling chest and

broad shoulders on display. Or that it was *arrogant* to flaunt those long, bare legs, which were currently sprawled out in front of him?

She kept away from men and all their complications—and with good reason. Experience had made her wary; but for once, all her latent fears and hang-ups about the opposite sex were put on hold as she stared at her boss with reluctant fascination.

Looking at him now, it was easy to see why women adored him. Why the newspapers had nicknamed him The Love Machine, when he'd been at the peak of his powers, and motor-racing champion of the world. Before her time, of course, but Carly had heard of him, even then. Everyone had.

His face had been everywhere—on or off the track. When he hadn't been standing on podiums, garlanded in the winner's laurels and spraying champagne over the adoring crowds, he had been an advertiser's dream. Magnified images of Luis Martinez wearing expensive watches, with that famously devil-may-care smile on his face, were regularly emblazoned over giant billboards. Off-duty, his fascination had been equally compelling. Hunky South American billionaires always provided good copy—especially as he was rarely seen without the requisite blonde clinging possessively to his arm. And if some perceptive journalist had once remarked that his jet-dark eyes looked almost *empty*—perhaps that only added to his appeal.

Because Luis Martinez wasn't just good-looking—even Carly recognised that. There was something *wild* about him. Something untamed. He was the trophy which was always just out of reach. The desired object which no woman could hold onto for long. That mane of

slightly too-long black hair gave him a reckless, buc-
caneering look and those black eyes were now studying her in a way which was making her feel distinctly
uncomfortable.

Turning away from his scrutiny, she looked at Mary
Houghton, who had been coming to his English mansion for weeks now. With her neat figure and shiny
hair, the physiotherapist looked as pretty as she always
did in her crisp white uniform, but Carly thought she
could see a shadow of hurt clouding the other woman's features.

'So there you are, Carly,' said Luis, his voice heavy
with sarcasm. 'At last. Did you fly in from the opposite
side of the world to get here? You know I don't like to
be kept waiting.'

'I was busy making *alfajores*,' said Carly. 'For you
to have with your coffee later.'

'Ah, yes.' He gave her a grudging nod. 'Your timekeeping may be abysmal, but nobody can deny that
you're an excellent cook. And your *alfajores* are as
good as those which I used to eat when I was growing up.'

'Was there something special you wanted?' questioned Carly pointedly. 'Because this particular kind
of baking doesn't lend itself kindly to interruptions.'

'As the world's worst timekeeper, I don't think
you're in a position to lecture me on time management,' he snapped, turning his head to look at Mary
Houghton, who for some reason had gone very red. 'I
sometimes think Carly forgets that a certain degree
of submissiveness is a desirable quality in a housekeeper. But she is undoubtedly capable and so I am
prepared to tolerate her occasional insubordination.

Do you think she can do it, Mary—can someone like her get me back to my fighting best, now that you are intent on leaving me?'

By now, Carly had stopped thinking about the Argentinian cakes which were Luis's favourites, or his arrogant sense of entitlement. She was too interested in the fraught atmosphere to even object to being talked about as if she were an inanimate object. She wanted to know why the previously cool physiotherapist was now chewing on her lip as if something awful had happened.

Had it?

'Is something wrong?' she asked.

Mary Houghton gave Carly a lukewarm smile accompanied by an awkward shrug of her shoulders. 'Not exactly…wrong. But my professional association with Señor Martinez has…come to an end. He no longer requires the services of a physiotherapist,' she said, and for a moment her voice sounded a little unsteady. 'But he will continue to need massage and exercise for the next few weeks on a regular basis to ensure a complete recovery, and someone needs to oversee that.'

'Right,' said Carly uncertainly, because she couldn't see where all this was leading.

Luis fixed her with a piercing look, his black eyes boring into her like twin lasers. 'You wouldn't have a problem taking over from Mary for a while, would you, Carly? You're pretty good with your hands, aren't you?'

'Me?' The word came out as a horrified croak.

'Why not?'

Carly's eyes widened, because suddenly all her fears didn't seem so latent any more. The thought of going anywhere near a half-naked man was making her skin crawl—even if that man *was* Luis Martinez. She swallowed. 'You mean, I'd be expected to *massage* you?'

Now there was a definite glint in his eyes and she couldn't work out if it was displeasure or amusement. 'Why, is that such an *abhorrent* thought to you, Carly?'

'No, no, of course not.' But it was. Of course it was. Wouldn't he laugh out loud if he realised how little she knew about men? Wouldn't she be the last person he'd choose as his temporary masseuse, if he knew what a naïve innocent she was? So should she tell him the truth—if not all of it, then at least some?

Of course she should tell him!

She shrugged her shoulders, aware of the heightened rush of colour to her cheeks as she mumbled out the words. 'It's just that I've…well, I've never actually given anyone a massage before.'

'Oh, that won't be a problem.' Mary Houghton's cool accent cut through Carly's stumbled explanation. 'I can show you the basic technique—it isn't difficult. If you're good with your hands, you won't have a problem with it. The exercises—ditto. They're easy enough to pick up and Señor Martinez already knows how to do them properly. The most important thing you can do is to ensure he keeps to a regular schedule.'

'Think you can do it, Carly?'

The silky South American voice filtered through the air and as Carly turned, the intensity of his gaze suddenly made her feel *dizzy*. And uncomfortable. It was as if he'd never really looked at her properly before. Or at least, not like that. She got the feeling that he had always regarded her as one of the fixtures and fittings—like one of the squashy velvet sofas which he sometimes lay on in the evenings if he'd brought a woman back here. But now his eyes were almost... *calculating* and she felt a stab of alarm as he assessed her. Was he thinking what countless men had doubtless thought before? That she was plain and awkward and didn't make the best of herself. Would it surprise him to know that she liked it that way? That she *liked* to fade into the background? Because life was safer that way. Safer and more predictable.

Pushing away the nudge of dark memories with an efficiency born of years of practice, she considered his question. Of course she could learn how to massage him because—as he'd just said—she was very good with her hands. She ran his English home like clockwork, didn't she? She cooked and cleaned and made sure the Egyptian cotton sheets were softly ironed whenever he was in residence. She arranged for caterers to arrive if he was hosting a big party, or for prize-winning chefs to be ferried down from London if he was holding a more intimate gathering. She had florists on speed dial, ready to deck his house with fragrant blooms at the drop of a hat or to float candle-topped lilies in his outdoor pool, if the weather remained fine enough.

What she wished she had the courage to say was that she didn't *want* to do it. That the thought of going anywhere near his body was making her feel...*peculiar*. And even though her dream of being a doctor was what kept her in this fairly mundane job—she didn't want her first experience of the therapeutic to be with a man with the reputation of Luis Martinez.

Imagine having to touch his skin, especially if he

was barely covered by a few meagre towels, as he was at the moment. Imagine being closeted alone in the massage room with him, day after day. Having to put up with his short fuse and bad temper in such an intimate setting. Luis Martinez she could cope with, yes, but preferably with as much distance between them as possible.

'Surely there must be somebody else who could do it?' she said.

'But I don't want anyone else doing it—I want you,' he said. 'Or do you have other things which are occupying you, Carly? Things which are making too many demands on your time and which will prevent you from spending time doing what I am asking you to do? Is there something I should know about? After all, I *am* the one paying your salary, aren't I?'

Carly's hands balled into two fists, because now he had her in a corner and they both knew it. He paid her a staggeringly generous amount of money, most of which she squirrelled away towards her goal of getting to med school.

She had the cushiest of positions here, which left her plenty of time to study. As jobs went, she would go so far as to say she loved working here. She loved it most when Luis was out of the country, which was most of the time. He had gorgeous homes in far-flung corners of the world, sited wherever he had business interests, and his English residence was usually bottom on his list of visits. She wasn't even sure why he bothered keeping this vast, country house until one day she had summoned up the courage to ask his burly assistant, Diego. 'Tax,' had been the ex-wrestler's terse reply.

Carly's role was to keep the house in a constant state

of readiness in case Luis should decide to pay an unexpected visit. In fact, he wouldn't be here now were it not for the charity car race which she thought he'd been insane to enter and which had ended with him smashing his pelvis and spending weeks in hospital.

She looked at him—thinking about his general high-handedness and arrogance and whether she would be able to tolerate it on a far more intimate basis. How could she possibly massage him without giving into the temptation to sink her fingernails into that silken olive flesh of his and make him squirm? How on earth would she be able to *touch* such a notorious sex god, without making a complete and utter fool of herself?

'I just wonder whether you might be better getting another professional in,' she said stubbornly.

He flicked a glance at Mary Houghton, who was still standing in exactly the same position and Carly saw his mouth twist with undisguised irritation. 'Can you give us a moment, please, Mary?'

'Of course I can. I'll...I'll talk to you when you've finished in here, Carly.' There was a pause, before Mary held her hand out. 'Goodbye, Luis. It's been... well, it's been great.'

He nodded, but Carly thought how *cold* his face looked as he propped himself up on one elbow, before shaking the physiotherapist's hand. Whatever Mary had said or done had not pleased him.

'Goodbye, Mary,' he said.

There was silence as she left the room and Luis sat up—impatiently gesturing for Carly to hand him the robe hanging from a hook on the back of the door.

She did as he wanted—quickly averting her eyes

until he'd covered up with the black towelling robe, but when he spoke, he still sounded irritated.

'Why are you so reluctant to do what I ask?' he demanded. 'Why are you being so damned stubborn?'

For a moment Carly didn't answer. Would he scoff if he knew that his proposed intimacy scared her? Or would he just be shocked to learn that she had allowed one horrendous experience to colour her judgement—and she'd spent her life running away from the kind of personal contact which most women of her age considered perfectly natural? Someone like Luis would probably tell her to 'move on', in the way that people did—as if it were that easy.

And this was about more than what had happened to her, wasn't it? She could see nothing but trouble if she agreed, because rich and powerful men like Luis *were* trouble. Hadn't her own sister been chasing that kind of man ever since she'd first sprouted breasts, and didn't she keep on going back for more—despite getting knocked back, time after time?

Thoughts of Bella's inglorious escapades flitted through her mind as she met Luis's luminous gaze. 'I don't want to neglect my housekeeping duties,' she said.

'Then get somebody else to do the cooking and the cleaning instead of you. How difficult can it be?'

Carly flushed. She knew that housekeeping wasn't up there with being a lawyer or a doctor, but she still found it faintly humiliating to hear Luis dismiss her job quite so flippantly.

'Or get in a professional masseuse who could do it better than I ever could?' she suggested again.

'No,' he said, almost viciously. 'I'm sick of strangers. Sick of people with different agendas, coming into my house and telling me what I must and mustn't do.' His mouth hardened into a forbidding line. 'What's the matter, Carly? Are you objecting on the basis that providing massage for your recuperating boss isn't written into your contract?'

'I haven't got a contract,' she said bluntly.

'You haven't?'

'No. You told me when I interviewed for the job that if I didn't trust you to give me your word, then you weren't the kind of person you wanted working for you.'

An arrogant smile spread over his lips. 'Did I really say that?'

'Yes. You did.' And she had accepted his terms, hadn't she, even if the logical side of her brain had told her that she'd been a fool to do so? In fact, she'd practically bitten his hand off, because she had recognised that Luis Martinez was offering her the kind of opportunity which wasn't going to come her way again. A place to live and a salary big enough to make substantial savings for her future.

The smile had now left his lips.

'I am growing bored with this discussion,' he snapped. 'Are you prepared to help me out or not?'

She recognised the implicit threat behind his words. Help me out or else.

Or else what?

Go out and find a new job? One which wouldn't leave her with so much free time to study for her exams? She frowned as she thought about the champagne bill from his last party and a new resolve filled her.

'I'd be prepared to do it, if you were prepared to give me some sort of bonus,' she said suddenly.

'Danger money, you mean?' he mocked. With a grimace he swung his long legs over the side of the massage bed, but not before Carly had seen a peek of hair-roughened thigh as the robe flapped open.

'Yes, that's right. Danger money,' she croaked, quickly averting her gaze once more. 'I couldn't have put it better myself.'

He gave a short laugh. 'Funny. I never really had you down as a negotiator, Carly.'

'Oh? And why's that?'

Luis didn't answer immediately, just concentrated on stretching his hips, the way that Mary had shown him. He wouldn't bother telling his plain little house-keeper that she had merely confirmed his belief that everyone had a price, because that might upset her, and there was no point in upsetting a woman if it could possibly be avoided. Often, of course, it couldn't. Usually because they weren't listening to what you were saying, or they thought they could change your mind for you.

Or they started falling in love with you, even though you hadn't given them the slightest encouragement to do so. His mouth hardened. That had been Mary Houghton's mistake. He'd seen it growing day by day, until in the end she could barely look at him without blushing. She'd made it clear that she was keen for a...*liaison* and, yes, he'd been tempted. Of course he had. She was a good-looking woman and hadn't he read somewhere that physiotherapists made great lovers because they knew how the body worked? But it had been highly unprofessional of her, and some deep-rooted and rather old-fashioned prejudice against such things had appalled him.

He turned his attention back to Carly. At least in her he had nothing to fear because sexual attraction was unlikely to rear its head. He found himself wondering if she bothered keeping a mirror in her bedroom, or whether she just didn't see what the rest of the world saw.

Her thick brown hair was tugged back from her face in a ponytail and she wore no make-up. He'd never seen mascara on those pale lashes which framed eyes the colour of iced tea, nor lipstick on her sometimes disapproving lips. A little blusher would have added some much-needed colour to her pale skin, and he'd often wondered why she insisted on wearing a plain blue overall during working hours. To protect her clothes, she said—though, from the glimpses he'd caught of them, hers were not the kind of clothes which looked as if they needed much in the way of protection. Weren't man-made fabrics notoriously hard-wearing? They were also very unflattering when stretched tightly over unfashionably curvy bodies like hers.

Luis was used to women who turned femininity into an art form. Who invested vast amounts of time and money making themselves look beautiful, then spent the rest of their lives trying to preserve that state of being. But not this one. Oh, no. Definitely not this one.

His lips flattened into a wry smile. What was it that the English said? Never to judge a book by its cover. And the old adage did have some truth in it—because despite her plainness and total lack of adornment, nobody could deny that Carly Conner had spirit. He could think of no other woman who would have hesitated for more than a second at the thought of—literally—getting their hands on him. Which of course was precisely the reason why he wanted her for the job. He needed to get fit, and he needed to do it as quickly as possible—because this inactivity was driving him crazy.

All he wanted was to feel normal again. He loathed the world passing him by, so that all he could do was watch it. Because inactivity left you with time to think. It left you feeling as if something was missing. He wanted to get back on the ski slopes. He wanted to pilot a plane again. He wanted the challenge of dangerous sports to fill him with adrenaline and make him feel alive again.

His mouth twisted as he levered himself off the bed.

'Hand me my crutches, will you, Carly?'

She raised her eyebrows.

He gave a small growl. 'Please.'

Silently, Carly handed them over and watched as he grasped them, straightening up to his full and impressive height. It still seemed strange to see a man as powerful as Luis needing crutches, but at least he was well on the road to recovery now. Almost unscathed, he had come through an accident the doctors said he'd been lucky to survive.

He hadn't raced professionally for five years, but the lure of an enormous charity prize organised by one of the big car manufacturers had proved too much to resist. That, and an inbuilt arrogance that he was indestructible…and a nature which loved to embrace danger in its many forms.

She remembered the day it had happened, when she'd received the phone call to say he'd been rushed to hospital. Her heart had been racing as she had driven through the narrow country roads, reaching the accident and emergency department and fearing the worst, to be told that he'd been taken to Theatre and they weren't sure how bad it was.

His entourage had been going crazy. There had been people rushing around all over the place and getting in the way of the medical staff. Security people. PR people. Diego, his swarthy assistant, had been dealing with the press, and his lawyers were busily engaged with threats of litigation, claiming that the racetrack had been unsafe.

Carly wondered if any of them had actually remembered that they were all there because a man was sick and wounded. And that was when her old pattern of wanting to care had kicked in. She had crept upstairs to the intensive care unit, where the nurse had let her sit with him and everyone else had been barred, on the grounds that any more excitement might hinder his recovery. She remembered thinking how *alone* he looked, despite all his money and success. There had been no family to visit. His parents were dead and he had no brothers or sisters. Carly had been the only one there for him.

All that night she had stayed put, holding his motionless hand and running her fingertips over it. Telling the unresponsive figure who dominated the narrow hospital gurney that he was going to be okay. But the experience had been a strangely powerful one. It had been a shock to see him looking so *vulnerable* and for a short while Carly's feelings towards her irascible boss had undergone a slight transformation. For a while she had felt almost *tender* towards him...

Until he had started recovering and had become his usual arrogant self. She had been elbowed out of the way then, when the first of a long stream of women had arrived, all vying with each other in their tiny leather miniskirts—because everyone knew that the ex-world champion was turned on by leather. She remembered turning up at the ward one day to find a stunning blonde in thigh-high boots groping him under the bedsheet. And Carly hadn't bothered visiting again. She hadn't seen him again until he'd discharged himself home against his doctors' advice.

But she suspected that the accident had changed him, as she knew that near-fatal accidents sometimes did. Even though the house was vast, it had seemed overcrowded with his people mooching around the place, not sure what to do with themselves while their boss was recovering. And Luis had been even more bad-tempered than usual. He hadn't liked people trailing in and out of his room to speak to him, saying that it made him feel like a dying king. Demanding peace, he had sent his entire entourage back to Buenos Aires—even Diego. Carly remembered their astonishment at being sent packing. And hers. Because once again, Luis Martinez really was on his own. Only this time, he was alone with *her*.

Emerging from her silent reverie, she realised that his eyes were trained on her and that he was waiting for the answer to a question which, in reality, was little more than an order.

'Yes, I'll do it.' She sighed. 'I'd better go and talk to Mary and get her to run over exactly what it is you need, though I don't know why you couldn't just have carried on paying for her to see you privately.'

She soon discovered why, when she found Mary Houghton in the garden room, staring rigidly out of the French windows at the rain-soaked gardens outside. The bright hues of the summer flowers looked like fragments of a shattered rainbow, but all Carly could see was that the physiotherapist's shoulders were shaking slightly.

Was the cool Englishwoman *crying*?

'Mary?' she questioned gently. 'Are you okay?'

It was a few moments before Mary turned round and Carly got her answer from the telltale glitter in the other woman's eyes.

'How does he do it, Carly?' Mary questioned in a shaky voice. 'How does he get usually sane women like me to fall for a man they don't even *like*? How come he's dumped me in the coldest way imaginable and I still end up thinking he's the greatest thing since sliced bread?'

Carly tried to crack a joke, anything to lighten the atmosphere and to take that terrible look of *pain* from Mary's face. 'Well, I've never been a great fan of sliced bread myself—which is why I always make my own.'

Mary swallowed. 'I'm sorry. I shouldn't have said anything. Especially not to you. You work for him all the time—you probably deserve my sympathy, instead of me asking for yours.'

'Don't worry about it. You're not the first woman he's reduced to tears and you won't be the last.' Carly shrugged. 'I don't know how he does it, to be honest. I don't think it's calculated, or even intentional. He just seems to have that indefinable something which makes women go crazy for him. Maybe it's inevitable when you're that good-looking and rich and power-ful and—'

'Do you know,' interrupted Mary, her voice suddenly urgent, 'that I've never fancied a male patient before? Never. Not once. The thought had never even crossed my mind—though obviously not many men like Luis Martinez end up on the hospital wards. I can't believe that I allowed him to see it.' She bit her lip. 'It's so… so…*unprofessional*. And so humiliating. And now he's asked me to go, and you know what? I deserve to be let go.'

Carly didn't know what to say. She found herself thinking that things were rarely what they seemed. She'd always thought of Mary Houghton as cool and unflappable. She'd seen her as one of those composed Englishwomen who knew exactly what they were doing and where they were heading. And yet one lazy look from the smouldering black eyes of Luis Martinez and she was as jittery as a schoolgirl who'd just seen her pop-star idol in the flesh.

Carly looked at her. *Maybe she should be glad of the hard lesson she'd learned all those years ago.* Because didn't they say that heartbreak was almost as painful as bereavement? And who in their right mind would want to be going through what the physiotherapist was clearly going through right now?

She looked at Mary. 'I'm sorry,' she said.

Mary pursed her lips together. 'Oh, I'll get over it. And maybe it's all for the best. Maybe I'll start dat-ing that sweet young doctor who's been asking me out for weeks, and forget about a man who's famous for breaking women's hearts. Now,' she said briskly. 'Let me show you what you need to do to get Luis back to full fitness.'

'If you're sure you're okay?'

'Carly, I'm *fine*!'

But Carly noticed Mary delving into her handbag for a tissue and that she blew her nose for a suspiciously long time afterwards.

CHAPTER TWO

CARLY COULD FEEL her heart racing like a train, because this was weird.

It was weirder than weird.

Her hands were unsteady as they positioned themselves above Luis's bare back and she drew in a deep breath, praying he wouldn't guess how nervous she was. Praying that she wouldn't behave like a ham-fisted failure as she began to do exactly what Mary had taught her. It wasn't difficult, she told herself fiercely. Massage was a skill, yes—but it was one that thousands of people did every single day.

But even though the thought of touching Luis's skin was making her mouth grow dry with fear, it seemed there was no way she could avoid it. He was paying her a bonus. They had agreed that this was a deal. And wasn't it crazy to have reached this age and still be scared of touching a man? She lowered her hands towards his gleaming skin and thought about the way she'd let the past impact so profoundly on the present. Was she going to let some worthless piece of scum ruin her life for ever?

Because if she was ever going to fulfil her dream of becoming a doctor, she was going to have to touch people like this every day.

Pressing the heels of her palms deep into his silken flesh, she began to move her hands, glad he couldn't see her face. Wouldn't he laugh himself silly to know that she was flushed with embarrassment?

It was distracting seeing him like this—wearing nothing but a pair of close-fitting black briefs. Catching sight of him and his billionaire buddies lounging around the pool during one of the few hot days last summer while she carried out a tray of drinks was not the same thing at all.

She thought how pale her hands looked against the olive hue of his skin and noticed that her fingers were trembling slightly as they moved over his warm flesh. But to her surprise her nerves soon left her once she got into some kind of rhythm. If she concentrated on the healing aspects of the task, it was easy to push away her uncomfortable thoughts. In a way, it was the opposite of working with pastry, which needed cool, quick movements. For this, her hands were warm and oily and her movements slow and deliberate. She pushed deep into his latissimus dorsi muscles and he gave a little groan.

'Is that okay?' she questioned nervously.

He gave a grunt and she wasn't quite sure if he was agreeing with her or not.

'I'm not hurting you, am I?'

Luis shook his head and shifted a little, the rough towel rubbing beneath his crotch, which was precisely where he did *not* want to focus his attention. *Santo cielos!* No, she was not hurting him—but he wondered if she was trying to torture him. Resting his cheek against his crossed arms, he closed his eyes, unable to decide whether this was heaven or hell. Or perhaps a mixture of both.

What the hell was happening here?

He could feel her hands moving further down his back, skating tantalisingly over the taut lines of his buttocks before alighting on the tops of his thighs. He swallowed as the minutes ticked by and suddenly he found himself lost in the sensations she was producing. If she was nervous, you would never have guessed it. Apart from that nervous flutter of her fingers at the beginning, she had taken to it as if she had been born to stroke at a man's skin like this. Who would ever have thought that his mousey little housekeeper had the touch of an angel?

Yet she had been the model of brisk proficiency from the moment she'd greeted him, with nothing but a brief smile as he had lain face down on the bed. She certainly wasn't flirting with him, which made him wonder what was making him feel so *aroused*. How could Carly—plain little Carly—manage to make him feel like this? Was it because she *wasn't* flirting with him and he wasn't used to that? For a moment he imagined her requesting briskly that he lift up his buttocks, so that she could slide her hands underneath him. He thought about her taking his rapidly growing hardness between her fingers and stroking him to a blessed and swift release.

His mouth dried.

'No, you're not hurting me,' he said eventually, when he was certain his voice wouldn't come out sounding like some kind of strangled groan.

She continued to work in silence. He could feel her fingers sinking deeper into his flesh and as the muscles began to loosen up beneath her touch he couldn't seem to stop himself fantasising about her some more. He wondered what her breasts might look like if she were to remove that hideous overall she was wearing. An image of pale mounds tipped with rosy points swam into his mind with disturbing clarity. He pictured his tongue tracing a slow, wet circle around one puckered nub and he shifted his aroused body again in a vain bid to make himself comfortable.

The movement must have registered, for her hands stilled.

'You're sure I'm not hurting you?'

Against the lavender-scented doughnut of a pillow on which his cheek was resting, Luis shook his head. 'No,' he said huskily. 'You have a very...*natural* touch. I can't believe you haven't done anything like this before.'

'Mary was very helpful. She showed me exactly what to do. She said that if I pressed firmly on key parts of the body...like *this*...that it would be effective. And then last night I studied lots of technique and tips on my computer.'

His instinctive groan of satisfaction made his words come out as a muffled drawl. 'You have nothing better to do on a Friday night than look up massage technique?'

There was a pause.

'I like to do a job properly. And you're paying me a very generous bonus to do this.'

Her emphasis on the financial made him feel comfortable about interrogating her, although it didn't occur to him until afterwards to wonder why he should be interested in her social life. 'So is there no irritable boyfriend wanting to know why your boss is demanding so much of your time?'

There was another pause, a slightly longer one this time. She seemed to choose her words carefully. 'I don't have a boyfriend, no,' she said. 'But if I did, I don't really think this job would be compatible with it. Not if it was a serious relationship.'

'Why not?'

'Because when you're here the hours are long and erratic and because I'm living in someone else's house and—'

'Not why a live-in job isn't compatible with a relationship,' he interrupted impatiently. 'You wouldn't need to be a genius to work that one out. No, I meant why don't you have a boyfriend?'

Carly rubbed some more oil into the palms of her hands. It was difficult to come up with a reasonable answer to his question. Difficult to come up with anything which sounded sensible when her hands were in contact with his skin like this. If she hadn't been feeling so disorientated by what was happening, she might have told him that her social life was none of his business. Or she might even have hinted that one dreadful experience had put her off men for ever. But she couldn't really think of anything except how gorgeous he felt. She was being bombarded with powerful sensations and none of them were welcome—or expected.

All the blinds had been drawn and the semi-darkened room felt claustrophobic because the dimensions seemed to have shrunk. Candles were wafting out a subtle sandalwood scent and there was faint whale-like music coming from the sound system, just as Mary had suggested. She knew these small additions were intended to create a relaxed atmosphere and maybe it was working for Luis, but it certainly wasn't working for her.

Because the unimaginable was happening. Instead of being frozen with fear, all she could feel was a slow-building pleasure whenever she touched him. She stared down at his olive-skinned body, because where else was she going to look? And even though he was wearing a pair of black briefs instead of those three terrifyingly small towels which had been covering him yesterday, they weren't nearly as much of an advantage as they should have been. Because yes, they provided a necessary barrier of modesty—but they also emphasised the very masculine outlines of his body. They made the rocky globes of his buttocks look as if they'd been coated in liquorice, and liquorice had always been her favourite kind of sweet.

'I'm not really interested in men,' she said at last, her words making a mockery of her thoughts.

'Ah. You prefer women?'

'No!' She was shocked by his openness, and unreasonably hurt by his assumption. She told herself that he was perfectly entitled to think what he liked about her, just as she was perfectly within her rights to tell him that her sexuality was none of his business. But something made her answer him. As if she wanted him to know. *Needed* him to know. 'I'm...straight.'

'Ah.' He turned his head to the side and she could see the faint smile which curved his lips. 'So why is there no man in your life?'

'It drives me mad when people say that. It's the first thing people ask a single woman.' She started massaging again, pressing the heels of her hands hard against the firm flesh, aware that she was running the risk of sounding defensive but suddenly she didn't care. 'You don't have a girlfriend, do you? But I certainly don't make it sound like some kind of character fault, or start interrogating you about it.'

'I don't have one particular partner, no, but I certainly have girlfriends from time to time. You, on the other hand, don't.'

Her hands stopped mid-stroke and she stared at them. She thought they looked like pale starfish in a sea of gold. 'How do you know that, when you're not here most of the time?'

'Because my estate manager keeps me up to speed with what's going on. I like to know what's happening with someone who has the entire run of my house while I'm not here, so obviously I enquire about you from time to time. Not that he tells me anything very interesting since, apparently, you live the life of a nun.'

Carly tensed, hearing the implicit criticism in his tone. 'There's nothing wrong with nuns,' she said.

'I didn't suggest there was. But you haven't taken any vows since you came to work for me, have you, Carly? Certainly not poverty or obedience,' he persisted mockingly.

'Actually, as an employer you do seem to require total obedience from your staff—though I can't deny that you pay very well.'

'Which only leaves chastity,' he said. 'Doesn't it?'

Carly's heart thundered again as she forced herself to restart the massage, trying to concentrate on the slow, circular movements instead of the bizarre turn of their conversation. 'What I do in my spare time is none of your business.'

'He said that you always seem to have your head in a book,' observed Luis, as if she hadn't spoken. 'And that you go to evening classes in the nearby town.'

'And is there something wrong with wanting to improve myself?' she demanded. 'Perhaps I should throw a wild party when you leave. Give the gardeners and the estate manager enough ammunition to earn me a reputation.'

'Why, do you like wild parties?' he challenged.

'No.'

'Me neither,' he said unexpectedly.

'So how does that work?' she asked, with a frown. 'When you throw them on a regular basis. The house is always full of people. Why, you could almost employ a full-time party planner.'

'I agree—they have become something of a habit. A hangover from my racing days when wild parties were *de rigueur,* but recently I have grown bored with them.' His bare shoulders rose in a shrug. 'I find that they are all exactly the same.'

Carly blinked. How peculiar. She'd thought he'd loved the crazy gatherings which all the locals talked about for weeks afterwards. When hordes of the rich and beautiful converged onto his country estate—some of them travelling from as far as Paris and New York. The women were usually the generic blondes he was so fond of, with their tiny dresses and seeking eyes. On more than one occasion, Carly had been standing making pots of coffee at four in the morning, while some poor creature sobbed her eyes out over the kitchen table, because Luis had taken some other woman to bed instead of her. On another memorable occasion, she had opened the door to the drawing room and found a

French supermodel lying completely starkers on a fur rug, waiting in vain for Luis and not realising he was already on a plane which was heading for Morocco.

'There.' Carly stopped massaging at last, suddenly aware of the slow trickle of sweat which was sliding in a path between her breasts. Was it the heat which was making them feel so much bigger than usual? Making their tips feel so uncomfortably hard and prickling against her uniform so that she found herself wanting to rub at them. And why was she suddenly looking at the golden gleam of his bare back and thinking it was so physically perfect that it would work as an illustration in the pages of an anatomy book? She swallowed. 'Feeling better?'

'I'm feeling…good,' he said indistinctly.

Hastily, Carly wiped her hands on a towel. She had to stop thinking like this. She had to start regarding him with the impartiality she'd always had before now. 'I think that's enough for now, don't you?' She kept her voice brisk. 'We can have another session before…er, before you retire for the night. You can get up if you like, Luis.'

But Luis didn't want to get up. Or rather, he didn't feel capable of getting up, not in the way that she meant and not without making it very clear that he was having very erotic feelings about her. He could feel the hard throb at his groin and the sharp aching in his balls and found himself in the unthinkable position of being aroused—*by Miss Mouse*. And he still wasn't sure how that had happened. Surely it couldn't just be because she was *touching* him, because if that was the case then he would have felt something more potent than irritation towards Mary—the physiotherapist he had just sacked.

The aching intensified, but his impatient squirm only made the hardness worse, instead of relieving it. He scowled into the stupid scented doughnut of a pillow. Weeks of doing nothing had driven him close to crazy with no work, no play and no sex. Worse still, his confinement had left him with time to think and he was a man who preferred to *do*. Stripped of his constant need for action, he was forced into the unwanted position of introspection.

His incarceration in hospital had made him stop and take a look at his life and realise what a circus it had become. He'd thought about his different homes dotted around the world and the swollen entourage who accompanied him everywhere, and it had been like looking at the world of someone he didn't know. When had he managed to acquire so many hangers-on? He remembered their barely disguised shock when he had sent them to his main base in Buenos Aires, with Diego at the helm. And the strange calm which had descended on the house once they'd gone, leaving him alone with his mousey housekeeper.

He shifted his thigh a fraction as he thought how efficiently Carly had slotted into her new role as temporary masseuse. It seemed she was as proficient at rehabilitation as she was at running his house for him. Minutes before his massage, she had overseen the daily ballet exercises intended to strengthen his damaged pelvis. She hadn't made any predictable jokes about men doing ballet, but had simply stood beside him, counting the small elevations of his legs, with a look of fierce determination on her face.

'How about a swim now, Luis?'

Her soft voice ruptured his disturbing thoughts and it was with a sense of relief that he realised that his erection had subsided.

He yawned. 'Is that a suggestion?'

'No, it's an order—since you seem to respond much better to those.' She pulled up the blind and peered outside. 'Oh, dear, it's raining again.'

'It's always raining in this damned country.'

'That's what makes the fields so green,' she said sweetly. 'Never mind. At least we can use the indoor pool.'

'But I don't like the indoor pool,' he growled. 'You know that. It's claustrophobic.'

'And this room isn't?'

'I'm not planning to swim in here,' he snapped. 'So why don't we just go outside and use the big pool? Live dangerously for once.'

Carly turned back from the window, her mouth flattening with a disapproval she couldn't quite hide as she looked at him. She knew that was the kind of crazy thing he did. She'd witnessed people diving into his rain-lashed swimming pool, fully clothed, and she'd come down early the next morning to find glasses full of rain and champagne. Once she had even found a pair of knickers hanging from one of the flagpoles and one of the gardeners had been forced to shin up and get them back down again. What must it be like to live a life as decadent as his? she wondered.

'Because I don't like to live dangerously,' she said repressively. 'And perhaps if you didn't, then you wouldn't have ended up occupying a hospital bed for so long and probably blocking it for someone who really needs it. As it happens, the grass is absolutely sodden and the tiles around the swimming pool will be wet and slippery.'

'Sca—*ry*,' he said sarcastically.

She didn't react to his taunt, even though he seemed to be spoiling for *some* kind of fight. What was the matter with him today? He was even more bad-tempered than usual—and that was saying something. She set her lips into a disapproving line. 'So unless you want to risk falling over and complicating your recovery, then I'd advise playing safe and using the indoor pool, which was designed with rainy days like these in mind.'

'Don't you ever get tired of being the sensible voice of reason?'

And don't you ever get tired of being the perennial bad-boy playboy? It was only with difficulty that she stopped herself from saying it out loud as she turned to face him. 'I thought that's what you were paying me for.'

'That, and your cooking.' He paused, his thick black lashes half veiling his eyes. 'So you don't like living dangerously?'

Emphatically, Carly shook her head. No, she certainly did not. On the contrary, she had always wanted to live safe. She had craved a security and stability which had always eluded her. But Luis didn't really want to know that, did he? He was asking the question in that throwaway way he sometimes did, like an owner throwing his dog a scrap of food from the table. He wasn't interested in her as a person; she was just a tiny cog in the giant wheel designed to keep his life running smoothly. 'Not really,' she said. 'You do enough danger for both of us.'

He gave an exaggerated sigh. 'Okay, Miss Sensible—you win. The indoor pool it is. Go and find your swimsuit and meet me in there.'

But his mocking was ringing around her head as Carly ran upstairs to change into her costume, because he had touched a nerve. Being sensible wasn't something most people aspired to but she'd always been that way. At school she had been the reliable first choice if you needed someone to help with your science homework, or to spend a whole playtime looking for a lost charm from somebody's bracelet. *Careful Carly*, they had called her and as a nickname she hadn't particularly liked it. It wasn't cool to be careful—it was just the way she'd been made.

She reached her room at the top of the house and shut the door behind her, leaning against it to get her breath back. The attic space was large, with sloping ceilings and a dramatic view over the gardens and the fields beyond. Up here she was among the treetops. Up here you could see the most amazing sunrises and sunsets, which filled the room with a rich red light. There was a little desk, on which she did her studying, and on the wall above the small fireplace hung the little watercolour her father had painted, the year before he'd become too ill to hold a brush any more.

Sliding open one of the drawers, she fished around and found her swimming costume, knowing that the last thing she wanted was for Luis to see her in it. She was too fleshy. Too pale. Too everything. And although she knew that comparison was pointless, she couldn't help thinking about the women who usually shared the pool with him. Leggy supermodels, wearing tiny bits of string which they called bikinis. She shivered as she stripped out of her bra and pants, her skin cold and resistant as she tugged on the one-piece. She thought how faded it looked and how, rather alarmingly, it seemed to have shrunk.

The rain was bashing hard against the window and some of the showier plants in the flower beds had been flattened to the ground. The dark blue petals of the delphiniums lay scattered on the sodden earth, as if some exotic bird had recently had its feathers plucked. Carly found herself remembering that expression her mother used to say: *Fine feathers make a fine bird.*

But now wasn't a good time to remind herself why her doll-like sister had always been given the cream of the crop, while she had been dressed in more practical outfits. After all, why would ungainly Carly be given the delicate clothes favoured by a thespian mother, desperate to create a mini-me image of herself?

When she'd been old enough to buy her own clothes, she had become more adventurous, until that disastrous night which had ended up with her at first wanting to die and then to just fade into the background. And she had become very good at doing that.

She thought about the questions Luis had asked her. Intrusive questions about her sex life or, rather, the lack of it. For a moment she forgot the indignation that her employer should be arrogant enough to question her about something like that. Suddenly she got a glimpse of her life as others must see it. As someone who never went out and never had boyfriends. Who lived in the billionaire's house and polished and cleaned it even when he wasn't there. As someone who lived in a staid little world which kept her safe, but which now seemed to mock her.

And Luis didn't know about her ambitions, did he? He didn't realise that behind her dull image was some-one who was going to do good some day. Someone who could hopefully use the brain she'd been given and not have to rely on her looks to better herself.

Pulling on a towelling robe, she hurried down to the pool to find Luis waiting for her and she couldn't help the instinctive shiver which ran down her spine. Sil-houetted against the enormous curved window which overlooked the woods, he was wearing nothing but a moulded pair of swim-shorts and, from where she stood, Carly thought he looked almost completely fit again.

Despite the severity of his injuries, he had certainly regained his physical strength very quickly—probably because he had been at the peak of fitness before the accident. His dark body still looked immensely tough, despite the crutches he was leaning on. Wavy black ten-drils of hair kissed the base of his neck and he seemed lost in thought as he stared out at the Indian Leaf trees whose summer blossoms were creamy-white against the greyness of the day.

He turned as she walked in, and something very peculiar happened to her as their eyes met across the turquoise pool. It was like the disorientation she'd felt when she'd massaged him earlier, only it was worse. Much worse. She stared at him across the echoing space and there was no sound other than the quiet lap-ping of water and the unnaturally loud pounding of her heart. She could feel her breath drying in her throat and suddenly her chest was tight and she was having trouble breathing. It was happening again and she didn't want it to happen. She didn't want to look at a man like Luis and *desire* him. She didn't want to feel this hot little ache at the pit of her belly or the sudden warmth which had started flushing over her skin. Why him, and why *now*?

Was it because she had touched him in an intimate way and broken a taboo which had haunted her for such a long time? She had run her fingers over his almost naked body and had been able to do so because everyone knew that the massage was a kind of *healing*.

But maybe she had been wrong. Maybe it had been more than that. What if that touch had woken something she'd thought was dead, but which had been lying dormant all this time? Something which was now assuming a life of its own and making her look at him with a terrible and tearing kind of *hunger*.

She blinked, wanting to clear her vision and make everything go back to how it had been before. She wanted to go back to thinking of Luis as a generous but extremely arrogant boss. She wanted to be troubled by nothing more onerous than trying to get her head round the book on quantum physics she was currently reading. Because she didn't *do* desire and all the dark stuff which came with it. Wasn't she a total failure in that department? *Hadn't she been told that in no uncertain terms?*

She saw him glance across as she slipped off her robe and that glance, more than anything, killed off some of the feelings which had been multiplying like bacteria inside her. Was that *disbelief* she could read in his eyes? Of course it was. He'd probably never seen a woman who wasn't a size zero. Looking at her curvy body, he might think that she usually finished up all the *alfajores* once he'd flown back to wherever was next on his exotic list of destinations. And he would be right.

Forcing a quick, professional smile, she walked towards him. 'Ready?' she questioned.

'I've been ready for quite some time,' he said acidly. 'But, as usual, you were late.'

'It took me a while to find my costume.'

'Sorry for the inconvenience,' he said sarcastically. 'Perhaps I should have given you more warning. Written it down in triplicate and signed it first.'

She decided not to react. To just pretend that nothing was the matter, but it wasn't easy when she was being confronted by a bare and powerful torso which was making her want to squirm with embarrassment. 'Anyway, we're here now,' she said brightly. 'Just make sure you go backwards down the ladder.'

'I think I know how to get into the damned swimming pool by now.'

Carefully, she took the crutches from him and propped them up against the wall. 'I was only trying to—'

'Well, stop trying,' he snapped. 'I'm fed up with people *trying*. I've been doing this damned regime for weeks and I think I've just about managed to get my head round it. Next thing you'll be teaching me how to cut up my meat using a knife and fork. Or maybe even start spoon-feeding me.'

For Carly, it was the final straw. Coming on top of the insecurity she was feeling at having to stand in front of him, shivering half to death in an unflattering swimsuit, and the fact that she had been shoehorned into a role she didn't want, something inside her flipped. She turned and glared at him. 'Do you have to be *quite* so bad-tempered, when I'm only trying to help you?'

There was a pause as their eyes clashed in a fierce and silent battle. She felt herself tense to find herself caught in that intense black spotlight and she wondered what snapped insult he was about to come out with next. And then, unexpectedly, he sighed.

'I know you are,' he said. 'It's only frustration which is making me so unbearable. The aftermath of this damned accident has gone on for weeks and sometimes it feels as if it's never going to end.'

'Yes.' She chewed on her bottom lip. 'I suppose that's one way of looking at it.'

He raised his brows. 'Unless you're about to tell me that I am pretty unbearable generally?'

Quickly, she glanced down at his bare feet, thinking how pale and perfect his toenails looked against the dark olive of his skin. 'That isn't for me to say.'

'No instant denial, then, Carly?' he mocked. 'Leading me to conclude that I *am* unbearable?'

She lifted her head then and met the mocking challenge in his eyes. 'You aren't exactly known for your sweet and even temper,' she said, and to her surprise he actually laughed as he lowered his powerful body into the pool.

'No, I suppose I'm not. Come on, Carly—aren't you coming in?' he questioned, hitting the surface of the water with the flat of his hand so that an iridescent little plume of spray went showering upwards and fell in tiny droplets which gleamed against his dark skin. 'Mary always did.'

I'll bet she did, thought Carly as she slipped into the

water beside him. Yet wasn't *she* doing exactly what Mary had been guilty of doing? She was having some *very* inappropriate thoughts about her boss, only she was also being a bit of a hypocrite, because hadn't she disapproved of the physiotherapist's behaviour?

She waded further into the water and shivered as the cool water reached her tummy. Goosebumps iced over her skin and she felt the tips of her breasts hardening again, just as they'd done earlier.

In an attempt to conceal it, she leaned back against the tiled wall and splashed water over her arms. 'You're supposed to do ten lengths.'

'I know I am, but I'm planning to do twenty.'

'Do you think that's wise?'

He gave her a hard smile. 'Let's find out, shall we?'

She watched as he struck out, making no concessions towards his injuries as he cleaved through the water like a golden-dark arrow. He swam with the same energy and determination which he applied to everything in life, but after twelve lengths she could see that he had grown pale and his mouth was tight with tension.

'Stop now,' she said, as he came up for air, his black hair plastered to his head like a seal. 'For heaven's sake—slow down, Luis. You're not in some kind of race.'

But he was stubborn, of course he was, and for him life *was* a race. She wasn't surprised when he shook his head and continued but when he'd finished, he was exhausted. Hauling his body out of the water, he propped his elbows onto the edge of the pool and rested his head on them, saying nothing until he had regained his breath.

At last he looked up at her, his eyes gleaming blackly from between wet, matted lashes. 'How was that?'

'You know exactly how it was. You did twenty lengths—double that recommended by the physiotherapist. You want praise for disobeying her instructions?'

'*Sí*. I demand praise. Heaps of it piled high onto my head. So why don't you wipe that disapproving look off your face for once, and tell me how good I am?' His mouth curved into a provocative smile. 'You know you want to.'

Carly stiffened as something unfamiliar prickled over her skin. Was he *flirting* with her? She stared at him, her eyes blinking. Surely not. Unless flirting was almost like a reflex action for him, a bit like a goldfish gasping for air if somebody tipped its bowl onto the floor. *It's just sweet-talk and it doesn't mean anything,* she told herself fiercely. *So don't act as if it does.* 'You probably overextended yourself, but, yes, you were good,' she agreed grudgingly. 'Actually, you were very good.'

He raised his wet eyebrows. 'Why, Carly,' he murmured. 'Praise from you is praise indeed.'

Flustered now, she tried not to let it show, dipping down below the surface of the water, mainly to try to distract herself again. But when she stood up again she could see that Luis's eyes had narrowed and it took a moment for her to realise that he was staring at her with fascination. Or, more specifically, he was staring at her breasts.

The stretchy fabric of her modest one-piece had suddenly become tight and shiny and was clinging to her like a second skin. Embarrassingly, she could feel her nipples pushing against the wet fabric like two little bullets.

Had he noticed that?

Oh, God. What if he had?

'I think you ought to get out now,' she said quickly. 'Before you get too cold.'

'Or too hot,' he amended, but his words were so indistinct that she told herself she must have misheard them. She *must* have done. Unless she was seriously imagining that Luis Martinez—one of the world's greatest lovers—was making a suggestive remark to *her*.

'Let's go,' she said, and dived beneath the water to escape his watchful black eyes.

She swam further than she had intended but she needn't have bothered, because the cold water failed to have the effect it should have done. And when she rose to the surface, gasping for breath, she still had that same terrible aching in her breasts when she looked at him.

CHAPTER THREE

IN A STREAM of impatient Spanish, Luis cursed loudly and eloquently. Outside, the wind howled and rain battered remorselessly against the tall windows. Never-ending rivulets slid down the glass as the sound of the summer storm served as background noise in the scarlet and gold drawing room.

When was this damned rain ever going to stop?

Redirecting his gaze to the table at the far side of the room, he watched as Carly bent over a tray and poured him a tiny cup of espresso.

He felt another unwelcome jerk of desire, jackknifed through his groin with an exquisite precision which made him want to squirm. He scowled instead.

He was bored.

Bored and frustrated.

And one must be as a direct result of the other, he reasoned. Because why else would he be feeling such powerful pangs of lust for someone like little Miss Mouse?

Unobserved, he let his eyes drift over her, trying to work it out. For once, the shapeless cut of her jeans managed to enhance her figure, though not through any deliberate intention on her part. When she bent over like that, the denim stretched tightly over her bottom and emphasised the generous curves of her derriere. She ought to wear close-fitting clothes more often, he thought hungrily. Just as he ought to be in his study an-alysing the stock market, or reading through the stack of emails which Diego had sent through to him earlier. His mouth tightened and the need to distract himself from her luscious body became paramount.

'Play cards with me, Carly,' he said suddenly.

She turned round to look at him, her expression at first startled, then decidedly wary.

'I don't play cards,' she said.

'Then I'll teach you.'

Still she hesitated.

'What's the matter?' he drawled. 'Afraid I'll corrupt you? One game of poker and you'll be gambling away all your hard-earned wages?'

Wishing that he would stop looking at her like that, Carly straightened up and carried his coffee across the room, putting it down on the table beside him.

Corrupt her? She wondered if he had any idea what a good job he'd already done in that department. Wouldn't he be appalled if he knew how much he was on her mind these days? If he realised that she lay in bed thinking about him at night, when the silence and the darkness of her room seemed to magnify her thoughts. Thoughts which felt like longing, but which were closely followed by terrifying memories. Yet even those memories weren't enough to prevent the tingling in her breasts, or the molten ache low in her belly as she lay beneath the feather-soft duvet.

She had felt...*frustrated*...but had found herself recoiling from needs which she had repressed for so long. She kept telling herself that all she needed was to maintain some kind of balance, until things got back to normal again.

But when would that be?

When her boss was well enough to go back to Buenos Aires, or New York, or France or wherever he was planning to take up residence next? When he put some natural distance between them, so that all these stupid feelings would fade away? When she could go back to the quiet, studious life she had forged for herself here and put him out of her mind.

And sitting playing card games wasn't going to help, was it? Not on top of all the increasingly intimate massage sessions and those long and distracting sessions in the pool. She needed to spend less time with him, not more.

'I don't think we have any cards,' she said.

'Yes, we do. In my bedroom,' he said. 'In the desk. Second drawer, on the left. Go and get them, will you, Carly?'

She raised her eyebrows.

He sighed. 'Please.'

'What if I told you that I don't particularly want to play cards.'

'Then I might be forced to pull rank.'

'So it's an order?'

He slanted her an arrogant smile. 'Most definitely it is.'

Carly turned and left the room without another word but her footsteps felt heavy as she mounted the stairs. She felt trapped—like a fly caught in the sticky temptation of a spider's web. The weather had effectively kept them prisoners in this big house so that sometimes it felt as if they were the only two people in the world.

And meanwhile, her dilemma was compounded by her growing feelings for him. Because even she recognised that something had changed.

In the past she had thought of him as a distant and demanding figure, but hadn't that been preferable to *this*? To finding that she was actually enjoying his company in a perverse sort of way. Just her and him and the worst summer rains the country had known for a decade. Cooped up and going stir-crazy, with the lanes around the estate thick with mud and puddles. Luis couldn't drive and he didn't want to take the train to London. And he told her that he didn't want people coming over, drinking his wine and eating his food, and taunting him with all the things he found himself unable to do.

The most disturbing thing of all was that Carly was discovering how much she *liked* having him all to herself.

Pushing open the door to his bedroom, she entered the oak-panelled suite which took up almost all the first floor of the stately home. She'd been up here earlier, making his bed as she always did, changing his expensive Egyptian sheets, which were inevitably tangled— even when he slept alone.

Walking over to his desk, she found her gaze drawn to the two photos standing at either end of the gleaming surface. One was of his mother with her sad eyes and raven hair and the other an iconic shot of Luis, taken the first time he'd become world champion. His hair was wet with the spray of champagne and he was holding a massive silver trophy aloft.

It was funny, she'd seen these photos countless times and most days she dusted around their heavy silver frames without really noticing them. But today she felt like an intruder snooping around. As if her role in this house had subtly changed and she wasn't sure how to deal with it.

'Carly!'

Luis's impatient voice rang through the house, and quickly she found the pack of cards and ran back downstairs to find him sitting where she'd left him.

He glared at her. 'What kept you?'

'I didn't realise I was being timed. I was just daydreaming.'

'And what were you daydreaming about?' he questioned silkily.

She could feel the hot lick of colour to her cheeks, terrified he might guess. 'Nothing,' she said quickly and walked over to the card table.

Wincing a little, Luis levered himself to his feet before joining her and, for some reason, he became aware of the lamplight making intriguing shadows on her rather square face. He noticed the way her breasts moved as she fidgeted with the cards. And he wondered what she'd say if she knew that he'd been sitting here wondering what she would look like naked. He pulled out a chair and sat down, wondering how long this madness was going to continue, and his mouth hardened. Because he had never slept with anyone on his payroll—and he didn't intend to start, not with Carly.

He held out his hand for the pack.

'So what are we going to play?' she questioned.

It was unfortunate that her innocent question only fuelled his frustration, and suddenly all he could think about was the brush of her skin against his as he took the cards from her and he wanted more of it. He wanted to play a game which had nothing to do with hearts or clubs or diamonds. He wanted to play a very grown-up game which involved baring those intriguing curves and feasting his mouth and his hands on them, until he had sated his inconvenient hunger.

He shook his head, trying to clear the powerful images from his mind. 'Do you want to try learning poker?' he asked.

'Is it easy?'

'Not really.'

'In that case, I'd love to.'

He raised his eyebrows. 'Don't say I didn't warn you.'

He shuffled the cards and dealt them and watched her brow pleating in concentration as he explained the rules to her. To his surprise he didn't have to repeat them and she seemed to grasp the concept of the game with remarkable speed.

He had expected—what? That he'd beat her without trying and soon become bored with effortless victory as had happened so often in the past? He was midway through the second game when he realised she was good. Actually, she was very good. And he was having to keep all his wits about him to compete against a mind which was more agile than he'd given her credit for.

She was bright, he thought in confusion. She was very bright.

'Are you sure you haven't played this before?' he questioned suspiciously.

'If I'd played before, then why would I have allowed you to explain all the rules to me?'

'Gamesmanship?'

'That's a very cynical viewpoint, Luis,' she said as she studied the fanned-out cards in her hand.

'Maybe life has made me cynical.'

She looked up and extended her bottom lip in an exaggerated pout. 'Oh, poor diddums!'

It wasn't an expression he knew but the meaning was clear and Luis found himself laughing in response. But that confused him even more, because women didn't usually amuse him, unless it was with the light, teasing comments they sometimes made when they were removing their clothes. Women had their place, but humour rarely featured in it. And suddenly he found himself intrigued by this badly dressed woman with her surprisingly street-sharp grasp of the complex card game. 'You do realise,' he said slowly, 'that I know practically nothing about you.'

She looked up and the light from the lamp shone directly into her face, turning her eyes the colour of clear, bright honey. And Luis suddenly found himself thinking: *They are beautiful eyes.*

'Why should you?' she questioned. 'It isn't relevant to my work. You don't need to know anything about me.'

'A woman who deflects questions about herself?' he drawled. 'Can this really be happening, or am I dreaming?'

'That's an outrageous generalisation to make about women.'

'And one which happens to be true. Generalisations usually are.' He leaned back against the chair and narrowed his eyes. 'So how long have you worked for me now? It must be a year?'

'It's two and a half, actually.'

'That long?'

'Time flies when you're having fun,' she said.

He heard the flippant note in her voice as he continued to study her. 'Being a housekeeper is an unusual job for a woman your age, isn't it?' he observed slowly.

'I suppose so.' She shrugged. 'But it's a good job if you don't have any qualifications. Or if you need somewhere to live,' she added, almost as an afterthought.

He put his cards face down on the table. 'You don't have any qualifications? That surprises me. You are clearly bright enough—judging by the way you've just picked up a relatively complicated card game.'

Carly didn't answer straight away and not just because his words sounded so patronising. She didn't want to tell him about her hopes and dreams—she didn't want to *expose* herself in any way to him because she sensed a certain *danger* in doing that. If it had been any other time, she might have distracted herself with a task which needed doing and hoped he'd forget about it. But it wasn't any other time—it was now—and she was out of her usual comfort zone. She couldn't pretend that she needed to go and see to something in the kitchen because she suspected he would overrule her. Luis wanted to talk and Luis was paying her wages. And what Luis wanted, he generally got.

'I've been trying to make up for lost time,' she said. 'Which is why I did those evening classes. And why I've taken a couple of the science exams I really ought to have taken at school.'

'You've been studying *science*?'

She heard the surprise in his voice. 'Yes. What's the

matter with that? Some people do actually *like* those subjects.'

'But they're not usually women.'

'Again, another outrageous generalisation.' She shook her head in mock despair. 'That's the second sexist thing you've said within the space of two minutes, Luis.'

'How can it be sexist if it's true? Look at the stats if you don't believe me. Men dominate the field of science. And maths,' he added.

'Which might have a lot more to do with teaching methods and expectations than because they have scientifically superior brains.'

His eyes glittered. 'I think we'll have to differ on that.'

Carly could feel herself getting hot as he ran a speculative gaze over her and once again she was aware of that whispering feeling of danger. 'As you wish,' she said, wanting to change the subject and talk about something else, but it seemed he was having none of it.

'Which science were you good at?' he persisted.

'All of them. Biology and chemistry. Maths, too. I loved them all.'

'So why—?'

'Did I flunk my exams?' She abandoned all pretence of playing the game and put her own cards down on the table. She didn't want to answer this, but she knew Luis well enough to recognise that he wouldn't let up. And pain grew less over time, didn't it? As the years went by you could talk about things which had happened and make them sound almost *conversational*. 'Because my father was...well, he was very ill when

I was younger and as a consequence I missed out on quite a bit of school work.'

'I'm sorry,' he said, and Carly almost wished he hadn't because it was harder to keep things in perspective when his voice had softened like that.

'Oh, these things happen,' she said.

'What exactly happened?' he probed, his dark eyes narrowed. 'What aren't you telling me, Carly? People have sick parents but still manage to pass exams.'

His persistence was as difficult to ignore as it was surprising, since he wasn't known for taking an interest in the personal life of his staff. And suddenly Carly found herself telling him. It was, she realised, a long time since she'd told anyone because people didn't want to hear hard-luck stories, did they? It was the modern trend to portray your life as if it were just one long, happy party; to act as if you were having fun all the time.

'It was one of those long-term chronic things,' she said, her voice growing quieter. 'He couldn't get out of the house much, so I used to come home from school, and sit and tell him about my day. Sometimes I'd read to him—he liked that. Then by the time I'd cooked supper and the nurse had come in to put him to bed, I'd be too tired to do my homework. Or maybe I was just too lazy,' she added, her attempt to lighten the mood failing spectacularly, for not a flicker of a smile had touched his suddenly sombre face.

'And did he recover?'

His voice was still doing that dangerous thing. That soft thing which was making her feel things she had no right to feel—certainly not about him. It was making her feel *vulnerable,* and she'd spent a lifetime trying not to feel like that. Carly pressed her lips together. She never cried about it these days, but the mind could still play funny tricks on you, couldn't it? Sometimes an innocent question could make your eyes well up without warning and she didn't want that happening now. Not in front of her boss. She shook her head. 'No. I'm afraid he didn't. He died when I was nineteen.'

His ebony gaze seemed to pierce right through her skin.

'And what about your mother?' he questioned. 'Wasn't she around to help?'

This bit was more difficult. It was hard to convey what had happened without making Mum sound like some kind of wicked witch, which she wasn't—she was just someone who could occasionally be a bit misguided.

'She wasn't very...*good* with illness. Some people aren't,' said Carly, injecting that breezy note into her voice which she'd mastered so well. The one which implied that she totally supported her mother's decision to live out her own failed dreams through her beautiful, younger daughter. She remembered the way her mum used to talk about Bella making it big through modelling, but saying that you needed to pump money in to get money out. And that had been what had driven her. What had made her bleed their dwindling bank account dry—a big gamble which had ultimately failed. And even if it had succeeded—so what? As if material success could ever cancel out all the sadness which had been playing out at home. 'My mother was busy helping my sister launch her career. She's a model,' she added.

'Oh?' Luis's eyebrows rose. 'That's a term which

usually covers a multitude of sins. Would I have heard of her?'

'You might have done,' said Carly. 'Though maybe not yet. She does lots of catalogue work. And last year she was hired for the opening of a new shopping complex in Dubai.'

'I see.'

Carly heard the trace of sarcasm in his voice and she bristled. Because that was the thing about families, wasn't it? You could criticise your own until the cows came home, but woe betide anyone else who attempted to do the same.

'She's doing a lot of swimwear shoots at the moment and lingerie modelling. She's *very* beautiful.'

'Is she?'

Carly could hear the doubt in his voice and all her own insecurities came rushing in to swamp her, like dark strands of seaweed pulling her down into the water so that she couldn't breathe. Did he think that someone like her was incapable of having a beautiful sister, with hair like white gold and naturally plump lips, which made you think she'd had Botox? A sister whose ankles and wrists were so delicate that sometimes you worried that they might snap, like spun sugar. Because Bella was all those things—and more.

And didn't she *have* to believe that her sister would one day achieve the success which she and her mother had yearned for? Otherwise it would make all those years of sacrifice and heartbreak count for nothing. It would make the memory of her father's reedy voice as he'd called in vain for his wife all the harder to bear. It would make the debts and the loss of their house seem a complete waste. And it would stop Carly from shrugging and accepting fate the way she'd learned to. Because the last thing she wanted was to feel bitter, when she remembered screwing up her application form for medical school into a tight little ball and hurling it onto the fire.

'Yes,' she said fiercely. 'She's the most exquisite woman you could ever wish to meet.'

For a moment, Luis didn't say anything. He thought her mother sounded shallow and uncaring, but he wasn't particularly shocked by that. She was a woman, wasn't she? And he had yet to meet a single one who could be trusted.

But it must have been hard on Miss Mouse. Even if she was trying to make it sound as if she was okay with it, he could see her struggling to contain her emotions. And for once he felt a certain empathy with her, even though dealing with a woman's emotions was something he tended to steer clear of. Because this was different. This wasn't someone who was breaking her heart just because she'd put on a couple of kilos, or because a man refused to buy her a diamond ring.

Instead, he saw a bright girl who was good at science, who had flunked her exams because she'd been busy caring for her father. But he wondered who had been looking out for her.

He remembered flitting in and out of consciousness after his recent operation, wondering who had been stroking his brow during the surreal night which had followed. The woman with the soft voice which had washed over him like a cool balm. Next day he'd asked the nurse if he had been hallucinating and she'd told him it had been the girl with the ponytail, in the old raincoat. He remembered frowning and wondering who she was talking about. A kind girl, the nurse had added, and that was when he'd realised that she'd meant Carly.

She had visited him a few times after that and in a strange way he had found himself looking forward to her visits—mainly because she always seemed able to plump up the pillows and make him feel even more comfortable than the nurses. She'd sat beside him rather primly and had suggested he breathe deeply and move his ankles around. Actually, in a quiet way she had been a bit of a *tyrant*, but he seemed to have responded well to her general bossiness. And then one day she'd just stopped coming, and that had been that.

He picked up his coffee and sipped it. Despite her occasional bursts of fierceness, her company had been surprisingly tolerable since they'd been alone in the house, even if she did insist on scurrying away to her room at every available opportunity. Even if she seemed to play down every womanly trait she possessed…

At least tonight she wasn't wearing that ugly uniform she always insisted on, though she had chosen a cotton shirt in yet another forgettable shade of beige. It was not a colour palette he would have ever chosen for her. With those eyes the colour of iced tea he might have dressed her in flame—or maybe scarlet. He gave the glimmer of a smile. Even if she was the antithesis of a scarlet woman.

His gaze flickered to her hands. Working hands, with short, unpainted nails which matched her scrubbed face and no-nonsense hairstyle. Briefly, he wondered why she was content to sublimate her femininity like this. Was it because she had stood for too long in the shadow of her beautiful sister? Or just that caring for her father during her formative years had blotted out her more frivolous side?

He thought that her childhood sounded pretty grim. Or maybe it was that all families were essentially dysfunctional. The wounds they inflicted never really healed, did they? He thought of his own family as the rain began to batter against the window again.

'This weather is crazy,' he said, his voice growing hard with frustration.

'Of course it is. We're in England.'

'But we don't have to be.' He put his cup down with a rattle and stared at her. 'Do you have a passport?'

'Of course I do.'

'Good.' He picked up his cards again. 'Then make sure you're ready to leave first thing tomorrow morning.'

'Leave?' Carly blinked. 'Leave for where?'

'St Jean Cap Ferrat. I have a house there.'

'You mean...' She looked at him in confusion. 'Cap Ferrat in the south of France?'

He raised his eyebrows. 'Is there any other?'

'But why do you want to go there, and why so suddenly?'

'Because I'm bored,' he said silkily.

Carly looked at him uneasily. She'd heard enough stories about his Mediterranean villa to know what it was like. It was where the beautiful people hung out. Where someone like her would never fit in. 'I...I think I'd prefer to stay here, if that's okay with you.'

'But it is not *okay* with me,' he returned, his voice edged with a steely arrogance which cut through her like a blade. 'You are being paid an enormous amount of money to make my life easier, Carly, which means doing as *I* wish. And number one on my wish list is to get out of this damned rain and feel a little warmth on my skin again. So why don't you wipe that dazed look off your face and start packing?'

CHAPTER FOUR

HATEFUL, ARROGANT MAN.

Even the beauty of her surroundings couldn't blot out Carly's indignation at the way Luis had spoken to her just before they'd left England.

You are being paid an enormous amount of money.

Yes, she knew that.

To make my life easier.

She knew that, too. So did that give him the right to treat her like a portable piece of property who could just be shifted around when it suited him? Her mouth tightened. But what Luis wanted, Luis got, didn't he? And if the South American billionaire decided to uproot to his villa in the south of France because he was *bored* and wanted to feel the heat of the sun on his body, then that was exactly what would happen.

But Carly forced herself to stay positive as she packed her suitcase, concentrating instead on the massive bonus he was paying her. It made her dream of getting to med school one step closer. It was so close now that she could almost *taste* it. All she had to do was tolerate the arrogant Argentinian playboy for a little while longer and then she would be free.

They had spent a surreal morning getting here,

boarding a private jet, which had flown them from London to Nice, where they'd been spotted by a lone paparazzi who apparently spent his days waiting for famous passengers to arrive on the incoming flights. Carly watched as he leapt in front of them, shooting off a role of film as Luis walked through the airport terminal.

He wasn't striding at his usual powerful pace, but his walking stick didn't seem to deter the attentions of a group of women who converged on him, looking like beautiful clones with their sun-kissed hair and frayed denim shorts. Instantly, they began to thrust pieces of paper in front of his face.

'Sign for me, Luis?'

'Want to come to a party later, Luis?' asked one, boldly trying to shove a card into the top pocket of his denim shirt.

But despite his waving them away with an impatient hand, the girls simply took out their camera phones and started clicking frantically instead.

'Does that happen very often?' asked Carly as they climbed into the powerful car which was waiting for them outside the terminal.

'Walking through an arrivals lounge when you get off a plane?'

'There's no need for sarcasm,' she said tightly. 'I meant, that kind of fan girl attention.'

He shrugged. 'Everywhere I go.'

'And does it get too much?'

He shot her a sardonic look. 'What do you think?'

She hesitated. 'I think that your life is…strange. That it manages to be both very public and very isolated at the same time.'

'Ten out of ten for perception,' he said mockingly.

She clipped her seat belt closed as the car began to pull away. 'Yet you didn't take any of those women up on their offers,' she observed, 'when many men in your position might have done.'

He gave a short laugh. 'You don't think that I've grown jaded with that kind of liaison? That those kinds of women are as interchangeable as the tyres I used to get through during a race?'

'That's a mean thing to say.'

'But it's true.'

The words came out more hotly than she had intended. 'Funny how it's never stopped you before.'

'Why would it stop me?' He raised his eyebrows. 'If a man is thirsty, he would be a fool not to drink. You think I should turn down some beautiful, beddable blonde because we have nothing in common other than the fact that our raging hormones seem hell-bent on collision?'

Carly shook her head. 'You are outrageous.'

His lips curved into a smile and his dark eyes gleamed. 'But you knew that already, Carly—I'm just answering your questions as honestly as I know how.'

Yes, he was, thought Carly. And didn't she *admire* his honesty, even if it made her feel uncomfortable at times? He wasn't pretending to be someone he wasn't, was he? Maybe the emptiness in his eyes was an inevitable consequence of having your appetite jaded by being offered too much, too young.

'So do you *like* being famous?' she asked suddenly.

'You make it sound as if I had choice in the matter, but I didn't.' He rested his palms on his denim-covered thighs and flexed his fingers. 'I didn't seek fame. All

I wanted was to race and to be the best in the world—
the acclamation was just an inevitable spin-off of that.'

But as he met her amber eyes he remembered that
there had been other spin-offs, too. Success on the scale
he'd known meant that you could write your own rules
as you went along and he'd done exactly that, hadn't he?
Big time. He had turned his back on responsibility. He
had taken from women but had never given anything
back. He hadn't needed to. He had known unbelievable wealth and adulation but nothing had ever filled
the dark space deep inside him. Maybe that was the
price you paid for fame.

'Maybe I shouldn't have taken on as much advertis-
ing as I did,' he said slowly. 'But I was young and the
success went to my head and it seemed crazy to turn
down that kind of money. And my sponsors were keen
for me to do it. Actually, that's an understatement. They
wanted someone to sex up the sport as much as possible
and I was considered perfect for the role.'

And motor-racing was as sexy as it got, Carly realised. Even she could see that. All that power and
testosterone and money—and Luis had exemplified
it all with those show-stopping good looks and hard,
sexy body. No wonder beautiful strangers thrust their
phone numbers at him at airports with innuendo in
their voices and hunger in their eyes. No wonder that
even women like her weren't immune to his charm.

'And once you're famous, you can't undo it,' she
said slowly. 'You can't go back to the person you were
before.'

'No. You can't. The world has an image of you and
there isn't a thing you can do to change it.'

'Well, that's not quite true. You could...' The words were out before she had time to think about them.

He raised his eyebrows. 'Could what?'

'Nothing.'

'Tell me. I'm interested.'

She shrugged. 'You kind of *bring* publicity on yourself by dating the sort of women who give tell-all interviews to glossy magazines after you dump them.'

'You think I should have them sign a confidentiality clause before I take them to bed?'

'I don't know, Luis—I'm your housekeeper, not your counsellor.'

Turning her head, she peered out of the window as the car ascended a terrifyingly narrow road which spiralled its way up a dizzyingly high, green mountain. 'Gosh, it's so beautiful out there,' she said.

'Are you deliberately changing the subject, Carly?'

'I might be.'

He laughed. 'Ever been to Europe before?'

She watched as a bright scarlet sports car squeezed past them in the opposite direction, screwing up her eyes as she wondered if it would make it. 'Just a package holiday to Spain—two weeks in Benidorm in a hotel with my mother and my sister. It was fairly... basic.'

'Then you may be in for something of a treat,' he commented drily as his phone began to ring and, pulling it from his pocket, he answered in Spanish.

The rest of the journey passed quickly and Carly wondered what her sister would say if she could see her now, in a chauffeur driven car, travelling through some of the most expensive real estate in the world. She probably wouldn't have believed it. Come to think of it, she was having a bit of difficulty believing it herself.

The car rounded a bend and she caught her first glimpse of Luis's house—a *belle-époque* villa which he told her he'd bought from an Arabian prince, a friend of a friend, who just happened to be a sultan.

For Carly, it was yet another illustration of his rarefied life, a life which she'd seen only fragments of before. But suddenly it was being pieced together in front of her eyes, like some kind of rich and lavish jigsaw puzzle. He knew sultans and kings. Supermodels and politicians converged on his houses like flocks of glamorous butterflies. But he had no real base, she realised. He flitted from gorgeous house to gorgeous house, but there was no place to call home. Despite all his expensive real estate, Luis Martinez was nothing but a rich and pampered gypsy.

She looked up at the villa as their car drove through the gates, thinking it was like some kind of sumptuous fortress. Dazzling white and shielded by tall dark cypress trees, it sat high in the hills overlooking little azure coves and inlets.

'Are there many staff?' she asked, suddenly nervous.

'Just the usual. And your French counterpart is called Simone. You'll like her.'

Simone was waiting to greet them in a vast reception area with corridors leading off in different directions, like the spokes of a wheel. Tall vases filled with orange roses and spears of eucalyptus were reflected back in large ornate mirrors. A classical statue of a young woman tipping water over herself stood in one corner.

Carly looked around, thinking that it was a bit like

being in a museum and that his French housekeeper was scarily chic. Simone's grey dress skated over her slim figure, her hair was cleverly tinted, and, though she must have been pushing fifty, Carly suddenly felt shabby in comparison.

'I'm going straight to my study,' said Luis. 'To answer some of Diego's increasingly hysterical emails, before he blows a fuse. Simone, this is Carly's first time in France.' He ran his finger thoughtfully over his broken nose. 'I think we might put her in the blue room overlooking the bay.'

There was a split second of hesitation. 'But might Mademoiselle Conner not disturb you, if your rooms are so close?' Simone's smile was fixed. 'I have made up one of the guest houses in the grounds, which might be more…suitable.'

'Carly hasn't travelled in Europe very much before. We might as well give her a decent view.' His eyes were as flat as hammered black metal. 'That won't be a problem, will it?'

'*Mais non!*' Simone gave a little wiggle of her hands. '*Pas de problème.*'

Carly realised that Luis was watching her and found her cheeks growing warm beneath that hard-eyed scrutiny. And suddenly she was conscious of something more than *consideration* in his dark eyes. Was he looking *at* her, rather than through her, or was she starting to imagine things? She felt her breasts growing heavy and her cheeks flushing, and she thought she saw his eyes gleam in response. *As if he had guessed what she was thinking.*

'That's very kind of you,' she said awkwardly.

'It's nothing. Enjoy the view. I'll see you later. Massage after lunch?'

'As long as it's not a heavy lunch.'

'You see how *stern* she can be, Simone?' he questioned mockingly. 'Don't worry, Carly, I will allow you to police what I eat, if it makes you feel better.'

His words only increased Carly's confused feelings. Was she misreading the signs again, thinking that he was flirting with her? Thinking that a man like him would be looking at someone like *her* with hunger in his eyes? But no matter how much the logical side of her brain tried to tell her that she was mistaken, her instincts were telling her that she was right. His eyes *had* grown smoky with something like desire and she wondered if Simone had picked up on it, too.

She watched as he walked off down the corridor, thinking how much he had improved. She doubted he would need that stick for much longer…soon he would be back to his fighting fit and glorious best.

She swallowed. And when he was? What then? She supposed she would just go back to ironing his sheets and keeping the house in a constant state of readiness for his infrequent visits. It would be as if this whole bizarre interlude had never happened.

And it would be better that way, she told herself fiercely. She wouldn't have to run her hands over his oiled flesh any more, nor feel droplets of water splashing on her skin as he broke through the surface of the water to emerge beside her in the pool, like some dark sea lion. They could slip back into that other, infinitely less threatening relationship they'd had before. The one where she just faded into the background of his busy life and he barely noticed her. And this would all be like a distant dream....

'I shall give you a quick tour,' said Simone. 'Though I warn you that the house can be a little overwhelming on a first visit. Don't worry about your suitcase—someone will take it to your room.'

She followed the Frenchwoman along one of the long corridors, trying to remember what led where, but as Simone had said—the place was a little overwhelming. Doors led off into high rooms most of which overlooked the sea. Carly counted two dining rooms, one with a glass ceiling, which Simone told her could be retracted to open up to the sky. On the ground floor was a gym leading out onto a large pool area with terrace, and on the upper floor was another terrace offering a wrap-around view over the mountains which towered over the back of the house. She thought it was the most beautiful place she'd ever seen.

When at last she was shown to her room, Carly stood open-mouthed trying to take in the Mediterranean view, and a bed made up with linen so white that she felt she'd have to scrub her skin before she dared climb in between the sheets.

'And this,' said Simone, 'is where you'll be staying.'

Suddenly, she could understand the Frenchwoman's reservations about putting her here, because it was a room which was fit for a king. And Luis had given it to *her*. Carly could feel a stupid lump rising in her throat. 'Here?' she questioned, horrified to hear the crack in her voice. 'You mean, I'm staying in here?'

'Yes, here,' said Simone, her voice now sounding almost gentle. 'I will leave you to change. Lunch will be served on the smaller terrace, just after two. Can you remember how to find your way back there?'

'I…think so.'

But after the housekeeper had gone, Carly walked around like someone in a trance, running her fingertips over the billowing white drapes which framed the fabulous view. Out on the terrace, there was a table and chairs and even a lounger. She would be able to read her textbooks out here *and* get some sun.

In the bathroom toiletries were lined up, like in some upmarket department store. Lavender-infused bath salts stood next to a big old-fashioned tub. Thick, soft towels lay in neat piles, like drifts of clouds. There was even a little vase of white freesia perfuming the air. Carly buried her nose in the petals. Flowers in the bathroom—imagine that! Another wave of emotion hit her and, try as she might, she couldn't seem to put the brakes on it.

Because for the first time in her life she didn't feel like second best. Like the geeky child who always dressed in practical clothes while her sister floated around in pretty little dresses. That same geeky child was now staying in a billionaire's home, in a fancy suite of rooms which had clearly been designed to accommodate his upmarket friends. She wondered what Bella and her mother would say if they could see her now.

But as she began to unpack the contents of her suitcase, she realised that this temporary change of circumstances didn't really change anything. You couldn't make a silk purse out of a sow's ear. She remembered what her mother used to say: *Oh, Carly's got the brains, but Bella's got the beauty.* And to her mother, appearances had been everything.

Carly looked around. Everything here was top of the range—all sleek and clean and shining. Everything except her. The full-length mirror reflected back a woman with a hot face, crumpled clothes and untidy hair. Was she really insane enough to imagine that Luis had been looking at her with *desire*?

She glanced at her watch. Surely she could do *something* with her appearance. If she got a move on then at least she could wash her hair and change into something more presentable for lunch.

But she still felt like an alien as she stripped off and stood beneath the cool shower, self-consciously aware of her fleshy body as she applied creamy soap and shampoo. Afterwards, she blasted her hair dry and had just pulled on a clean set of bra and pants, when there was a knock on the door.

Perhaps it was Simone. Grabbing her discarded towel and holding it in front of her, she walked over to the door and pulled it open.

But it wasn't Simone who stood there.

Carly felt as if someone had just pulled the rug from beneath her feet because suddenly her knees felt shaky.

It was Luis.

Luis, whose black hair was ruffled and damp—presumably because he was fresh out of the shower, just like her. Luis, whose fine linen shirt was clinging to his torso, outlining every hard sinew. And suddenly her perception of him underwent a dramatic shift. This was the man whose half-naked body had become almost normal to her. So why did the fully dressed version suddenly seem way too intimate? She wondered what it was about those faded jeans and damp hair which made her bones feel as if they had turned to jelly. As if she were in danger of melting at his feet.

Because wasn't that what all women did around him? What she had sworn she would *never* do?

Her fingers dug into the soft towel held chastely against her breastbone. She should have felt embarrassed by her own near-naked state. She should tell him she wouldn't be long and close the door on him.

Or *he* should have felt embarrassed at seeing her that way. Shouldn't he apologise for disturbing her and tell her that he'd see her outside on the terrace?

But he didn't.

And neither did she.

They just stood there staring at each other like two people who had just been introduced and she could hear her heart pounding like a drum. Her breasts felt heavy and there was a soft, molten ache between her legs and in the middle of this confusing state came anger, and fear. Because she didn't *do* this kind of stuff. She didn't feel desire any more. She didn't want to. Because desire was unpredictable—and, more importantly, it was *dangerous*.

She shook her head slightly. 'I didn't hear the bell,' she said, licking her dry lips.

He frowned. 'What bell?'

Act normal, she told herself. Pretend that nothing's happening. Because nothing is. 'The lunch bell.'

His eyes narrowed. 'That's because nobody's rung it.'

'Oh. Right. Did you…' she shrugged her shoulders, telling herself this was crazy, but still she stayed rooted to the spot '…er…did you get all your emails answered?'

'No.'

'Diego won't be very pleased.'

'I imagine he won't,' he agreed drily. 'But right now I'm not really thinking about Diego.'

'Oh. R-right.'

Luis felt his throat grow as dry as sandpaper and even her stumbled response didn't dissolve his growing hunger. He knew he should leave *right now* but he couldn't seem to drag his eyes away from her. Not because she looked particularly sexy, because she didn't. Her pale legs and faded bra straps were unremarkable and, for him, it was no big deal to think that beneath that towel she was almost naked. He was used to naked women.

But this was Carly and, for once, her long hair was loose. Freed of the usual tight ponytail, it looked like silk and smelt of bay leaves and he found himself wanting to run his fingers through it. To twist one thick strand possessively around his wrist and to draw her head close enough to kiss her. He wondered what those unpainted lips would taste like. He wondered how the lush curves of her generous body would feel if they were moulded against him.

But it was more than that which drew him. More than the rampant and unexpected lust which was raging around inside him, and a sexual frustration which was making him ache.

She looked clean. That was it. Clean and pure. Her face was untouched by artifice and her iced-tea eyes were wide and dark. She looked like snow before it got trampled on. Before it became all grey and slushy.

And he was the kind of man who did the trampling, wasn't he? He stamped on women's hearts and hardly even noticed he was doing it. He was cruel and insensitive—that was what they said. And she was the last kind of woman he should be lusting after.

But none of that seemed to matter. All he could think about was the aching in his groin which felt as if he were about to *explode.* 'Carly,' he said unsteadily, even though he hadn't been planning to say her name like that.

Her eyes widened. She licked her lips again and made them gleam. 'What's…wrong?'

Her words whispered over his skin like silk and suddenly Luis found himself fighting temptation as he'd never had to fight it before. In the past, if he wanted a woman—he would simply take her, if she was willing. And they were always willing.

But even though her lips had parted with unconscious longing, she was staff, and everyone knew that sleeping with your staff was a recipe for disaster. Even if she weren't, she was all *wrong* for a man like him. She was caring and wholesome. She was the clean light to the darkness which filled the space where once he'd had a soul. What right did he have to mess with her? To take her just because he could and then to leave her broken-hearted afterwards?

'No, nothing's wrong,' he said abruptly. 'I thought I'd show you the way to lunch because I know how easy it is to get lost in this place, but, as usual, you're late. What is it with you?' He scowled at her. 'I'll meet you on the upper terrace in fifteen minutes—and for God's sake, get a move on.'

CHAPTER FIVE

THE INCIDENT AT her bedroom door unsettled her more than it should have done. Carly told herself that Luis had seen her in the swimming pool loads of times so a glimpse of her unexciting bra strap was hardly likely to send him into paroxysms of delight.

But while she might not be very experienced, neither was she stupid. She could read people and their body language—they were two of the traits which made her believe that one day she might make a good doctor. And she had *seen* the way he had looked at her when she'd stood wrapped in her towel. That hadn't been shock or revulsion she'd seen in the Argentinian playboy's eyes, it had been hunger—potent and powerful and almost tangible.

And hadn't she felt it, too? Hadn't what had silently passed between them made her feel as if she were being swept away by something? As if some dark and invisible wave were dragging her towards something outside her control? She found herself thinking how cruel nature could be, that her body should be so attracted to someone who was out of bounds for about a million different reasons.

She knew her cheeks were still flushed as she joined

Luis for lunch that day and she knew, too, that something between them had changed. That no matter how hard she focused her mind, she couldn't seem to make things the same as they'd been before.

Suddenly a new and achingly raw awareness had sprung up between them. She tried not to let it affect her work, but how could it not? The nervous trembling of her fingers when she massaged him reminded her of the first time she'd done it. She found herself missing the confidence which she'd acquired with practice. But what she mourned most was the loss of the ease between them. When for a while she'd felt as if they were almost equals. When she could say exactly what was on her mind and sometimes even make him laugh.

Now there was a terrible and fraught kind of *atmosphere* whenever they were alone. Their curious alliance must have been more fragile than she'd thought or maybe she really *was* naïve after all. Because now he seemed to go out of his way to avoid her unless absolutely necessary, closeting himself in his study and immersing himself in work and leaving Carly largely to her own devices.

Their days settled into an awkward kind of routine. Carly woke early and swam in the pool, long before any of the other staff were around, slightly worried that it might appear presumptuous of her to be enjoying the 'facilities'. She would swim furiously in an attempt to rid herself of the night-time demons which had been haunting her. And afterwards, she would lie floating on her back, looking up as the sun rose higher in the blue sky.

After that, she would take Luis through his exercises and give him a fairly rigorous massage before breakfast—a pattern she repeated three times throughout the day. And whenever she got the opportunity, she would scuttle away to some largely hidden corner of the vast complex to tackle some reading.

There had been a couple of visitors, each arriving unannounced on separate occasions—Carly had heard their giggles long before she'd seen them. A beautiful blonde and a foxy-looking redhead, who had sat wearing big sun hats and tiny bikinis, draping themselves around the pool without ever managing to get themselves wet.

And Carly had forced herself to stem the unreasonable jealousy which had risen up inside her. She told herself that, *of course*, Luis would have women round—he usually did—and she should be glad that he was showing very obvious signs of complete recovery. Though she noticed that neither woman stayed the night. Each was dispatched home in one of his luxury cars, usually a sign that he was bored.

He had been out a couple of times, too. His driver had taken him along the coast to Monaco, where, according to Simone, a Hollywood actress had taken over a famous restaurant to give a lunch in his honour.

That had been the day when Carly had uninterestedly pushed her *salade Niçoise* around her plate, telling herself not to behave like a possessive child. Of course he would leave her behind! Or had she really pictured herself bursting in on some glamour lunch wearing one of her pastel-coloured T-shirts with her knee-length denim skirt?

At least she'd managed to get through two books she'd been meaning to read for ages, and the fresh air, good food and regular exercise meant that, physically, she felt better than she'd done in a long time, despite her lack of sleep.

One afternoon, her thoughts were travelling along the fascinating labyrinth of quantum physics when a dark shadow fell over the page and she glanced up to see Luis blocking out the light. Behind him the turquoise waters of the infinity pool danced in the sunlight and beyond that was the infinitely darker blue of the sea. But the only things she noticed were his powerful body and that battered straw hat he always wore in the sunshine, and her mouth dried.

'What are you reading?'

She screwed up her eyes, wishing her heart would stop doing that noisy, drum-like thing. Wishing that by now she would have acquired some sort of immunity to him. 'I didn't know it was time for your massage,' she replied.

'That's an odd title for a book.'

'Very funny.' She held up the cover so he could see it.

'And why are you lying in the sunshine reading...' he narrowed his eyes, and read '..."*Quantum Theory Cannot Hurt You*"?'

'Stop laughing at me. You know why. I told you before that I like science.'

'I like cars, but I don't spend my time lolling round the pool reading maintenance manuals. There are plenty of novels in the library—just help yourself.'

'Thanks, but I don't particularly want to read a novel. This is...'

'What?' He lifted his walking stick and used it to point at the dog-eared dust jacket. 'Heavy? Indecipherable?'

'Completely fascinating,' she said quietly. 'In my opinion.'

He rested his stick against one of the sunbeds and gave short laugh. 'You know, you really are something of an enigma, Carly. What are you planning to do with all these qualifications you keep accumulating? Sooner or later, you're surely going to run out of exams to take.'

She hesitated. 'And is there something the matter with that?'

He gave a shrug. 'You'll just become one of those people with a stack of diplomas you never use.'

'Who says I'll never use them?'

He smiled. 'Science may make you *understand* why cornstarch is vital when making *alfajores,* but it isn't really necessary, is it?'

Carly felt a stir of resentment as she met the mocking question in his eyes, because wasn't that just *typical* of him? There was no praise or even a glimmer of surprise that his housekeeper should have been working hard at exams as she went about her lowly job. It hadn't even occurred to him that she might want more from life than this. The world revolved around Luis, didn't it? Stung by his attitude, she turned on him.

'Maybe I'm not just stockpiling certificates,' she retorted. 'Maybe I'm going to use the exams to make something of myself.'

'Like what?'

'Like, a doctor.'

'You? A doctor?'

Any momentary doubt that it might not be a good idea to tell your employer you were planning on leaving immediately dissolved. Was he arrogant enough to think that she'd be fulfilled for the rest of her life keeping house for him and making sure his favourite cakes were on the table whenever he was in town? Watching and waiting in the background while he lived his life, without having any real life of her own.

'Why not?' she flared. 'Do you think I'm incapable of being a medic?'

'I hadn't really given it a lot of thought.'

What he meant was that he hadn't given *her* a lot of thought. Oh, he might have felt the odd flickering of desire—because she was a woman of child-bearing age who was closeted up with him, and that was how nature had programmed him to react. But he didn't really think about her as a *person*.

Carly stared at him. 'If you must know, I've already applied for medical school and I have a deferred place waiting for me. I'm planning on going just as soon as I've saved up enough money to support myself during the course. I've dreamt about being a doctor for a long time and I don't intend to give up on my dreams any time soon.'

She sat up and pushed her sunglasses on top of her head, but the jiggling movement of her breasts seemed to have distracted him. Or maybe he'd just grown bored with hearing about her dreams. Whatever the reason, he was suddenly staring at her as if he couldn't drag his gaze away. He was staring at her and glaring as if he liked what he saw and yet resented feeling that way—all at the same time.

'You've got a tan,' he said.

Following the direction of his gaze, she glanced down to see the glimpse of white where her shoulder strap had shifted. 'A bit.' She smiled, trying for a little levity to lighten the heavy atmosphere which had suddenly descended on them. 'That is what tends to happen when you expose your skin to the sun, Luis.'

'And you've lost weight.'

'Have I?'

Their eyes met. 'You know you have.'

'If I have, it wasn't intentional.' She shrugged. 'This climate doesn't...well, it doesn't give me much of an appetite, and Simone's been serving those delicious salads. And I've been swimming every morning—in this weather it seems criminal not to. All that helps.'

There was another factor, of course. One which she wouldn't be confiding in him any time soon—and the main reason why her normally healthy appetite seemed to have deserted her.

She wondered what he would say if he knew. If he'd be shocked to learn that these days she had grown to dread and long for their massage sessions, in equal measure. That just the thought of going anywhere near his warm skin started a terrible aching deep inside her. And it was getting worse. She found her hands wanting to linger on his flesh. She wanted to bend her head to the base of his neck and kiss the dark tendrils which curled there. She wondered how her attitude towards men and sex could have changed so radically. Was it possible that all her hard-wired fears of intimacy had been melted by daily exposure to Luis Martinez and his magnificent body?

'Don't you own a bikini?'

His impatient question startled her and Carly looked at him. 'A bikini?'

'You know, the garment of choice for most women

your age rather than something your grandmother might be seen wearing.'

Her cheeks grew hot as she looked down to where her thighs were outlined against the cushions of the sunlounger. 'I'm the wrong sort of shape for a bikini.'

'And what sort of shape is that?'

She lifted her gaze to his. 'Too fat.'

'You are not too fat,' he said impatiently. 'You're curvy, yes—but in all the right places. And men like curves. Actually, they like to see them, instead of them being hidden away behind shapeless clothes which are deeply unflattering.' His mouth hardened. 'You ought to give it a try some time. Stop moaning about the way you look and try doing something to change it, if it makes you unhappy.'

'You do say the nicest things, Luis.'

'Maybe it was something you needed to hear,' he said, unrepentantly.

She snapped her book shut. 'What time is it?'

'Ten after four.'

'Then we'd better go for your massage.'

'If you say so, Carly.'

'I do say so.'

But Luis didn't move. He couldn't. Because massage was the last thing he was thinking about right then. From here all he could see were her legs. Legs which had turned a shade of the *dulce de leche* he used to eat as a child. A paler shade than the syrupy sweet which used to seep out from the *facturas* pastries his mother used to make—back in the days before betrayal had slipped its lethal knife into his world and changed it for ever.

He felt that familiar little stab of pain but it was

overridden by the infinitely sharper spiralling of lust. He dragged his gaze away from her legs but today she was like a beacon who seemed to glow golden just about everywhere. Even her hair had caught the sun and there were pale licks of colour nestling in amid the sedate brown, making it look as if she'd spent hours at an expensive hairdresser's. He shifted his position a little, but it had little effect on the heavy aching at his groin.

'Give me fifteen minutes,' he said tersely. 'I need to make a phone call first.'

'Fifteen minutes it is.' She scrambled up from the lounger as if she couldn't wait to get away from him. 'I'll see you in the massage room.'

He watched her go and the sway of her hips made him harder still. Her swimsuit was riding up and revealing more of her bottom than she probably would have liked, if only she'd been aware of it. He suspected she would be appalled if she knew just how much of her creamy buttocks he could see, because she was a prude, no question. She dressed like a prude and she acted like one, too.

Yet he knew enough about women to realise that she was as jumpy as a box of newly lit fireworks whenever he was around. And then some. Did she think he was blind to the way her cheeks went pink whenever he walked unexpectedly into the room? Her newly acquired tan wasn't deep enough to conceal *that*. Did she think he hadn't noticed that her breasts were diamond-nubbed and straining, whenever they were in the pool together? Or that during his massage sessions her hands had gone back to that same trembling she'd had at the beginning.

It was a powerful kind of chemistry, and if it had been anyone other than Carly she would have made a pass at him by now. And in truth, that probably would have been enough to deflate his interest—or certainly to cut it short. The easy lay had never been a problem; it was the potentially unobtainable which had always intrigued him. He realised that he'd never met anyone who had actively fought her attraction to him before. It was incredibly…arousing.

Propping his walking stick against the lounger, he pulled his cell phone from the pocket of his robe and called his office in Argentina. For a while he allowed his mind to be taken over with the practical considerations of his business empire, while his assistant read out the list of bullet points she had prepared for him. Most concerned his global building projects: the luxury apartments being constructed on Uruguay's most beautiful beach and the new hospital in Santiago del Estero. As he listened to her neat summary, he realised that everything was going according to plan. The conservation measures he was instigating in the south of his country had been so successful that he'd been asked to chair a Pan-European convention in the fall.

But as he mentally filed away the information he was given, different images started crowding into his mind. Images which were painful and unwelcome. He tried to block them out, just as he'd spent the last four months blocking them, but for once it wasn't working. He stared at his walking stick and suddenly found himself remembering the accident with a crystal clarity which made him flinch.

It was all too easy to recall that strange split second of calm, moments before impact. And then the deafening crumple of metal as his car had smashed into the side of the track. He closed his eyes as he remembered the stench of burning rubber and the first hot lick of flames as the car had ignited around him. The distant sirens and muffled shouts of his rescuers had grown louder with their sense of urgency and panic. He remembered being trapped in that metal coffin, thinking that he was about to die.

And if he had died? What would he have had to show for his life? A bloated bank account and a shelf full of trophies. His mouth hardened. It wasn't much of a legacy, was it?

The sound of a bird calling out from one of the trees brought him back to the present. He looked around at the luxury pool and the villa which rose like an elaborate white cake out of the tiered green gardens. Dusky-pink roses and starry-white jasmine scented the air and his senses suddenly felt saturated. How beautiful it was, he thought, and, ultimately, how fragile. It could all be over in a heartbeat.

Couldn't it?

He felt something flicker and power into life inside him as he began walking towards the massage room, like a man in a trance.

Quietly opening the door, he blinked against the subdued light to see Carly with her back to him, lining up bottles of aromatic oils in a neat row. He stared at the set of her shoulders and the ponytail which hung down her back and he knew the exact moment when she heard him enter, for her long fingers stilled on a small vial which looked like some alchemist's potion. She had changed into her uniform and the ice-blue dress stretched across the broad beam of her bottom, emphasising its generous curves.

He also knew the exact moment when his painful recall became transmuted into desire. Only this time it wasn't the low-grade variety which had been nagging away at him for weeks. Suddenly it was gathering all the force of a tidal wave—whipped up by soft *dulce de leche* flesh and eyes the colour of iced tea.

He could smell the subtle bayleaf scent of her hair as she turned round and flicked her ponytail back and the gesture made her breasts jiggle beneath the uniform dress. Automatically, his gaze lingered on them and it took all his concentration to lift his eyes to her face.

'You…startled me,' she said.

'That wasn't my intention.'

'Where's your stick?'

With a start he looked down at his empty hands, only just noticing that he'd left it behind. 'I didn't even realise,' he said. 'I must have left it by the pool.'

'I'll go and get it for you.'

'No,' he said suddenly. 'I don't need it any more.'

'I think that's something your doctor should decide.'

'My doctor's not here, Carly.' He began to walk across the room towards her. And suddenly he was walking completely unaided, consciously free of support for the first time in months and he gave a low shout of laughter at the sense of exhilaration he felt. 'But you are.'

'I'm not qualified to give medical advice.'

'I don't need any medical advice,' he said, his shadow falling over her face as he came to a halt right in front of her. 'At least, not for what I'm planning to do.'

'Oh? And what's that?' she questioned lightly, as if

there weren't a hundred dark undercurrents flowing between them. As if her darkened eyes weren't unconsciously begging for him to kiss her.

'You're an intelligent woman, Carly. Don't ask questions to which you already know the answer.'

Her eyes were huge as she looked at him, but they were wary, too. She shook her head and he could see the rippling movement of her throat before she spoke, as if she were trying to swallow something which was stuck there. 'I don't know what you're talking about.'

'Oh, please. Don't *pretend*, Carly. You're too clever for that. Unless you're trying to deny the chemistry which has been building for weeks, or that you want to kiss me as much as I want to kiss you. You're driving me out of my mind with frustration, and I have the feeling that if I don't do something about it soon, then one or both of us are going to go crazy.'

Carly was trembling as he reached out and coiled his fingers around the back of her head and the unthreatening nature of the gesture meant that she found herself sinking into it. And once she had let him touch her, she was lost. She tried to think logically. To be that person who was good at science. To concentrate on the million reasons why this shouldn't happen. But all she could think of was how mesmerising it felt to have the tips of his fingers rubbing at her scalp like that, as if he was giving her an impromptu head massage. As if the tables had turned and he was the one now in charge. Oh, yes. He was definitely the one in charge. She could feel her eyelashes fluttering and the lids suddenly felt unbearably heavy. 'We can't do this,' she said desperately.

'Why not?'

'You know why not. I work for you—'

'I'll give you dispensation, starting from now.'

'That's not funny.'

'It wasn't intended to be funny. I've never been more serious.'

He was still stroking her scalp and Carly knew she should pull away before it was too late. *So why didn't she?* Because she liked his fingers in her hair and his black eyes looking at her like that? Or because all those feelings she'd thought were dead were now flickering to life inside her, and she was afraid to move in case they disappeared again?

Their eyes met and held.

'We can't,' she said again, more desperately this time.

'Stop fighting it. We can do any damned thing we like,' he said harshly as he pulled her face towards his.

But unlike his words, his kiss was soft. Soft and insistent and innocent enough to make her relax, until she felt her lips parting through no conscious effort of her own. She felt the flicker of his tongue against the roof of her mouth and, automatically, she coiled her arms around him, clinging to him with an eagerness which surprised her. She had watched him and wanted him for weeks and at last she was touching him.

And suddenly she was consumed by her need for him. The past became nothing but a desolate place which was retreating by the second. The present was here. Now. And she wanted to live every single second of it.

Did she make some kind of sound? Was that why he lifted his head to stare down at her with a gleam of

pleasure in his black eyes? His mouth gave a flicker of
a smile before he lowered his head towards hers again.

She didn't know how long that second kiss lasted,
only that it was underpinned with a new sense of purpose. He levered her up against the wall, pushing the
flat of his hand above her head for support, while with
the other he stroked her face. And not just her face.
His fingers moved down over her neck, drawing tiny
little lines along her collarbone, and she shivered in response. Next thing she knew, they were skating down
over her breastbone and she moved her body restlessly.
She heard him give a soft laugh as he pulled at the zip
of her uniform dress. She felt that first little tug of re-
sistance before he slid it down to her waist and the material parted easily, leaving her breasts to slide free.

She felt the rush of air which cooled her skin and
heard his muffled murmur of appreciation as he drew
away to look at her. He didn't seem to notice her func-
tional bra—nor to care that it was chosen with support
rather than frivolity in mind. There was nothing but
dark intensity on his face and a look in his eyes she'd
never seen there before.

'Perfecta,' he uttered, cupping one breast in the
palm of his hand, as if he was weighing it. His thumb
flickered across one nipple and, despite the barrier of
the bra, her puckered flesh tightened in a rush of pure
pleasure.

'Oh!' she gasped.

'Still think we "can't"?' he mocked.

She couldn't think of anything except the way he
was making her feel. His hand had slithered down to
her dress and he was rucking it up. Her body felt hot.
Her skin was suddenly too tight for her body and her

pounding heart too big for her chest. She closed her eyes, hardly daring to breathe for fear that he would come to his senses, and stop.

But he showed no signs of stopping. On the contrary, he was now pushing her towards the narrow massage bed, which lay like a sacrificial table at the centre of the room, and she felt her bottom collide with the soft, leather surface. Instinctively, she dug her fingers into his neck, terrified that she was going to slip to the floor and take him with her and shatter all the sensual magic. Momentarily, his mouth curved into a hard smile.

'Relax,' he murmured. 'I wouldn't be doing this if I didn't think I was capable of following through.'

The sexual boast broke into the sweet fug of desire which had descended on her and the magic began to dissolve in a way which was chillingly familiar. Her body went from heated need to icy revulsion in one sobering second. Only this time she wasn't with some sleaze of a guy at a party, who was still smarting with rage at another woman's rejection. This was Luis.

Luis her boss.

Luis who bedded actresses and supermodels.

What was she doing?

Panic swept into her mind like the dark beat of flapping wings. With all the detachment which her scientific brain was capable of, she pictured the scene as others might see it. As Simone might see if she walked into the massage room. Carly with her uniform open to the waist—her breasts hanging out and her legs parted. And her billionaire boss with his hand up her skirt, eager to slake his frustration on the most accommodating woman to hand. Despite her lacklustre looks and lowly job, he had decided that he wanted to have sex with someone as unlikely as *her*. Someone who just happened to be in the right place at the right time.

Or the wrong time.

Appalled at herself, she pushed at his chest with the flat of her hand. 'No!' she said.

Perhaps he thought she was playing a game. As if she had suddenly decided to adopt the role of tease, because he dipped his head to brush his lips over hers. 'Oh, Carly,' he said, very softly. 'Just shut up and kiss me again.'

But the kiss was no longer working. It no longer felt like magic. Her mind was playing tricks with her as she started to remember that other kiss. The forced entry of an alien tongue, and then…then… The blood in her veins was now so icy that it hurt.

'No,' she said again, splaying the flat of her hand over his chest.

And maybe this time he realised she meant it. That her words weren't just the flutter of someone saying something because they felt they should. She could see surprise flickering over his face, as if nobody had ever stopped him before, and she wondered how she could have been so stupid.

Of course nobody had ever stopped him before.

She slid down from the massage bed but her fingers were shaking as she yanked the zip of her dress back up and tugged her skirt into place.

'What are you doing?' he demanded.

'What does it l-look like? I'm calling a halt to this before it gets completely out of hand.'

'I don't understand. One minute you're up for it, and the next you're acting like I'm the big, bad wolf.' His face darkened. 'I'm not crazy about women who play games. What's the matter, Carly?'

'What's the *matter*?' Moving away, she gripped onto the aromatherapy table for support, her heart racing so hard that she felt dizzy. 'Where shall I begin? With the total lack of professionalism we've both just demonstrated?'

'I told you that I was prepared to overlook that.'

Carly shook her head. She never got it right where men were concerned, did she? Maybe she was just one of those women who had *victim* or *walkover* written all over them. She looked at Luis, at his magnificent body in the faded jeans and white shirt and the way his sensual mouth seemed to form a natural, wilful pout. The wild black hair hung in tendrils around his collar and he looked just as much a pin-up as he'd ever been.

As if someone like him would seriously be interested in someone like *her* in normal circumstances. 'Well, I'm not prepared to overlook it,' she said. 'Because no woman likes to think of herself as a substitute.'

His eyes were suddenly watchful. 'What the hell are you talking about?'

'Oh, come on. This is *me*, Luis, not someone you've just picked up at a party. I've been in your life long enough to know what you're like. You're renowned as being a ladies' man. As a man who loves women.'

'Your point being?' he questioned coldly.

'That you're known for your love of supermodels and actresses. In all the time I've worked for you, I've never seen you date someone who...' *Say it, Carly. Just come right out and say it.* 'Someone like me!' she finished. 'Someone ordinary, who you're only making a pass at because I just happen to be around.'

He rubbed his finger up and down the uneven surface of a nose which had once been broken by a jealous husband, but when he spoke, his voice was curiously calm. 'You don't think I could have one of these leggy *supermodels* or *actresses* in my bed within an hour or two, if I wanted? That it might be more straightforward if I did?'

'So why don't you?' she challenged.

'Because it's you I want,' he said savagely. 'It may be wrong and it may be inexplicable, but I. Want. You. And you want me, too.'

Carly stared at him. His voice had roughened and grown hard with desire, but only one word stood out. His feelings for her were *inexplicable,* were they? He couldn't understand why he wanted her. Yet wasn't he only telling her what she already knew? That this could only ever be a one-off, which was only ever going to end in tears.

And she couldn't let it happen, no matter how much she wanted him.

She wondered how to handle it. She could storm out without any kind of explanation, but that wouldn't solve anything. From what she knew about human psychology, she guessed that flight might only sharpen his decidedly alpha traits. He might be fired up enough to hunt her down and kiss away all her doubts and she might not be strong enough to resist him again.

But if she told him the bare facts, then wouldn't that act as a natural repellent? He was a playboy, yes, but she suspected he had the double standard so common to many of his type. Didn't men like Luis see women as either good girls, or whores? If he knew the truth about her, he might *respect* an innocence which would put her off-limits to him, and stop this from happening ever again.

She met the hungry glitter of his gaze.

'Well, it's not going to happen, because I'm...'

'You're what?'

She tried to swallow down the complex mix of feelings, but suddenly it was no good and the words came spilling out of her mouth. 'I'm a virgin!' she burst out, and saw the narrow-eyed look of comprehension on his face. 'Yes! Now do you understand, Luis? I'm a freak—a weirdo—a twenty-three-year-old woman who has never had sex!'

And with that, she turned and ran from the massage room as if some deadly snake had slithered down from the mountain and was intent on biting her.

CHAPTER SIX

HE DIDN'T COME after her.

He didn't follow her to her sumptuous room over-looking the bright blue bay. He didn't push his way in and try to kiss away every one of her objections, which seemed to be diminishing as the minutes ticked by. Carly stood staring out at the sleek white yachts she could see skimming across the distant water and felt the plummet of her heart. Had she really thought he might? Hadn't she *hoped* he might?

Well, yes. If honesty was the name of the game, she *had*.

She bit her lip as doubt washed over her. Even if Luis had decided that making love to her was a bad idea after what she'd just told him, at least he could have reassured her that she wasn't some sort of freak, even if she'd used that description herself. He could have laughed it all off as behaviour which had just got out of hand. He could tell her what she already knew, that there was definitely chemistry, but that it would be a very bad idea to act on it. Then they could forget what had happened and go back to how it had been before.

She turned away from the window. Could she do that? Pretend that he hadn't kissed her breasts, or rucked up her skirt like that? Or that she hadn't enjoyed every glorious and forbidden second of it, until his boast reminded her just what kind of man she was dealing with.

Walking over to the mirror, she saw herself as Luis must have seen her. Her skin was flushed, her hair wild and her eyes didn't look like her eyes any more. She swallowed. This was a Carly she didn't recognise.

A Carly she'd thought was lost for ever. A woman who could feel desire and act on it, just like any other woman.

Throwing her discarded uniform into the laundry basket, she washed her face and changed, but as she brushed her hair and tied it back into a ponytail she wondered how she was going to fill the hours until supper. And what on earth she was going to say to Luis when she saw him again. How *could* she have told him about her virginity like that?

Her muddled thoughts were disturbed by a knock on the door and her dread was complicated by the thunder of her heart when she opened it to find Luis standing there.

But on his face wasn't the anger she had been anticipating. Wasn't that a trace of *amusement* she could read in his dark eyes?

'You have to realise,' he said drily, 'that if you want a man to run after you, it's usually better to choose a man who can actually run.'

She swallowed. 'I didn't want you to run after me.'

'Oh, but I think you did,' he said, dark eyebrows rising. 'Aren't you going to invite me in?'

'I don't think that's a good idea.'

'You have a better one? Like pretending nothing happened?'

'Nothing *did* happen.'

'No?'

She shook her head. 'No!'

His eyes narrowed. 'Look, why don't you open the door properly and let me in, so that we can have this conversation in private?'

'Is that an order?'

'If that's what it takes—then yes, it's an order.'

Carly hesitated, but she could see from his expression that he wasn't going anywhere. He wanted to satisfy his curiosity. He wanted to know *why* and at the end of the day he was still her boss, wasn't he? If they *had* to have this conversation then surely it was better without the risk of Simone or one of the other staff coming past and overhearing them.

'Oh, very well. Come in, if you must,' she said ungraciously, opening the door wider.

Luis walked into the room, his heart beating out a primitive tattoo as she closed the door behind him. He had just spent the last hour telling himself that this was a bad idea and that he should forget what had almost happened.

But he couldn't forget it. Or maybe he didn't want to. He couldn't forget the look of shame on her face as she'd blurted out her innocence to him. And he couldn't forget the way she'd made him feel when he'd kissed her. It had felt sweet and soft and powerful. But most of all it had felt dangerous, and he had always been hooked on danger.

He heard her footsteps behind him and turned to look at her. Beneath the light tan her face was tight with tension and she was chewing the inside of her lip. He found himself wanting to take that look of anxiety away. He wanted to make her melt again, only this time, he wanted to do it slowly.

'So why are you here, Luis?'

'Not to apologise, if that's what you're thinking.'

She seemed to have difficulty meeting his gaze. 'Then, why?' she whispered.

'I want to know why you spoke about your virginity like that.'

She flinched, as if his bluntness had startled her, but she treated his question in the same way she might have treated a polite enquiry about the weather. 'And how was that?'

'As if you were ashamed of it.'

Now some of her poise seemed to desert her because she stared at the floor and started rubbing her toe against the Persian carpet. There was a long pause before she lifted her head to meet his gaze. 'Why should that surprise you?' she said. 'It's not exactly something to be proud of, is it? We live in an age where we're bombarded by sexual images, and people who don't conform to the norm of having amazing sex all the time are regarded as freaks. Most women of twenty-three aren't like me.'

'You make it sound like a burden,' he said.

'In many ways, it is.'

He narrowed his eyes. 'Yet when I gave you the opportunity to liberate yourself from this state of self-imposed purdah, you turned and ran away.'

Her knuckles clenched. 'It was very generous of you to offer to "liberate" me,' she hissed. 'But I'm not some *charity case,* eager for the big stud Martinez to show me where I've been going wrong all this time.'

He raised his eyebrows. 'And where have you been *going wrong*?'

'It doesn't matter.'

'Yes, it does.'

'Please don't push it, Luis.'

'Why not? I think you should talk about it.'

And suddenly all the fight seemed to leave her. Her shoulders slumped as she sat down heavily on the edge of the bed and looked up at him. 'What do you want to know?'

'Everything.'

'That's a big ask.'

'I know it is.'

For almost a minute Carly didn't speak, trying to convince herself that he had no right to demand to know these things. Until she reminded herself that she had started the ball rolling. She had told him or, at least, told him some of it. She must have realised that some-one like Luis would demand to know the full story.

She hadn't talked about it for years. Not since it had happened. She had taken it and buried it in a dark place somewhere deep inside her. She hardly ever thought about it now, only when she awoke from those occa-sional nightmares, the ones where she was clutching her throat and unable to breathe. Did that mean that on some subconscious level it still troubled her? And mightn't it be good to get it off her chest to someone, even if that someone just happened to be her boss?

'So why, Carly?'

His soft question slid in through all her defences, and suddenly she was back there. Back with those lights flashing and music pounding and that horrible dizzy feeling, which had ended with her bent double at the bottom of a frosty garden, being sick into one of the flower beds. In the bright, sunlit bedroom of the luxury Mediterranean villa, it seemed as if it had all happened to someone else. But it had happened to her.

'I was at a party,' she said tonelessly.

'When?'

'I was sixteen, but I probably looked older. I hadn't been out of the house for weeks because of Dad, so I went with a schoolfriend to this big party on the edge of town. For once, I was wearing make-up and I'd borrowed some of my friend's clothes and I felt excited. And there was this…this guy…' She stumbled over her words, trying to present them in the fairest possible light. Because hadn't she asked herself again and again if she'd somehow *deserved* what had happened to her? Wasn't that what women always did in situations like this? 'I'd had a couple of drinks—and so had he. He'd probably had a bit more than a couple, come to think of it.'

'So he was drunk?'

'A bit,' she said. 'But mostly he was just in love with someone else. Someone who didn't want him.'

'You're not making any sense, Carly.'

'Aren't I?' she said and she gave a hollow kind of laugh. 'Okay, then, I'll spell it out for you. I was supposed to be his substitute lover for that evening, though I didn't know it at the time. I was the lucky person he'd picked to make him feel better about himself. To make him know that he was still desired. Surely you can guess what happened next?'

'Oh, I can guess, but I'd rather be told.' His mouth

had grown hard. 'You say you want to be a doctor. Well, you'll make a much better doctor if you don't cling onto the past and use it like some kind of security blanket.'

There was a pause which seemed to go on for an uncomfortably long time.

'He started to kiss me,' she said eventually, her voice a stilted whisper. 'And then to touch me. At first I liked it. I liked the way it made me feel. But then....'

'Then what, Carly?'

His words sounded distant. As if they were coming from somewhere far away.

'He...' She winced with pain and shame. She could almost feel those fingers probing her, digging into her dryness and telling her she should have been wet. Telling her that she was frigid and useless. The clamp of those teeth was sharp on her breasts and the sound of her knickers being ripped apart seemed deafening. She had attempted to scream, but he had blotted out the scream with the vodka-soaked slick of his mouth. 'He...' Her voice shuddered to a halt as, wordlessly, she shook her head.

'*Raped* you?'

His appalled question broke the spell and Carly opened eyes she didn't even realise had been closed. She shook her head again. 'No. Not that.'

'But he touched you...intimately?'

'Yes.'

'Aggressively?'

'Oh, yes.'

'That's a definition of rape in many of the statute books,' he gritted out and there was a dark anger on his face she'd never seen before. 'What stopped him?'

'Someone came into the room to collect their coat and disturbed us.'

'And then you called the police?'

She didn't answer, not straight away, and in a way wasn't this the bit she was most ashamed of? That she had succumbed to pressure and other people's expectations and allowed them to take control of the situation.

'No. I decided against it.'

'You decided against it?'

'That's what I said.'

There was a split second of a pause. 'Do you want to tell me why?'

Carly met his eyes and their dark light washed over her. Dark light was a contradiction in terms, wasn't it? But that was what she was getting from him. And it was disarming. It was like a deep bath at the end of a long day. Like holding out your cold hands in front of a blazing fire.

'What stopped you from reporting it?' he said.

'My mother did,' she said baldly.

'Your *mother*?'

'She said it would be impossible to prove, that it would be his word against mine, and she had a point. He was insanely rich and well-connected, and could have hired the best defence lawyers. I was just an ordinary girl with a sick father and no money. I wouldn't have stood a chance. My name would have been mud. It would have been just one more thing to add to the stack of dark things which were building up at home. And it wasn't as if he actually *raped* me.'

'But what about the person who came in to collect their coat? Couldn't they have been called as your defence if they witnessed the attack?'

She gave a bitter laugh. 'It was a friend of his,' she said, 'who described it as "horseplay".'

For a moment he winced, as if her pain were his pain. *'Cabrón,'* he bit out, his eyes darkening as he walked over to the bed and sat down beside her.

Carly tensed, but the arm he placed around her shoulder felt protective, not seductive. Although she guessed that in some way it *was* seductive. He seemed to represent safety and she'd never really had that before. She wanted to lean against him and drink it in, but she forced herself not to. She had learnt to stand on her own two feet and she didn't need to lean on anyone, but, even if she did, it certainly shouldn't be Luis, because he was the antithesis of safe. Luis was all about danger.

'So that's when you started sublimating your femininity,' he said slowly.

'I don't know what you're talking about.'

'Oh, I think you do.' He nodded, as if something was suddenly making sense to him. 'That must have been when you started scraping your hair back into that damned ponytail, which means nobody ever gets to see it. Probably around the time when you stopped wearing clothes which might flatter you, or the make-up which most women your age wear. You must have thought that if you didn't draw attention to yourself then you wouldn't attract the wrong kind of attention. That by being invisible, people would look through you rather than at you, and it wouldn't ever happen to you again.'

His perception was unsettling and Carly could feel the sting of tears at the backs of her eyes. But she blinked them away, because to break down and cry in front of him would be the final humiliation. 'You think that suddenly you're qualified to act as some kind of amateur shrink, just because I've told you my sob story?'

'It's not a sob story, Carly. It's the truth. And I want to help you.'

'Well, I don't want your help,' she said, pulling away from his grasp and staring out at the terrace, where a fat bee was disappearing into the scarlet trumpet of an hibiscus flower.

'You might not want my help.' His voice was quiet. 'But you want me.'

Forcing her attention away from the pollen-brushed bee, she jerked her head round to look at him. Suddenly she realised that she was sitting on a bed next to him and she shouldn't be. She shouldn't be within six feet of him. And she definitely shouldn't be staring into his eyes like that and losing herself in their dark luminosity. 'No, I don't,' she whispered.

'Then try saying it as if you mean it.' His mouth flickered into a hard smile. 'Except we both know you can't.'

'I can't believe you're saying this. Do you really think it's…*acceptable*…' her voice shook '…to start talking about desire, in the light of what I've just told you?'

'Yes,' he said fiercely. 'Absolutely I do. What happened to you was bad, and the guy who took advantage of you was a piece of scum, but it happened a long time ago and you can't let it write the script for the rest of your life. Sex isn't *wrong,* Carly. It's natural. It's one of the greatest pleasures in life and you're missing out on it. Don't you see that?'

His fierce words were impossible to brush aside and

suddenly Carly realised that she felt better for having told him. She felt lighter—*cleaner*. As if she'd scrubbed years of grime away from her skin and stepped out into the sunlight.

And Luis had been the catalyst for that.

She stared at him. 'I'm wondering where we go from here,' she said. 'Do you think we can we go back to how it's been before?'

'Possibly.' He took one of her hands in his and turned it over, studying her palm as if he was examining her lifeline, and when he looked up again there was a question in his eyes. 'But I don't want to. And neither do you. Not really.'

He had lifted his fingertips to her face and was tracing a feather-light path down over her cheek and Carly had to resist the urge to close her eyes, because it felt so *right* to have him touching her. She swallowed as his thumb moved across the cushion of her bottom lip and suddenly it began to tremble.

'Luis,' she said, but it came out in a way she didn't recognise. As if she was making a protest without really meaning it.

And he smiled, as if he had just won a battle she hadn't even realised they were having, before lowering his voice. 'Tell me something, Carly. Are you saving your virginity for the man you will one day marry?'

His blunt question shook her out of her dreamy state and she blinked at him in surprise. 'That's a strange question to ask at a time like this.'

He shook his head. 'It's exactly the right question to ask because I need to know what's important to you.'

She wanted to tell him that she wasn't sure she could answer coherently when his thumb was rubbing her lip like that, but she didn't want him to stop. 'Then no. The answer is no. I wasn't *saving* it for anyone. It's not like money you put in the bank. It's just that I'd never met anyone who—'

'Makes you feel the way I do?'

His murmured assertion should have sounded unbearably arrogant, but it didn't. Because that was the truth, too. She shook her head. 'No.'

He leaned forward and replaced his thumb with his lips, brushing them over hers in a way which made her tremble even more.

'I want to be your lover, Carly,' he breathed. 'I want to show you how to enjoy pleasure, for pleasure's sake. You have helped heal me—so let me now heal you.'

'S-sexual healing?' she questioned unsteadily.

'If you like.'

She drew her head away from his. 'It's…it's a crazy idea.'

'Why?'

Why?

A million reasons flooded into her head. Sex wasn't supposed to be something you just *did*, was it, like some cold-blooded experiment carried out in laboratory conditions? Sex was supposed to be about passion. A lot of people thought it was only about *love*.

She looked into the hard gleam of his eyes and suddenly she understood what that journalist had meant when she'd written that article. His face was rugged and beautiful, yes, but his eyes really did look *empty*. As if you could jump into their black depths and never reach the bottom. And surely only a fool would choose to be intimate with a known heartbreaker like Luis Martinez.

Yet the detached, scientific side of her personality was impressed by his honesty. He wasn't spinning her lies by making promises he couldn't fulfil. He was offering to teach her the art of sex.

She imagined turning him down. Of going back to being the woman she'd been before. Carly the invisible. Carly the scared. But she hadn't felt invisible when he'd kissed her. Or scared. She had felt three-dimensional and desired—properly desired—for the first time in her life. Hadn't it come as a huge relief to discover that the creep at the party hadn't destroyed those kind of feelings for ever? That deep down she was still a functioning woman, with a woman's needs.

And didn't she want that? Wasn't it time for her to truly leave the past behind?

'So how would it work?' she questioned casually, but maybe her nonchalant tone didn't fool him because she saw him smile in response. '*If* I were to agree.'

'I hadn't actually given much thought to that,' he said. 'I thought that might have been a little...*presumptuous.*'

'I suppose it might.' But Carly didn't care about *presumptuous*; she just wanted him to begin. She wanted him to kiss her again and make her feel the way she'd done before. She wanted his hands on her breasts and in her hair. She wanted to know what would happen if that low ache deep inside her was allowed to keep building and building...

Letting her eyelashes flicker to a close, she elevated her chin, silently inviting him to kiss her. But his soft laugh made her eyes snap open.

'Oh, no,' he said softly. 'This is not how I intend for your seduction to happen, *querida*. It will not be here, or now. It will not be fast and furious with us grappling on your bed like a couple of greedy teenagers. It will be a slow and considered feast. A banquet guaranteed to satisfy all the senses, rather than something devoured without tasting properly. I want you to be sure that this is what you really want.' His lips curved into a slow smile. 'And when you do, there will be no holds barred.'

She wanted to contradict him. To listen to the small part of her brain which was questioning her own sanity. But the heat in her blood had other ideas and so she shrugged, as if it were no big deal. 'So...'

'So.' He stood up very quickly, as if he didn't quite trust himself to sit chastely beside her on the bed any more. 'You will meet me on the upper terrace at eight o'clock. I will instruct the chef to prepare something cold and dismiss the staff for the rest of the night. We will not be disturbed.'

A shiver of anticipation whispered over her skin.

'I should like you to wear a skirt or a dress and to leave your legs bare,' he continued. 'Oh, and make sure your hair is down. I don't want to see you with that damned ponytail.'

'Anything else?' she questioned, her sarcasm hiding the sudden hurt she felt.

'Yes. And this is probably the most important provision of all.' He looked down at her, his shadow suddenly enveloping her like a dark cloak. 'I need you to promise that you won't fall in love with me. I can do sex—very good sex, as it happens—but I don't do love. Do you understand, Carly? Because I mean it. And if you think this is going to end in wedding bells and clouds of confetti, then you're mistaken.'

Carly was in no doubt that he meant it. She could tell from the implacable note in his voice and the steely glint of his eyes. And while his arrogance was shocking, once again she couldn't help admiring his honesty. Luis would never spin her any impossible dreams, would he?

'There's no need to worry about that,' she said. 'Believe me, I have no desire to waft up the aisle in a cloud of tulle and then listen to a load of boring speeches. I'm going to be a doctor, not a housewife, and I'm certainly not in any danger of falling in love with you, Luis. I know you too well.'

He smiled. 'That's what I like about you, Carly. I like your clear-headed way of thinking.'

But as Carly looked into the hard glitter of his eyes she suddenly found herself wondering if she had taken on more than she could handle.

CHAPTER SEVEN

CARLY BECAME PROGRESSIVELY more nervous as she got ready for dinner that night. Her mouth had grown dry and her hands were trembling and she thought seriously about abandoning the whole idea and telling Luis it had all been a horrible misunderstanding. Could she really go through with losing her virginity to a man like him, who had laid out his exacting guidelines from the start? She thought about what he'd said about her appearance, about what she should and shouldn't wear for her seduction. He had been positively *brutal* in his assessment of her physical appearance, hadn't he?

Yet he'd said nothing which wasn't true. Dull anonymity had been her aim and it seemed she had achieved exactly that. But while fading into the background had worked brilliantly when she'd been his housekeeper, he had told her quite emphatically that it was inappropriate for her new role...

As what?

His lover?

She licked her lips as she pulled the scrunchy from her hair.

Or just someone who was jumping in way out of her depth?

She soaked in a long bath, then hunted around for something suitable to wear but that made her feel even worse. She had convinced herself that she didn't *care* about pretty clothes, but as she surveyed her plain skirts and T-shirts she wished that someone would suddenly appear with a magic wand and transform her wardrobe into something frivolous and...*pretty*.

She did the best she could, but it wasn't easy for someone who had become a stranger to titillation. She had no idea how to primp herself to look good and gain a man's attention. She hadn't worn make-up in years, and her only jewellery was a tiny pearl on a gold chain, which her granny had given her. She fastened it around her neck with still-shaky fingers, but when she surveyed her completed image in the mirror she knew she couldn't go through with it.

Her mother had been right all along. You really couldn't make a silk purse out of a sow's ear. What would Luis say when he saw her with her scrubbed face and her cheap clothes and a pair of sandals which were currently showcasing her unmanicured toes? How could she possibly trot down to the terrace like some sort of prize pony and prepare to give him her virginity?

She began to pace the room, but that only increased her paranoia. What if she phoned him and told him she'd changed her mind? He might be irritated, yes, but he would understand. *Wouldn't he?* He might even be relieved.

But still she hesitated as she walked over to the bed, where her cell phone sat on the table beside it.

What would she say?

A soft knock on the door was followed by someone

opening it and suddenly Luis was walking into the room. His face was dark with question as his narrow-eyed gaze swept over her.

'Have you started walking in without being invited?' she said.

'I thought I'd better come and find you,' he answered. 'But judging from the expression on your face, your no-show on the terrace might indicate something more than your usual poor timekeeping.'

She shook her head and suddenly she didn't bother to hide her feelings behind a wall of pretending not to care. 'Luis, I *can't.*'

He was walking towards her and she could feel the loud bashing of her heart against her ribcage. Though he was dressed down in jeans and a linen shirt, nothing could disguise the glossy patina of power which moulded itself to him like a second skin. Suddenly, he looked like the towering superstar he really was and Carly felt herself begin to shrink in comparison. *How on earth had she put herself in this situation?* What had he said about those beautiful women at the airport? *As interchangeable as the tyres I used to get through.*

Was she out of her mind to contemplate having sex with him?

He was staring down at her. He was so close that she could almost feel the warmth of his body and smell the sandalwood of his soap. She was aware that the bed was within touching distance and she felt torn now—wanting him to reach out for her and terrified of making a fool of herself if he did.

His voice was soft. 'Can't what?'

She bit her lip. 'Can't go through with this.'

'Lesson number one: expressing doubt is not the

most flattering way to greet your prospective lover. And neither is standing there with a look of horror on your face.'

'Luis, I'm serious.'

'Relax,' he said. 'And let me look at you.'

She lifted a self-conscious hand towards her collar as his gaze roved over her. The pink T-shirt was new and the plain denim skirt made her hips look less curvy than usual, but even so... 'I've got nothing particularly fancy to wear. And anyway, I certainly wasn't anticipating *this*.'

'But that's what makes you completely lovely,' he said unexpectedly. 'Your lack of calculation and your absence of expectation. Your naturalness is refreshing.'

She stared at him suspiciously. 'I thought you didn't like what I wore?'

He shrugged. 'I don't, particularly. You certainly don't make the best of yourself, but your simplicity has an appeal all of its own. Even the most hardened cynic can have his head turned by a pair of shining eyes and the glow of healthy skin. And at last you are showcasing one of your most beautiful assets.' He lifted a handful of hair and let it fall down around her shoulders. 'Your hair is the stuff of male fantasy. And right now, you are the stuff of *my* fantasy.'

'Luis,' she said breathlessly, realising that some of the tension had left her, only to be replaced by a new and very different kind of tension, and she saw from the darkening of his eyes that he felt it, too.

He moved his hands to her waist and pulled her close and her heart began thumping dangerously as she felt the warmth of his body against hers.

'Carly,' he said softly. 'Sweet, unexpected Carly.'

She didn't say anything and part of him was glad, because for the first time Luis felt the whisper of doubt, and maybe her words might have compounded that doubt. He saw the way she looked at him—all darkened eyes and parted lips. All innocence and wonder. And as he moved closer he was overcome by a wave of lust far sweeter than he had anticipated, and hot on its heels came the dark stir of his conscience.

His mouth tightened.

He must not hurt her.

He would not hurt her.

'Come here,' he said. He cupped her face with both his hands and slowly brought his head down as he began to kiss her.

At first, he kept it light and teasing—a touch of the lips so fleeting that it barely made contact, though he could taste the subtle flavour of her toothpaste and, for some reason, that drove him crazy. And then he deepened the kiss, flickering his tongue inside her mouth as he began to explore her fully clothed body, and she came to life beneath his touch.

It was the most instant and mind-blowing transformation he had ever encountered. Suddenly, she was all fire. The hands which had been lying inert on his shoulders now moved to curl possessively around his neck as he pulled her even closer.

She kissed him with a passion which took him by surprise. He groaned as she tangled her fingers in his hair and melded her pelvis against his. Her lack of guile and experience was making him feel... Luis heard the roar of his own blood. He wasn't sure *how* it was making him feel. Only that, for all his words about wanting a seasoned seduction, he was suddenly peeling off

her T-shirt with the same kind of hunger as a hormon-
ally charged teenager. Maybe even more. Because at
seventeen everything had been out there waiting for
him. Back then he had been completely entranced by
women and yet to discover just how devious they could
be. He soon found out that what you saw was never
the truth. That thick cascades of hair were usually as
false as the stories they spun you. That breasts this
large usually owed more to the skill of a plastic surgeon, than to nature.

But not with Carly. He swallowed. God, no. Carly
seemed...*real*.

He unclipped her bra and drew back as her breasts
tumbled out—the fleshy mounds pale and her nipples
the colour of cappuccino. She went to cover them up
with her hands but he halted her.

'What are you doing?'

'I know they're too big,' she said.

'Are you kidding?' He smiled. 'They are perfect.
Your nipples are exactly the right size for a man's
mouth. Shall I show you how well they would fit into
mine?'

It pleased him that she blushed as she let him remove
her hands, leaving those caramel-coloured circles bare
to his gaze. He saw her eyelids flicker as if she was
fighting something inside her and then they closed as
he bent to lick his tongue over one.

'Luis,' she moaned.

But now he said nothing; his teasing dialogue forgotten. In truth, he was in no fit state to talk. He felt
himself grow harder as he sucked at her nipples and
teased them with his teeth until she was making wild
gulping little sounds at the back of her throat. Her

denim skirt was restricting and it was with unfamiliar difficulty that he tugged it down over her hips and thighs, before it pooled at her feet. And when at last he put his hand between her legs her panties were very wet.

Gently rubbing at the moist panel of fabric, he carefully pushed her down on the bed and then drew away from her.

'Stay right there,' he commanded unsteadily.

Her voice trembled. 'You think I'm in any fit state to go anywhere?'

'You are a woman who constantly surprises me,' he said drily. 'So I wouldn't care to make a wager on that.'

Carly watched as he tugged the clothes from his body with an impatience which seemed charged with extra urgency, though his hand was completely steady as he placed a condom on the locker beside her phone.

She had expected to be daunted by the sight of seeing Luis completely naked and aroused and ready to make love, but she wasn't. The truth of it was that her starved and eager body felt nothing but *relief* as he finally dropped his boxer shorts to the floor and joined her on the bed. She could feel the rough hair on his chest squishing against her bare breasts as he kissed her. His hand skated down to her hips, his fingers slipping beneath the elastic of her panties, before sliding them down over her knees.

He kissed her breasts and he kissed her belly. He touched her intimately until she was writhing with pleasure and a hunger which had become all-consuming. Suddenly, she didn't feel like Carly any more—she felt like... Her head tipped back. She felt like a woman. A *real* woman, and suddenly the inequality of their experience didn't matter. Greedily, her fingers explored his body in a way she'd wanted to do for so long. So very long. She touched the angled bones and honed muscle. She skated her fingers over the silken surface of his skin and then she dragged her lips from his, grazing them along his jaw, before finding the warmth of his ear.

'Please,' she whispered, barely conscious of what it was she was asking for.

'Please, what?' he murmured, his fingers moving down to part her moist labia so that she jerked with pleasure. 'This?'

She supposed she must have nodded or said something, or maybe it was obvious just from the eager way she clung to him how much she wanted him. She felt him reach out for the condom and the tearing open of the foiled package sounded unnaturally loud to her highly sensitised ears. She knew a moment of trepidation as she felt him prepare himself, but then he was moving over her and she could feel the engorged tip of him pressing against her.

She looked up into his face and the weirdest thing was that the look which passed between them seemed like the most intimate thing which had happened so far.

'Luis,' she whispered.

'It may...hurt a little,' he said, his voice doing that soft and unsteady thing all over again. 'I don't know. I'll do my best to make sure it doesn't.'

And then he was easing himself into her. Slowly. Deliciously. Filling her as if her body had been nothing but an empty space, just waiting for him to fill it. It didn't hurt like the books and the stories sometimes said it did. There was a moment of acute discomfort—

but then it was gone. And that was the moment when pleasure began to swamp out trepidation and doubt and every other negative feeling and replaced them all with satisfaction, and joy.

He moved inside her. He coaxed her and teased her. He made anything seem possible. At first she thought the shimmering of something hovering on the edge of her understanding was a flicker of something impossible. But when it happened again she began to stiffen with fear that she might somehow miss it. Like closing your eyes when you were looking at a rainbow and when you opened them again it was gone.

'Relax, *querida*,' he murmured as he made another deep thrust inside her.

Perhaps it was the '*querida*' which took the fantasy one stage further, which made her believe that anything *was* possible. She was poised on the brink of something magical, reaching out for something which kept slipping beyond her reach…and then suddenly it was happening. Her body was contracting and it was all about everlasting rainbows as Luis tipped his head back and gave a helpless kind of groan.

And Carly's body seemed to splinter into a million beautiful pieces.

CHAPTER EIGHT

CARLY COULDN'T SLEEP, and in the end she gave up trying.

Slowly, she got out of a bed which was still rumpled and scented with the unfamiliar smell of sex. Looking down, she saw the indentation of the second pillow; tangible evidence that for the first time in her life she had not slept alone, and she felt her skin shivering with pleasure as she remembered.

She had slept with Luis.

She had given her virginity to the Argentinian play-boy with an eagerness which was making her blush even now.

Scooping mussed hair back from her face, she laid her palms over her hot cheeks. Because not very much sleeping had taken place, had it? It had been one long night of discovery.

She swallowed, remembering how nervous she'd been. How she'd been fretting and pacing in her bed-room, too scared to go down to supper. But somehow he had made it all okay. He had come to her room and started kissing her and, instead of being some big deal, it had just seemed to *happen*. As if it was all perfectly natural and normal, just as he'd said it should be. She had made love with Luis Martinez and he seemed to have enjoyed it just as much as she had done.

Supper had been forgotten and it had been almost ten when he had pulled on his jeans and brought back some of the neglected food from the terrace. They had eaten grapes and slithers of mountain cheese in bed, and he had opened a bottle of wine called Petrus and given a small smile when she had pronounced it 'really nice'.

And he had gone to his own room just as dawn had begun to filter through the sky in streaks of red and gold. Bending his dark head, he had kissed her and told her it would probably be easier if he wasn't there in the morning.

He was right about that, too. She knew that. It was nothing but stupidity which made her wish that he'd stayed all night; a flicker of yearning which she knew was dangerous and pointless. So she forced herself to concentrate on the practical instead, which she was good at. She told herself that no way would he want his staff to know how he'd spent the previous evening and she couldn't think of anything worse than Simone discovering him leaving her bedroom, looking tousled and unshaven. Something like that would only make her own position more difficult…though she hadn't actually given a lot of thought as to what was going to happen now.

Now that Luis had taken her as his lover.

Padding barefooted into the bathroom, she pulled on the fluffy robe which was hanging on the back of the door and knotted it tightly at her waist. She certainly wasn't going to do the whole guilt trip—not with herself and not with him. Even if it never happened again, she would always be grateful for the way he'd made her feel. He had set her free from the past. He'd made her realise that she was capable of experiencing the same kind of pleasure as anyone else.

What had he said to her before it had all happened? The one phrase which had stuck out in her mind.

I like your clear-headed way of thinking.

She knew why he'd said that. Because she'd told him she wasn't hung up on love, or marriage. Because she'd convinced him that she was able to regard this sexual experience with complete objectivity.

So why did she suddenly want to hug her arms around herself and dance around the room, while music played loudly inside her head?

The sun was higher now, turning the sea a deep shade of rose, and when she walked out onto the terrace the air felt still and clear. The house was quiet but her head and body were buzzing and for once the thought of losing herself in a few pages of quantum physics didn't appeal. She would catch up on her emails, then see what the day would bring. And if Luis had decided that one night was enough—well, she would have to accept it like a grown-up.

She logged onto her email account and found three messages from her sister. The first was titled Where are u? The second consisted of nothing but a long row of question marks, and the third announced, rather more dramatically, WHAT THE HELL IS HAPPENING?

Carly clicked onto this one first, but unusually the email wasn't peppered with smiley faces or descriptions of her sister's latest modelling jobs. For once, the message was all about Carly.

Saw a photo of your boss at Nice airport and it looked like YOU in the background. I said to Mum that nobody else would wear a T-shirt like that in the Côte d'Azur!!! Are you really in the south of France with Luis Martinez—and if so what the hell is going on?????

Carly smiled. She wondered how Bella would react if she told her the unbelievable truth. *Yes, I am here with Luis. In fact, I told him about my past and he's decided to teach me everything he knows about sex, which is fairly comprehensive as I'm sure you can guess.* Imagine drafting *that* into an email!

She clicked to reply.

Yes, it's true. I've been helping Luis with his rehab after his accident, and he decided it would be preferable if he got better in the sunshine. It's absolutely gorgeous here. Aren't I lucky? Love, Carly xxx

She hit the send button just as someone tapped on the door, but before she had a chance to answer—it opened quietly and Luis walked into the room. He was freshly shaved and his black eyes were alive with vitality and a spark of something else which already she recognised as desire.

'Hello,' he said softly as he closed the door behind him.

Carly's hand crept up to her throat as she realised that the white bathrobe was deeply unflattering and probably added at least ten extra pounds to her frame. 'I thought you'd decided that it was better not to risk being seen here.'

'Maybe I've changed my mind.'

'I haven't even brushed my teeth.'

'Then go and brush them now,' he instructed silkily. 'Because I like the taste of your toothpaste.'

She escaped into the bathroom and when she returned, it was to discover that Luis had dropped his clothes on the floor and was in her bed—completely naked amid the still-rumpled sheets.

'What are you doing?'

'Isn't it obvious?'

'But…what about the staff?'

'What about them? The only member of my staff I'm interested in is standing right in front of me, wearing far too many clothes.' He patted the empty space beside him. 'So come over here, *querida*, before I grow too impatient.'

Carly swallowed down the sudden apprehension which had risen in her throat. It would probably be better to resist him, when even now the gardeners would be arriving and the chef sending his assistant down to the markets in Nice to buy fresh fish and vegetables for the day. To tell him that this was an extremely unwise move and surely they could arrange a rather more discreet meeting later.

It would be much better.

So why was she walking towards the bed and pulling back the sheets?

And why was Luis shaking his head like that?

'No. Not yet. Lose the robe,' he instructed silkily. 'And don't tell me you're shy, not now, when I happen to know more about your body than any man on the planet.'

It was difficult to act nonchalantly when the harsh light of day was showing no mercy to her too-generous curves, but Carly did her best. 'I'm glad to see that nothing ever manages to deflate your ego,' she said, unknotting the robe and letting it fall to the floor, before quickly sliding between the sheets and colliding with his warm, hard body.

'Not just my ego,' he said as he guided her hand to his groin and bent his head to kiss her. 'Mmm. Toothpaste.'

He kissed her until she relaxed. Until her body had begun to call out to her with a hunger which was already familiar and impossible to ignore. And again, Carly was lost as her whole world became centred on what he was doing to her.

She closed her eyes as he cupped her breasts, his palms rolling rhythmically over her peaking nipples. She squirmed with pleasure as he moved over her, parting her thighs and positioning himself there. She gasped as he entered her with one long, slow thrust, her head tipping back as he began to move inside her. Her fingertips roved over his skin, greedily exploring all the different textures, from the hard, hair-roughened thighs to the silken expanse of his broad back.

She wanted to revel in this feeling of intimacy and pleasure, but her orgasm rushed upon her with the speed and power of a freight train crashing over eggshells. She heard him cry out almost immediately, that strangely vulnerable moan he made as he shuddered into stillness inside her. She cradled her arms tightly around him and snuggled up close, her head resting comfortably on his shoulder.

And then she fell asleep.

When she awoke he had gone, just as he'd done last night, and when she appeared at the breakfast table, Simone informed her that Monsieur Martinez had gone into Nice on business and she didn't know when he'd be back.

The morning seemed to pass like an eternity and Carly found it impossible to concentrate on anything. He didn't return until late in the afternoon and by the time he came to her room to find her, she was convinced he was regretting what had happened.

'Where have you been?' she blurted out, before she could stop herself.

He raised his eyebrows.

'I'm sorry. It's none of my business.'

He gave a short laugh as he pulled her into his arms. 'I needed space, and I needed to do some business without any distractions. But now I find I'm in the mood for distraction.'

He pushed her down onto the bed, removing her clothes with almost clinical efficiency, and as Carly looked into the hungry gleam of his black eyes she guessed that this was a demonstration that sex could be fast and furious, too.

Afterwards, she lay there feeling slightly dazed, drawing little circles on his skin and realising that he knew far more about her than she did about him. And in her dreamy post-orgasmic state, she felt she could ask him anything.

'Luis?'

'Mmm?'

She turned onto her side, propping herself up on her elbow so that spills of hair fell down over her shoulders and covered her breasts. 'Have you never wanted children of your own?'

His mouth tightened as he brushed away the curtain of hair to expose her nipple. 'Another word of advice,' he drawled. 'As a post-coital topic, fatherhood isn't really a winner. Be warned, any dreamy little references to babies is likely to send any future lovers running off into the sunset. They might worry that you're starting to fall in love with them.'

She ignored the stab of disappointment that he seemed totally without sexual jealousy; she didn't think *she* could have been quite so casual about any future lovers he might have. But she stuck to her guns. To consider the question logically, as she had been taught. 'You think a question about children automatically means I'm falling in love with you?'

'I know the signs,' he drawled.

'Well, in my case you are misreading them,' she said coolly. 'I'm interested purely from a human interest point of view. Most men want to recreate—it's in their DNA. Continuation of the human race, that sort of thing. You've built up a massive empire, you're a millionaire many times over, surely you want your own flesh and blood to inherit all that?'

Luis rolled onto his back and stared up at the ceiling. It was a topic he usually snapped the lid on—fast. He didn't like women probing and it bored him when they searched for feelings which weren't there. He wondered why was she was spoiling things by asking him this kind of question.

Yet Carly wasn't looking for the kinds of things which most women wanted, was she? A question he'd normally consider loaded, and which he would deflect with ease, sounded different when it came from her. With Carly, he had laid out all his ground rules from the start. She knew what he would or wouldn't tolerate. She was ambitious for a career, not marriage, and perhaps that was why he felt relaxed enough to answer her question.

'I think the human race will survive very well without any miniature versions of Luis Martinez,' he said drily.

'Any particular reason?'

'I can see that you're going to make a very good doctor.' He turned his head to meet her eyes. 'Since you're very persistent with your questions.'

'You're stalling.'

'So I am.' His eyes gleamed. 'What do you want to know?'

'Oh, I don't know. About your life. Where you grew up. Why you're so adamant you don't want children.'

He linked his fingers together and put them behind his head, allowing a slow stream of memories to pass through his mind. 'I grew up on a big ranch outside Buenos Aires,' he said. 'Where we farmed cattle in great rolling sweeps of land with the biggest skies you ever saw.'

She wriggled a little closer. 'We?'

'Me, my mother and my father. We were quite unusual in that there weren't loads of children running around. But I guess that made us especially close as a family, and my parents...' He shrugged. 'Well, they adored me, I guess. The farm was hugely profitable, my father had business interests in the city which were equally successful...'

'So everything was lovely?' she prompted as his voice faded away.

'For a while.' He looked at her and when he spoke again his voice had grown hard. 'My mother had a friend called Amelita, and she and her husband had

a son about my age. Vicente was like the brother I'd
never had, and the two families used to do everything
together. We skied in the winter and hit the beaches in
the summer. We ate Christmas dinner around the same
table. We were all like one great big unit.'

He paused, not sure why he was telling her all this.
Not sure that he should. Was it because she had shared
her secrets with him and something was telling him
that he needed to redress the balance? Or because he
suspected that she was insistent enough to keep probing if he didn't?

'Go on,' she said.

He stroked her hair. 'I developed a love of speed
early on and my father built a small go-kart circuit on
our property for me to practise on, which was pretty
innovative at the time. Vicente and I spent hours bomb-
ing around that dusty trail. Then at sixteen, I moved
away to the San Luis province so that I could use the
famous Potrero de los Funes track. I didn't come home
that often, but when I did, things seemed different. I
thought that my father and Amelita had grown...close.
Closer than was right. I used to see the way she looked
at him. The way she dressed around him. For a while I
managed to convince myself that I must be mistaken,
because I *wanted* to be mistaken. And she was my
mother's best friend.'

He swallowed. His own sexual experience had been
at a fledgling stage—he was barely out of single fig-
ures himself at that time. But he had been hit on often
enough to realise that his mother's best friend really
was coming onto his father. He remembered trying to
talk to him about it and being shocked by the old man's
sudden spurt of rage; his gritted threat to punch his

only son. He had allowed himself to be placated by the furious denials which had followed, because hadn't it been easier that way, even if deep down he had known the words to be lies?

'And then one afternoon I rose early from my siesta,' he said slowly. 'The day was so still and so hot that I felt I could hardly breathe. I walked outside, seeking the shade of the trees, but it was no better there. There was no relief to be found anywhere. And then I heard a sound, something which seemed out of place in my home. I found myself walking towards the summer house and that is where I found them. My father and Amelita...'

Carly's hand flew over her mouth so that her words came out muffled. 'And were they...?'

'Not quite,' he said, repressing a painful shudder of recall. 'Amelita was in the middle of some kind of tacky striptease at the time, while my father...' His voice shook with rage. 'And all this while my mother slept in the house nearby. It was the lack of respect as much as the betrayal which made me want to kill him.'

He stopped speaking and she didn't say anything. She moved her hand to his face to try to comfort him, but he shook it off as if a fly had landed there.

'It all came out, of course. These things always do,' he said. 'I suspect Amelita made sure that it did, since my father was one of the richest men in Argentina. And predictably, it blew everyone's world apart. My mother never really recovered. She felt the sting of the double betrayal, of being cheated on not just by her husband, but by her best friend, too. She moved out of the ranch and bought a place in the city, but she stopped eating.

Stopped caring, really. She used to stay in her rooms, afraid to leave, haunted by the fact that people would be looking at her and mocking her. Didn't matter what I did or what anyone said, she refused to listen, and she died just three years later.'

'Oh, Luis. I'm so sorry,' she whispered.

He shook his head as he tried to hold back the tide of dark emotion which he had battened down for so long. But for once in his life, it kept on coming and some instinct told him that maybe it was better this way. He had never told anyone, and if he told someone who ultimately didn't matter, then couldn't he loosen some of his own dark chains? Because one thing he knew was that Carly would never go anywhere with this. He could see the makings of the doctor in her already, not just in her firm but ultimately gentle care of him, but in a moral compass, which was rare. She would not need to swear the Hippocratic oath to have her discretion guaranteed.

'You want to hear the rest?' he questioned bitterly. 'Because it doesn't make for a particularly happy bedtime story.'

'I want to hear it,' she said.

'The husband of my father's mistress also felt humiliated by the public laughing stock he'd become, but he sought a different remedy than the self-imposed isolation of my mother. He took what he thought was the only honourable way out. He put a revolver to his head and blew his brains out. It was Vicente who found him.'

She drew in a deep, shuddering breath. 'Oh, Luis.'

He stared up at the ceiling again. 'So there you have

it. Now do you see why I don't believe in family life and happy ever after, Carly?'

There was a pause. He could almost hear her thinking aloud as she sifted through all the possible words and tried to find the right ones to say. Except that there were no right words. He knew that.

'Not...really,' she said tentatively. 'I mean—those were terrible things which happened, but they weren't really anything to do with you, were they? None of that was your fault. Just because of the way your father behaved, doesn't automatically follow that you would do the same. Infidelity and betrayal aren't hereditary, you know.'

He turned to look at her again. He could see empathy clouding her eyes and he couldn't help admire her kindness, as well as her perception. Because Carly was clever, he realised. Clever enough to realise that there was more.

'But I've lived a life on the racing circuit,' he said simply. 'And I've seen what it does to men—especially to champions.'

'What do you mean?'

He shrugged. 'There are characteristics which make men like me succeed. We're driven—literally—by the desire to win. We spend years in pursuit of the elusive perfect lap and when we achieve it we want to repeat it, over and over again. There aren't many of us at the top, but when you get there you realise that it is both a seductive and a dangerous place to be. People revere you. They want a piece of you. Especially women.'

'Women who are *"as interchangeable as the tyres I used to get through"*?' she quoted quietly.

'Exactamente.' His face tightened. 'I have seen the

strongest marriages break down under the strain of all the temptations the sport has to offer. When the adrenaline is flowing and some sexy little creature puts on a skirt the size of a handkerchief and presses her breasts against your windshield, most men can't say no. Most are arrogant enough to feel they *don't have to* say no.'

'So.' She sat up, folding her arms across her naked breasts. 'What you're really saying is that world champions get given so much forbidden fruit, that they find it impossible to exist on normal fare like most normal people?'

He shrugged. 'If you like.'

'But you no longer race for a living, Luis,' she said. 'So how does that even apply?'

'My father wasn't a racer,' he said stonily. 'He was a farmer who'd been married for twenty-one years. Who used to tell me that my mother was his soulmate.'

'So what you're really saying is that you think men generally are incapable of fidelity?'

'That's one way of looking at it,' he said slowly. 'Yes. I think that's right.'

'So men really are the weaker sex?'

'Or the more realistic?' he countered coolly. 'How can two people possibly make promises of fidelity to each other, when they have no guarantee of keeping them?'

Carly didn't respond. His words had made her heart sink, even though she knew she had no right to be hurt by them. He had never promised her anything other than what he'd just given her, had he? In fact, he had explicitly warned her off the very things he had just been talking about. She pushed back the sheet and got out of bed. 'I need to use the bathroom,' she said.

She walked across the bedroom and closed the bathroom door behind her, though maybe you were supposed to leave it open in circumstances like these? She realised what a novice she still was and how little she knew about how to interact with a man on such an intimate basis. She told herself that she couldn't complain about his honesty, just because he was telling her something she didn't want to hear. She had to accept this on the terms he had offered her, or she would end up getting her heart broken.

She flicked cold water over her face and practised a few convincing-looking smiles in the mirror so that when she walked back into the bedroom she felt almost calm. At least, until she saw him sitting propped up against the bank of snowy pillows, looking very dark and rugged.

His black eyes seemed to pierce through her still-tender skin. 'Would you like to go out for lunch tomorrow?' he questioned.

'Lunch?' She blinked, because she had assumed that they would assume their normal boss/employee relationship during daylight hours. She had thought that they would be together only in bed. 'You mean—not here?'

He gave the faint flicker of a smile, as if her lack of imagination had amused him. 'No, not here. There is a whole beautiful coastline out there, *querida*—with some of the most famous restaurants in the world just waiting to be eaten in. There are beaches and mountains and tiny villages which are like stepping back in time. And since this is your first visit to France, I think it's time I showed you some of them.'

'But…I thought you'd decided it was best if we weren't seen together?'

'And maybe I've changed my mind.' His mouth tightened. 'I don't live my life trying to please other people, and neither should you.'

CHAPTER NINE

HE TOOK HER to Juan-les-Pins, to a restaurant on a beach, where he was recognised immediately. But Carly was still too busy thinking about what he'd told her to take much notice of the heads turning to watch them as they walked over the sand-covered boards to a table which looked directly over the lapping blue waves. She thought about his sad upbringing and the conclusions he'd drawn. Conclusions which had only been compounded by his championship status in the glamorous sport of motor racing.

He didn't think that men were capable of fidelity.

It had been a bald statement to make to someone you'd only just seduced and the message had been plain, even for someone as naïve as her. He was warning her off. Telling her to keep this bizarre liaison in the right place and not start building any fantasies. Because he wasn't stupid. He must guess that being sexually awoken by a man like him would be powerful enough to turn the head of any woman, no matter how much she protested that she wasn't looking for love or marriage.

They ordered shellfish salads, and iced lime juice flavoured with coconut, and Luis devoured his food with a voracious appetite before noticing that she wasn't doing the same. He put his fork down and looked at her, dark eyebrows disappearing into the tangle of his dark hair.

'Lobster not to your satisfaction?'

She prodded at the pink flesh with her fork and forced a smile. 'The lobster's lovely.'

'Is that why you're not eating any of it? Or is it because you're upset about what I told you yesterday?'

'I'm not *upset*. I'm grateful you felt you could be so honest with me. I'm just feeling a bit…'

He put his glass down. 'A bit what?'

She shrugged. 'Nothing.'

'Tell me.'

'Oh, I don't know. Overwhelmed, I guess.' Her gaze shot around at the tables, which all seemed to contain at least one female who looked as if she'd be at home on a catwalk. 'All the women here look amazing. As if they've spent the entire morning getting ready to have lunch in a chic restaurant, while I—'

'Look like someone who has spent the morning being ravished by a man who can't seem to keep his hands off her? Who is growing hard just by looking at her.'

'Luis,' she said faintly, her breath catching in her throat, because when he looked at her that way she just wanted to lean across the table and kiss him.

'Don't you think that any of them would prefer to be in your shoes?' His gaze dropped to floor level and the hint of a smile curved his lips. 'Or flip-flops, in this case.'

'Which were never bought with the intention of being worn in some ultra-smart restaurant on the Côte d'Azur.'

He glanced up. 'But you don't dress to be seen, do you, Carly? Or to be looked at. You dress to be invisible and to blend into the background. I thought that was the whole point.'

She could hear the white umbrella above them flapping in the light breeze which was coming off the sea. 'And I told you why.'

'But the reason no longer applies, surely? If I've set you free from your hang-ups about sex, then doesn't it follow that you might be a little more experimental about what you wear?'

'You think I look awful,' she said, in a wooden voice.

'I think those pale shades you like don't do you any favours. Your colouring is so fair that you need something more dramatic to set that off. If you don't like your appearance, then change it, but don't keep doing nothing and then complaining about it, because it's boring.' He leaned back in his chair and subjected her to a cool look. 'And there's no need to look at me quite so reproachfully. You *did* ask.'

'And you certainly didn't p-pull any punches in telling me,' she said.

'What would be the point of that? We're back to the whole question of honesty again.' He shrugged. 'Maybe it's time you stopped hiding some of your more spectacular assets and tried something new. So grab your bag.' He lifted his hand and signalled to the waiter for the check. 'I'm taking you shopping.'

'I don't like shopping.'

'You will. Like eating avocado—it's a taste which can easily be acquired.' His black eyes gleamed. 'So come quietly, *querida*, because I am still not fit enough to put you over my shoulder and carry you.'

Carly bit back a smile. When he looked at her that way, she felt powerless to do anything but agree. She didn't feel like herself any more; she had become one of those women starring in a rom-com, their lives transformed by a gorgeous man with a big wallet and a lot of attitude.

Clamping her hands down over her hair, they sped along the Croisette in Cannes in his open-top car before coming to a halt outside a screamingly smart boutique, where a burly man in uniform took Luis's car keys and went off to park for him.

But Carly's mood evaporated when she peered through the plate-glass windows at the glamorous sales assistants who were grouped around inside.

'I can't,' she whispered. 'I can't go in there.'

'I thought we'd decided to dispense with the self-deprecation?' he drawled. 'You can do anything you want. Starting right now.' He laced his fingers in hers. 'Come.'

Carly felt faint. He was holding her hand in public! He was walking inside as if he owned the place and telling one of the sales assistant that hc wanted to see her in 'hot' colours.

'Scarlet,' he said. 'And definitely flame. And I think we might try yellow, too.'

Slipping into seamless French, he spoke animatedly to the woman, using his hands to draw curving shapes of a voluptuous body in the air. They were taken to a private area at the back of the store, where he showed no embarrassment about running his fingertips along a line of frothy lace bras, or deliberating between the virtues of the thong versus the camiknicker.

Carly's throat had grown dry with nerves. She felt

big and ungainly, like a giant in a land of tiny people.
She wanted to tell him she'd changed her mind, until
she remembered that it hadn't actually been her who
had made it up in the first place. It had been Luis who
had taken command of the afternoon, overriding all
her objections and deciding what needed to be done.
And judging by his relaxed attitude as he sat on one
of the velvet sofas, sipping a tiny cup of espresso, this
wasn't the first time he'd adopted this particular role.
Maybe it was just a rite of passage for all the women
who shared his bed. Though surely the usual rangy
supermodel would do more justice to one of the delicate pieces of underwear which had been brought to
the cubicle for her to try?

But to Carly's surprise, the wispy bra was deceptively supportive and the camiknickers transformed
her rounded hips into an area of her body which suddenly looked glossy, and…inviting.

When she pulled on a yellow and white polka-dot
dress, with its full skirt and shiny patent belt, she barely
recognised the reflection which gazed back from the
mirror, but even the sales assistant gave her a wide
beam of approval.

'*Mais, elle est jolie,*' she said, on a note of surprise.

Luis gave a slow smile as Carly stood in front of
him. 'Very pretty,' he agreed, picking up a straw sun
hat with a yellow ribbon on—his black eyes piercing
into her as he placed it carefully on her head. 'Now are
you going to start believing in yourself?'

She could feel the silk next to her skin and the crisp-
ness of the petticoat beneath the fifties-style dress and,
almost shyly, she nodded.

He smiled, his gaze alighting on a stick-like mannequin clutching a plastic bucket and spade at the far end of the store. 'I think we'll take a look at some bikinis while we're here.'

Soon they were laden down with glossy carrier bags, tied with bright pink ribbons, and Carly was persuaded to keep on the yellow dress and the matching espadrilles.

'You've bought me far too much,' she whispered, her heart pounding as Luis cupped her face in his hands, causing the sun hat to wobble precariously.

'That's for me to do and for you to accept. And now I'm going to take you home and show you something which is vital to the repertoire of any lover,' he said, brushing his lips over hers in a grazing kiss.

Carly was back on that same dangerous high as they sped along the mountain road. She kept trying to tell herself that none of this had any real substance, no matter how wonderful it felt. But her heart was stubbornly refusing to listen to what her head was telling her. She had told him she wasn't looking for the things which most women wanted—that her desire for love and marriage had been eclipsed by her ambition to be a doctor. But suddenly she was discovering that falling in love with Luis would be as easy as falling off a chair.

He took her straight to his bedroom when they got back, but she barely had time to register that this was the first time she'd ever been in his room because he was closing the door and walking towards her, with a look of fierce intent on his face.

His eyes were glittering as he began to peel off her yellow dress before carefully draping it over the back of a chair. Beneath it she was wearing some of the new lingerie he'd chosen and she saw his eyes narrow as he ran his gaze over her.

'Perfecta,' he said softly.

'I'm not perfect,' she said, until she saw the expression on his face. 'Th-thank you.'

'That's better.' He gave a small nod of approval as he cupped the embroidered swell of her breast. 'Because right now, you are completely perfect to me.'

Carly would have defied a marble statue not to have responded to that statement. She tried to play down its significance as he pushed her onto the silken rug and took off her new camiknickers, before putting his head between her thighs. She stiffened at the shock of the sudden warm intimacy of his tongue licking against her moist flesh. Her fingers started tugging at the wayward waves of his hair so that he lifted his head, his dark eyes gleaming as they surveyed her.

'Luis?' she said uncertainly.

'You just have to relax,' he said. 'I'm not going to hurt you.'

Wasn't he? She closed her eyes. She suspected he was going to do exactly that. Because there were different kinds of hurt, weren't there? She'd learnt in biology that the human heart was vulnerable in so many ways.

But her mind emptied as his tongue began to explore her. She clung to him as he whispered soft incitements in Spanish. And after she had sobbed out a powerful orgasm which left her dazed and shaking, she wondered how she was going to live without this kind of pleasure.

Or live without him.

She could taste the unfamiliar flavour of sex on his mouth as he slid up to kiss her.

'Unzip me,' he said.

She swallowed. 'Are you going to corrupt me even more?'

'I'm going to try.'

He taught her how to suck him. He showed her how to pleasure herself, while he watched. He took her to Monaco and Antibes and Saint-Paul-de-Vence, where they ate lunch in a famous restaurant, where paintings by Picasso and Miro hung on the walls. They ate *plateau de fruits de mer* in Nice and drank champagne in a little place called Plan-du-Var, high up in the mountains. Back at his luxury villa he would strip off her clothes with hungry hands and their sex would have a hot, hard urgency. And when she had gasped out yet another orgasm, he would stroke her skin and murmur that her body was everything a woman's body should be. By the end of that week, Carly was reeling—her senses so exquisitely stimulated that she could barely eat or sleep.

And all she could think about was Luis.

It was as if he had entered her bloodstream like a powerful drug. Suddenly, she began to understand something about the nature of addiction. You tried something which you knew was bad for you, and suddenly you were hooked. Hooked on a feeling which even a novice could recognise as love.

But none of this was real. That was what she kept bringing it back to. It was a brief fairy tale which was bound to end. Her feelings weren't real and neither was this situation. Seduced by his skill as a lover, she had found it easy to forget she was also Luis's employee. But she was. Nothing had really changed and now she was wondering what was going to happen when they left here.

'You've been very quiet,' he observed late one afternoon as they lay beside the pool and she tried, unsuccessfully, to read.

'I'm just sleepy.'

'Don't be evasive, Carly,' he said softly. 'I thought we had agreed to be honest with each other.'

She laid the book down on her stomach, her heart clenching as she looked at him. The growing ache inside her was making her realise she couldn't carry on like this. She couldn't keep burying her head in the sand and pretending the future wasn't out there. She couldn't keep pretending that she didn't care for him, because she did. 'I've been thinking.'

'About what?'

'Well, a couple of things really.' For a moment the world seemed to hold its breath and everything around her seemed to be green and blue and beautiful. The flickering gleam of sunlight danced on the pool and the sky was as blue as those rain-smashed delphiniums she'd seen in the garden back in England. She didn't ever want to leave here, but some day soon she was going to have to. Because they were living in a protected bubble and sooner or later the bubble was going to burst. 'About what's going to happen when we go back to England.'

Luis tipped his sun hat forward, so that the shadow of the brim fell over his eyes, because somehow it was easier to know that his face was in darkness. He thought about her question and how he was going to answer it. She was only saying what had been on his mind for days, and he knew he couldn't keep ignoring his commitments elsewhere. He had a doctor's appointment in London next week and a growing stack of engagements, which he couldn't put off any longer. He had meetings in Dublin and Buenos Aires and was due to make a visit to Uruguay, to oversee the second stage of his beachside development.

But this wasn't just about the logistics of his life; it was about how he was going to deal with a situation he had created. How he was going to extricate himself from it, with as little angst as possible.

He sighed. He liked Carly. He liked her a lot, but the longer this went on, the greater the likelihood that she would get hurt, because that was what he did to women. That was his *process*. And he didn't want to hurt her. He didn't want tears or recriminations. He didn't want her to degrade herself by trying to hold onto what they could never have. He wanted her to go away and be the fantastic doctor he knew she could be.

'I don't think that's going to be a problem,' he said.

'Maybe not. But we still have to face facts, don't we, Luis? There's no point pretending that nothing's happened, is there?'

Beneath the shadowed brim of his hat, Luis frowned. What did she think had *happened*? They'd had sex. She had been unfulfilled and uptight and crying out for some kind of affection. And he had given it to her. He had set her free. His mouth hardened. *That had been the deal*.

He looked at her, at the zingy new orange and cerise bikini which moulded itself to her magnificent curves. She'd left her hair loose, the way he liked it, and her skin had now turned a deep, caramel colour.

He'd done her a favour. And he would do her an even bigger one by setting her free.

'I don't think it will be a problem,' he said coolly. 'In fact, I'm planning on leaving almost as soon as we get back to England. I have a number of global projects which will keep me occupied for most of the winter. We'll hardly see one another, probably not until the spring.'

'Oh. Oh, right.'

There was no disguising her shock or her disappointment. He could see she was doing her best to smile, but he knew enough about women to realise that behind her dark glasses those iced-tea eyes would be blinking away the first prick of tears. Because he made women cry, didn't he? That was something else he was good at. He made them long for something he was incapable of giving them. He felt a twist of something which felt like regret, but it was gone in an instant.

'And you'll soon be going off to med school, won't you? You're going to be a doctor. The best doctor in the world.'

Carly was about to tell him that it would be at least a year before she could afford to do that. Because even with the bonus he was paying her, she still needed to pay her rent and feed herself through six long years of study. For someone who hadn't done any formal education for such a long time, she wanted to give one hundred per cent of herself to her course and not distract herself with part-time jobs.

Until she realised the implications of what he was saying, and all the practical considerations about her future slipped from her mind. She realised what was happening and suddenly she felt sick. Luis was ending it. Now. As clinically as he was able to remove her clothes, he was now taking a scalpel to their relationship. He intended going off round the world and when he returned, they would act as if nothing had happened.

Because nothing had.

They'd had sex, that was all. All it was ever intended to be. Only a fool would imagine that the act of *making* love would make someone *fall* in love.

And she was that fool, wasn't she? That fool who had started looking at him with a warm glow in her heart and stupid little fantasies building in her mind.

She swallowed.

She was only that fool if she let herself be.

Quietly, she closed the pages of her book. 'That's right,' she said, hoping her face didn't betray the pain in her heart. 'I will. The best doctor in the world,' she repeated.

He glanced over at her. 'And what was the second thing?'

She stared at him. 'The second thing?'

'You said you had a couple of things you wanted to talk to me about.'

Had she? Carly blinked and then remembered. In the parallel universe of a few minutes ago when there had still been hope in her heart, she had been about to tackle a few home truths. She had wanted to tell him something she thought he needed to hear, but now she thanked heaven that his words had stopped her in time.

Dimly, she registered the sound of an approaching car in the distance, then the slamming of a door and the clatter of heels. But the momentary intrusion was dwarfed by the cold and tearing pain inside her. There was no going back—or going forward. She and Luis were finished. It was over.

She stared into his face. 'It doesn't matter now,' she said, just as Simone began to walk out from the back of the villa, closely followed by someone with long blonde hair and a tiny denim skirt. Someone who looked oddly familiar but who really shouldn't be here.

Carly blinked. It was weird. Like seeing a double-decker bus in the middle of the desert. They were both things you recognised, just that one of them was in the wrong place.

Simone's face was expressionless as she looked at Carly. 'Your sister has arrived.'

'My sister?' said Carly in confusion, as the blonde in the miniskirt came clattering towards them.

CHAPTER TEN

CARLY SAT BOLT UPRIGHT. 'Bella?' she said, her voice rising in surprise. 'What…what on earth are you doing here?' But deep down, she knew. The reason was fairly obvious and lying sprawled on a sunbed which her sister was now standing beside as she slanted him the widest smile in her repertoire.

'Well.' Bella pushed a spill of platinum hair away from her tanned face. 'You told me you were here in Cap Ferrat and I happened to be in the area—'

'What are you doing in the area?' asked Carly, but Bella was shooting her a furious *don't-ask-me-any-awkward-questions* type of look and years of deferring to her sister's wishes was a hard habit to break, especially when you were already feeling emotionally wobbly. She forced a smile. 'Luis, I'd like you to meet my sister, Bella. Bella, this is Luis Martinez, who is—'

'Ex-champion motor-racer of the world,' purred Bella. 'Yes, I know.'

'Oh, that was a long time ago,' said Luis smoothly. 'Nice to meet you, Bella.'

Bella was staring at him with open admiration as he sat up and pushed back his battered straw hat.

'I hope I'm not intruding,' she said.

'Not at all,' he answered. 'As you can see, your sister and I were just catching the last of the afternoon sun. Would you like some coffee? A drink, perhaps?'

'Ooh, a drink would be wonderful. I've been doing the most horrendous shoot all day and I'm knackered. The photographer has practically had his lens up my bum all day.' She licked her lips. 'I don't suppose you've got any champagne?'

'I think we might be able to find some.' He glanced up at his French housekeeper. 'Simone—I wonder if you'd mind...?'

'Oui, monsieur,' said Simone briskly. *'D'accord.'*

'Here, let me get you a chair,' said Luis, and he stood up, a movement which seemed to completely captivate Bella, before walking across to the far side of the terrace towards a small cluster of sunbeds and chairs which stood there.

He was barely out of earshot before Bella turned to Carly, her mouth hanging open in amazement. 'What have you been *doing* to yourself?' she demanded. 'I hardly recognised you! My God—that *bikini*!'

Carly automatically tugged at the frilly bikini bottoms. 'You don't like it?'

'I'm not sure. I don't know if it's really *you*. It certainly looks expensive. What the hell is going on, Carly? How come you're lying out here with Mr Hunky and looking like you were born to it?'

'I've been... I've been helping with Luis's rehabilitation.'

'Is that what you call it? Looked pretty cosy when I arrived, I must say.' Her eyes narrowed. 'You're not...'

On her face was an expression which Carly had never seen before. Yes, there was amazement and disbelief, but surely that wasn't *jealousy* she could read there?

Bella flicked a strand of platinum hair over her shoulder. 'You're not…*involved* with Luis Martinez, are you?'

Carly looked her straight in the eye. 'Oh, come on, Bella, can you really see someone like Luis bothering with someone like me?'

'No,' said Bella slowly. 'I suppose when you put it like *that*.'

Carly was relieved when Luis arrived back with a chair, though less pleased when Bella removed her high-heeled sandals and proceeded to glug down a glass of the pink champagne, which Simone had just delivered on a tray.

She had forgotten just how glamorous her sister was. How a similar composition of genes could have ended up making someone who looked so different from her. They both had the same amber-coloured eyes, but that was where all similarities ended. Bella's were fringed with heavy dark mascara, which made her look like some kind of startled young deer. And her figure was amazing—nobody could deny that. She had always exercised to within an inch of her life and never ate carbs after six and it showed. Oh, yes. It showed. She could see Luis looking at her, his black eyes narrowed with interest, and Carly felt her heart beginning to sink with the inevitability of it all. Of *course* he would find Bella attractive. Any man would.

She found herself accepting a glass of champagne, even though it was only five in the afternoon, and the bubbles shot straight to her head as she sipped it.

'Carly tells me you're a model, Bella,' said Luis.

'Yes, that's right. Though I still haven't made it *quite* as big as I'd like. At least, not *yet*.' Bella smiled at him from behind her curtain of white-blonde hair. 'I suppose you must know plenty of people in the industry?'

'Some.'

'Perhaps you could introduce me sometime?'

'Perhaps,' he said, non-committally.

Carly sat listening in horrified fascination as Bella ladled out abundant amounts of charm. Was Luis enjoying talking to her sister as much as he appeared to be? She watched him smile as Bella told him a story about the elastic snapping on a pair of bikini bottoms as the photographer homed in for a close-up.

'But about three men dashed over to the rescue with their beach towels!' she said.

'I'll bet they did,' observed Luis.

Carly tried to smile but her mouth seemed stuck in some kind of awful rictus. The alcohol was making her feel *disassociated*…as if she was a spectator in all this and not a participant. She saw Bella glance down surreptitiously at her watch.

'What are you guys doing tonight?' she asked casually. 'You're not free for dinner, by any chance?'

'Sorry.' Luis gave her a quick smile. 'But Carly and I have an engagement which we can't get out of,' he said, without missing a beat.

Carly blinked at him.

They did?

'But we must see you some other time,' he continued. 'Just give us a little more warning next time.' He reached down and picked up his cell phone. 'And in the meantime, I'll have my driver take you back to wherever it is you're going.'

Carly could see the flicker of annoyance on Bella's face, the sulky pout which had made her pretty face crumple. The look which always used to get their mother eating out of her hand, but which seemed to be having absolutely no effect on Luis.

She could feel cold dread building inside her as she wrapped her sarong around her to see Bella out, waiting for the outburst she knew was inevitable—and she wasn't disappointed.

'You do realise you're in danger of making a complete and utter fool of yourself?' hissed Bella as they reached the front door.

'I don't know what you're talking about.'

'Oh, please! It's written all over you, and I'm your sister—I know you better than anyone. It's obvious to me that you're sleeping with him and that you can't tear your eyes away from him. I don't blame you for that—he's pretty amazing—the only surprise is that he's chosen someone like you. I don't want to be cruel, Carly, but you need to hear the facts. And you're heading for a crash if you don't pull yourself together, because it's clear what he's doing.'

Carly felt as if she'd been carved from wood. 'And what's that?'

'He's just playing Pygmalion,' Bella continued, really getting into it now. 'Transforming his mousey little housekeeper into someone who's happy to lie by the swimming pool, bursting out of her bikini. But it's nothing but a *game* for him. Don't you see? He's been bored—and incapacitated—and it's just something to keep himself occupied. He'll drop you just as quickly as he picked you up, and then where will you be?'

There were a million things she could have said in

response, but Carly just said the words she knew were expected of her, like someone who was reading from an autocue. *And wasn't Bella only speaking the truth?* 'Thanks for the advice—I'll certainly bear it in mind,' she said. 'Maybe we can meet up when I get back to England?'

Bella stared at her as if waiting for more and when it didn't come, she spoke again. 'And hopefully you'll have seen sense by then.'

'Hopefully.'

Bella shook her head and her blonde hair swayed. 'You're a fool, Carly Conner.'

Carly watched as her sister strutted across the forecourt of the villa and climbed into the car which was waiting. She stood there for a long time after the electronic gates had closed, until there was nothing but a tiny black dot in the distance, spitting up clouds of dust as it drove down the hillside.

She walked slowly back into the house. Now what?

Back to the poolside to finish her glass of champagne and for a conversation she didn't really want to have? Yet deep down she knew she didn't have an alternative. She couldn't avoid the truth for ever.

Luis had obviously been swimming while she'd been saying goodbye to her sister. His dark hair was dripping and his olive skin was sleek with little droplets of water. He walked along the edge of the pool and stretched and suddenly it was as if her vision had cleared. As if she was able to step out of the fog of lust and love which had clouded her judgement up until now. She saw him as Bella must have seen him. Famous, gorgeous, rich. One of the great playboys who'd had dalliances with some of the most beautiful women in the world. Had she *really* thought she could stand in their shadow for long? Even if he had managed to make her feel better about herself, did she really think she was able to hang onto him? To make him *love* her?

He looked up and met her eyes.

'She's gone,' she said flatly.

'Yes.' There was a pause. 'She's nothing like you, is she?'

'Not really.' Carly forced a smile. 'Were you attracted to her?'

'Was I attracted to her?' he repeated slowly. 'Why do you ask a question like that?'

Carly reminded herself that he had taught her not to have hang-ups about sex, so didn't that mean that she should start thinking about it the way that the rest of the world did? Like some kind of casual exercise to be enjoyed. 'Most men are.'

'Are they?' he said, his tone now ominous. 'What, did you think I wanted to bed your sister, Carly? Or perhaps to live out the fantasy of taking the two of you at the same time?'

Her skin had turned to ice. 'D-did you?'

He gripped his hands into two tight fists, which hung down by the powerful shafts of his thighs, his face darkening like thunder. 'No, I did not,' he gritted out. 'Just what kind of man do you take me for?'

Carly had never seen him so angry. His black eyes were cold and his shadowed jaw looked as hard as granite. 'I know what kind of man you are,' she said. 'Remember?'

'I may have had a chequered past, but I have treated you with nothing but respect since we became lovers,' he ground out. 'I've been up front with you every step of the way and as considerate as I know how. But it seems you couldn't wait to throw it all back in my face by making veiled suggestions that I might enjoy some sordid little tryst with your sister.'

'I didn't—'

'Yes, you damned well did!' Ruthlessly, he cut across her words, advancing towards her as he had done so many times before, only this time his face was not softened by desire. This time it was hard and cold with fury. 'Maybe in the past, my behaviour might have justified you making such a negative judgement because, God knows, I've certainly been no angel. But there are *limits* to what I would consider acceptable behaviour.'

'Luis—'

'Do you really think I would be willing to replicate that kind of massive betrayal, after what I told you about my mother?'

'I'm sorry,' she said woodenly.

'Even if you could think so little of me, do you really think so little of yourself? Haven't you learned anything, Carly? That sex is not wrong and that you can be just as confident and as beautiful as you make up your mind to be.' He shook his head. 'But you're still allowing yourself to be that same scared woman underneath, aren't you? Still so eager to believe the worst about yourself. What's making you do that? Do you miss the cloak of invisibility you wore for so long? Do you find it so terrifying to be out in the real world that you're looking for some excuse to escape from it again?'

She shook her head as his accusations rained down on her like spiky little hailstones. And even though she wanted to blot out what he was saying to her, somehow she was finding it impossible. *Was* she an emotional coward, eager to think the worst about everyone because it was easier that way?

Or was he?

'Maybe you're right,' she said, pushing her hair out of her face. 'But if I'm having difficulty adapting to normality maybe that's because none of this *is* normal. I feel like someone who has jumped into the wrong end of the swimming pool. I'm out of my depth and I don't fit in. Not here. Not anywhere, really.'

'Then *find* your depth,' he said grimly. 'You're an intelligent woman. Don't tell me that you're planning to go to medical school at the age of twenty-three and then start playing the shrinking violet again. You are capable of so much, Carly. Of anything you want, if only you have the courage to reach out and grab it.'

Carly sucked in a deep breath, terrified that tears were going to arrive just when she least needed them. Because although his words were intended as an encouragement—and they were—they were also intended as a farewell. Her lips wobbled for a couple of seconds before she could trust herself to speak. 'You're very good at dishing out advice, aren't you, Luis? But I wonder how good you are at taking it.'

He gave a bitter laugh. 'Why, is this now going to become some kind of tit for tat?'

'It's more about redressing the balance than scoring points,' she said, hating the sarcasm she heard in his drawled response, hating this new distance between them which was growing bigger by the second. 'You wonder why I was so eager to jump to the wrong conclusion about you wanting my sister? Well, why shouldn't I think something like that, when you told me emphatically that you didn't think men were capable of fidelity?'

'Now you're twisting my words.'

'Am I? Or am I just putting my own interpretation on them?' She stared at him. 'Because I don't think that you do believe that, not really. I think that's just your excuse for staying away from commitment.'

'My *excuse*?' he demanded.

'Yes.' Her voice dropped to a whisper. 'I think you were hurt so badly by what happened with your parents. I think you felt completely betrayed by your mother's friend and your father and maybe even by your mother, too, for allowing herself to fade away and leave you. I think the pain was so bad that you vowed never to let anyone get that close to you again. So you didn't. You lived the life you could, the life which was expected of you, the playboy with all the different homes and all the different women. But no matter how many there were it was never enough, was it? They could never fill that hole deep inside you. At the end of the day, you were still all alone. And you always will be if you carry on like this.'

'That's enough!' he bit out and suddenly he wanted to lash out at something. Anything. He wanted to smash his fist into that marble statue on the opposite side of the terrace and see it lie in shattered pieces. He wanted stop the hurt which was enveloping him in something so dark and clammy that suddenly he couldn't breathe properly.

'You may be planning to major in psychology, but so far you're way off course!' he snapped. 'Is this supposed to make me *want* you, Carly? Am I supposed to be *grateful* for this brutal character assessment of yours? To be so in awe of your unique *insight* that I will somehow see the light? And what do you suppose will happen next, hmm? Play out the scene for me, *querida*, so that I can see it for myself. Do I now drop down onto one knee and ask you to become my wife?'

The breath dying in her throat, Carly stared at him. His caustic words were like having a blade rammed straight into her heart, but she told herself that maybe he'd done her a favour. Because hadn't this liberated her from any dormant hopes she might have nurtured, no matter how much she'd tried to deny them? Wouldn't she now be free of the fantasy that, deep down, Luis might actually *care* about her?

She shook her head. 'I may have been innocent,' she said slowly. 'But I'm not stupid. And if ever I was going to marry anyone it certainly wouldn't be a man who didn't even have the courage to look at himself properly.'

His eyes narrowed. 'You accuse me—*me*—of lacking in courage?'

She shook her head. 'Oh, I'm not talking about the kind of courage which made you put your foot down on the accelerator and take your car through a gap so tiny that most men wouldn't have seen it. I'm talking about the emotional courage to face your demons and put them to rest. Just as I've had to do. I'm sorry I said that about Bella—that was just a lingering hang-up from my own past. I had no right to accuse you of that, and I should have been strong enough to stand up to her.'

But she knew why she hadn't answered Bella's question about her involvement with Luis and why she hadn't dared stand up for herself. Because she didn't believe in the strength of what she and Luis had together. She hadn't wanted to see the pity or the glee in her sister's face when it all ended. And it seemed that her instinct had been right.

'Anyway,' she continued. 'At least this has given us the ending we both knew was inevitable, even if it hasn't been quite as amicable as we might have wanted. We both know that I can't go back to being your housekeeper.'

There was a long pause before he spoke. 'No. I guess you can't.' He flicked her a glance from between narrowed black eyes. 'So what will you do?'

She took a moment to compose herself. To behave as if they'd been talking about nothing more controversial than the weather. And didn't some stupid part of her wish that he'd fought a bit harder to get her to stay? 'I'll find another job until next September. I should have all the funds I need by then to take up my place.'

He frowned. 'But you told me that there was a deferred space available now. So in theory, you could go this September—if you had the funds.'

'Which I don't.'

'You could if I gave them to you. And before you say anything—don't. I can afford it and I want to. Please, Carly. Don't let pride stop you from taking what I am able to give. At least that way, you'll get your happy ending.'

She looked at him and thought that she wasn't the only one who could be naïve. Did he really think that this was her happy ending? She thought about the father who had betrayed him and the mother who had slowly slipped away from the world. She thought about how alone he was, amid all his trophies and homes and enough money in the bank to secure the future of the children he would never have.

And something made her say it. Made her kick her pride into touch and have the courage to declare what she'd known for a long time now. Couldn't she give *him* something, too? Not money, but something much more precious.

Hope.

'Okay, I'll take it. And I want you to know that I am very grateful to you for your…generosity, in all its many forms.' She sucked in a lungful of air but her next words still came out in a breathless rush, full of nerves and apprehension.

'But you should know something else, too, and that is that I've grown to love you, Luis. And I'm sorry about that, because I know it's the last thing you ever wanted. I didn't want to fall in love with you, but, somewhere along the way, I did. And I'm not saying it because I want anything in return, because I don't. I don't expect anything. I'm saying it because, deep down, you *are* loveable. And you need to believe that. It's not because you're sexy, or rich and not because you have a whole roomful of silver trophies and can fly a plane. You are loveable because you can be a very kind and thoughtful man, when you let yourself be. And maybe one day you might start believing in that enough to open your heart and let someone in.'

Her words died out to the sound of silence. There wasn't a flicker of response from the rigid figure who stood in front of her, though she thought she saw something flare briefly in the depths of those empty black eyes. But then it was gone, and he smiled. That easy, charming smile he could turn on like a tap, a smile which was as cool and as transparent as water itself.

'Interesting hypothesis,' he said, in a voice which sounded faintly bored. 'But you know that I'm not really interested in the emotional stuff you women are so fond of spouting. All I will say, for what it's worth, is that I think you're going to be a brilliant doctor.'

Carly stared at him. *He had completely ignored what she'd just said.* Had treated her words with contempt. Of course he had. Why should she be surprised when he was just being true to himself? He didn't *do* that emotional stuff and he never would. He'd told her that all along.

And it was that which made her quickly turn and walk towards her room, before she added to her humiliation by letting him see her cry.

CHAPTER ELEVEN

LUIS STARED OUT of the window, without really seeing the sombre grey of the November day. Why was he feeling like this? As if there were some heavy weight on his shoulders which was perpetually weighing him down? As if there were something gnawing away inside him, which he couldn't work out how to fix. And that didn't make sense. Especially since he'd kept so busy after putting Carly on a plane back to London and saying goodbye to her.

He had left the Côte d'Azur and travelled to New York, where he'd hired a personal trainer before getting straight back behind the wheel and winning a charity race in Brazil. He remembered staring at the gleaming trophy and thinking it would have been around the same time that Carly was starting at med school in England. And he couldn't shake off his feeling of disappointment that she hadn't bothered to contact him to say well done.

He knew their relationship was over—he was the one who had ended it, wasn't he?—but the race had been big news internationally, and hadn't he expected some kind of acknowledgement? If not exactly praise, then surely *something*. Perhaps a faintly mocking communication noting that he still seemed hooked on danger, but congratulating him on winning the race, all the same.

But there was nothing.

Not a phone call. Not a postcard.

Nothing.

Never had a silence seemed quite so deafening.

He remembered feeling disbelief, closely followed by a slow and simmering anger. After all he'd done for her she didn't even have the generosity of spirit to say *well done*.

He had buried himself in his work, throwing himself into every new task with the enthusiasm of someone who was just starting out in the cut-throat world of business.

But something inside him had altered. Something he hadn't expected. He found himself looking at things differently. He started making changes he suspected had been a long time coming. He sold two of his houses and a whole heap of office space in Manhattan. He realised that he preferred life without all the hangers-on and so he reduced the size of his entourage, and told Diego so. A Diego who kept looking at him from between narrowed eyes and asking was he *sure* he was okay?

Was he okay? Luis had felt his mouth harden in response to the question. Of course he was. Physically, he'd never felt better. His brush with death had made him look at the world with a sharper focus. His senses felt raw and heightened. In many ways, he had never been so grateful just to be alive.

Yet all he could think about was Carly. Carly lying naked in his arms, with her hair spread over his chest, talking in that soft, sweet way she had. Carly running her finger along his jaw and teasing him. Carly sending him a silent glance, which would make him think about something in a way he hadn't thought about it before.

He tried going to parties to get her out of his head, and there were plenty of parties. Slick, pared-down affairs in minimalist New York loft spaces or wild, poolside extravaganzas held outside the city.

Trouble was that he couldn't look at a swimming pool without thinking about her.

He couldn't look at a damned bed without thinking about her.

He would find himself standing motionless while some impossibly glamorous woman came onto him in a way which made his stomach crawl. And that was when he started to get worried.

He tried looking at the situation logically. He was only fantasising about her because she'd been like no other lover he'd ever had. Because she had walked away without a backward glance and seemed happy to leave it that way.

Yet she'd been part of his life for a long time, way before they'd become lovers. He told himself he was interested to see how her ambition was playing out— hell, didn't he have some sort of *right* to know?

And now he was back in England on the second round of interviews for a new housekeeper to replace her and it was proving harder than he'd imagined. The first stream of women he'd seen had been hopeless, even though they'd all been eager for the job. But there was something wrong with each and every one of them. Too flirty, or too unimaginative. Several had been no good at cooking and one even had a criminal record she'd tried to conceal. He had rejected them all and demanded that Diego find him someone more suitable.

He looked down at the list of 'more suitable' candidates in front of him. On paper some looked promising, but his heart wasn't in it. He thought how long it had been since he'd eaten a decent *alfajor.* How long since he'd played poker. Or had sex. How long since he'd been made to laugh, or argue or defend himself in the presence of a sharp and amusing mind.

And that was when it hit him, harder than an opponent's wheel flying off during a practice lap.

He didn't want a housekeeper. He didn't want someone to replace Carly, because she was irreplaceable. He wanted... He closed his eyes. He knew what he wanted but it was a big ask. Too big an ask, surely, after what he had done. He flinched as he remembered the way she had looked at him, with that hesitant expression on her face. How she must have met nothing but coldness in his eyes in return. But that hadn't stopped her, had it? She had taken a deep breath and told him she loved him—even though it must have taken an almighty leap of courage and faith to do so. She had hung on in there and said what she needed to say. She had conquered her own insecurity and told him that he was a loveable man. She had done that *because she thought he needed to know.* And how had he reacted? He had treated her declaration with contempt and acted as if she'd said nothing at all.

He shook his head as the door opened and he saw Diego's swarthy features set in a questioning look.

'Shall I show in the first applicant, boss?'

But Luis was already rising to his feet and shaking his head.

'No,' he said fiercely as a powerful sense of resolve washed over him. 'Forget the interviews.'

'But—'

'I said, *forget* them. I have something I need to do.' His heart was pounding as he slid his phone into his pocket and reached for his jacket. 'Somewhere I need to go.'

He drove down to Southampton in his bright red car, only just staying inside the speed limit. The sky was low and the air filled with drizzle and, even though it was only late morning, all the cars on the motorway had their headlights turned on so that shafts of golden light cut through the sombre greyness.

The medical school was situated in a green swathe of land on the edge of the city and it was nearly lunchtime by the time Luis finally parked up. He turned up the collar of his leather coat as hordes of students streamed past him and as he looked into all the unknown faces he wondered why the hell he hadn't bothered to call her first.

You know why you haven't called her.

Because she might just have told you to go to hell, and you just might have deserved it.

He made his way to some reception office and saw the girl behind the desk turn very pink when he asked where he might find a first-year student called Carly Conner.

'We're…we're not really allowed to give out that sort of information,' she stumbled.

He leaned over the desk and used a smile which had

never failed him. 'Do you think your medical school would like a substantial donation?'

She nodded.

'Then why don't you tell me where I might find Carly Conner?'

He was informed that the first-year medical students were on their way to lunch and the girl hadn't finished giving him directions before he was weaving across some courtyard towards a cafeteria, which was packed with crowds of students.

And that was when he saw her.

At first he almost didn't recognise her, because she looked *different*. As if she belonged. She was laughing and talking to a small nucleus of people, a bag loaded with books slung over her shoulder.

He felt the clench of his heart as he stood stock-still and watched her and maybe somebody noticed him because suddenly heads were turning in his direction. Across the crowded courtyard he saw the colour drain from Carly's face as she looked up and met his gaze.

She didn't move and, at first, neither did he. He felt as if the blood had frozen in his veins and he would be stuck to that spot for ever. And then he began walking towards her, his legs feeling heavy and wooden and somehow disassociated from him.

The students with her had formed themselves into a protective semicircle and Luis automatically picked out some young Adonis with hair like buttered corn and eyes of startling blue, who seemed to be unconsciously squaring up his shoulders as Luis approached.

She tilted her chin as he got closer and now he could see why she looked so different. She had changed in ways which were both subtle yet startling. Her hair was still long, but now it was weaved into a complex plait which hung down over one shoulder. And she was wearing *make-up*. Luis swallowed. Not much, just a lick of mascara and a slick of something which was making her lips gleam. She looked…amazing.

In her jeans and short jacket she somehow managed to fade into the crowd and yet to stand out from it. And instantly, he understood why she had refused to take the expensive clothes he'd bought her, for she would have no use for them here, in her new life. His heart clenched as he thought of the yellow and white spotted dress still hanging in the wardrobe of his French home. Of the space beside him in a bed which had never seemed empty before she had gone and left it.

'Hello, Carly,' he said.

Her expression was wary as she looked at him. She didn't look exactly overjoyed. In fact, that was an understatement. Her face had grown pale and tight and her eyes were cool.

'I'm not going to ask why you're here,' she said in a low voice. 'Because obviously you've decided you wanted to see me, but you really might have given me some warning, Luis.'

He was not expecting a reprimand and for a moment he was…*shocked*. He thought how any other woman would have hurled herself into his arms and the slight deflation he felt was almost certainly something to do with his ego. *And mightn't that be a good thing?* he questioned with a self-awareness which suddenly made him feel uncomfortable.

'I thought that if I'd warned you, you might have

refused to see me,' he said, his gaze training hard on her face. 'Would you?'

She shrugged as if she didn't really care. 'I don't know.'

'You need any help, Carl?'

The Adonis had stepped forward and Luis held onto his temper with difficulty as Carly shook her head again.

'No, I'm fine,' she said.

'I need to speak to you, Carly,' said Luis softly, flicking a dismissive glance towards the youth. 'In private.'

For a moment she hesitated. He saw emotions he didn't recognise, and some he did, crossing those iced-tea eyes, before she looked down at her watch.

'I've got half an hour before my next lecture, so you'll have to be quick.'

'I thought you were never on time.'

'That was in the old days. I've changed.' Defiantly, she met his eyes. 'We can walk in the grounds. Come with me.'

He was barely aware of the total silence which suddenly descended on the courtyard, or the excited chatter which rose up before they were barely out of earshot. The grass was sodden beneath their feet as they left the courtyard and the bare branches of the trees were etched in forbidding lines against the low sky.

'What are you doing here, Luis?' Her breath was like a cloud of smoke as it billowed out into the cold air.

He swallowed. He hadn't really planned what he was going to say because hadn't some cynical side of his nature wondered whether this might just turn out to be a form of catharsis. That he would take one look at her and wonder what all the fuss had been about. Why he'd been unable to sleep or to think of anything much which didn't involve Carly Conner with her clever mind and soft body and that way of prising out secrets he'd locked away from everyone else.

But it wasn't turning out that way. It was as he had suspected all along. His heart was tight in his chest, as if an iron band were squeezing all the blood out of it, and his pulse was racing with a feeling which felt like excitement and exultation and apprehension all rolled into one. He'd experienced something like it when he'd been waiting on the starting line at the notoriously tough twenty-four-hour race at Le Mans, or any of the other myriad dangerous racetracks he'd tackled during his race career, but nothing like this. *Nothing like this.*

He stared into eyes as cold as chips of ice and suddenly it all came spilling out from a place deep inside him. 'I love you,' he said simply and waited for her reaction as he repeated the words in a voice he'd never heard himself use before. 'I love you, Carly Conner.'

Carly shook her head and her hands clenched into tight fists. She wished she hadn't forgotten her gloves because then she could have avoided her fingernails digging into her flesh like this. But the sharp pain helped her focus on her anger, and anger was the safest thing she had to hang onto right then. She glared at him. How dared he do this? How dared he come here and disrupt the life which she was building for herself—day by day? How dared he, by coming out with something he probably didn't mean, undo all her good work of trying to forget him? How dared he come here and try to *break her heart* all over again?

'You don't "do" love,' she snapped. 'Remember? It's top of your list of requirements for lovers—that they won't dare to expect anything like that from you. No wedding bells or clouds of confetti for you. *Your words,* Luis. And I don't have time for meaningless declarations. If you're missing sex then f-find someone else. That shouldn't be a problem for someone like you.'

She made to walk away but his hand reached out and caught her arm and she wanted to shake him off, but she couldn't. *How could he do that?* she wondered desperately. How would her physiology lecturer explain it? How could just one touch from a man make you defy all your instincts? Send your pulse rocketing and fill your mind with thoughts you were intent on not having…

'You're right. I didn't *do* love,' he agreed, still holding onto her arm. 'Because it has never happened to me before. I never thought it could. I'd only ever seen love as a negative. As dark and destructive. As full of pain and lies and betrayal. I didn't realise that it could make you feel a part of something bigger than yourself. Could make you feel as if you were really alive. And you showed me that, Carly. You showed me that like nobody else ever could.'

'Stop it,' she whispered. 'Please, Luis. Just go away.'

He shook his head. 'I'm not going anywhere until you've heard what I've got to say. I miss you more than any words can say. Nothing seems to make sense without you there, and I was a fool to let you go.'

'You didn't *let me go,*' she said. 'You pushed me away. You know you did.'

'Yes, I did,' he said heavily. 'I hold my hands up to

that. So maybe it follows that I don't deserve your love, Carly. That I shouldn't be given a second chance, because I threw it all back in your face.' He swallowed. 'So if you tell me that you no longer love me and that you don't want me in your life, then I'll turn around and walk away from here and I will never bother you again. I give you my word on that.'

She stared at him and sucked in a deep breath. 'I don't love you.'

His eyes narrowed. 'I don't believe you.'

'You arrogant bastard.'

'If you didn't love me, then you wouldn't be looking at me like that. Your eyes wouldn't be asking me to hold you properly, nor your lips parting because you want me to kiss them.'

'Luis—'

'And I want that too, *querida*. So much. I want to kiss you and never stop.'

She stared at him and her mouth was trembling but not nearly as much as his hands as he reached out to pull her into his arms. 'Answer me honestly, that's all I ask. Do you still love me, Carly Conner?' he growled. 'Will you marry me and have my babies?'

'Babies?'

She pulled away from him and he saw her frown, like someone who was preparing for a cloud to burst on top of their head. 'But I'm going to be a doctor, Luis. I've worked hard to get here and I'm not going to give it up. I've got six long years of training ahead of me. Six years of me being based in the south of England, while you continue with your jet-setting life elsewhere? Is that going to work out? I don't think so.'

'You don't think it's possible?' He gave a low laugh.

'Believe me, anything is possible if you want it enough. And I want you more than I have ever wanted anything. I respect your ambition and I am prepared to work around it, to support you in whatever you want to do. Because while I can see that there are practical difficulties to be overcome, they are completely irrelevant. There is only one thing which is important and that is my next question and I think you owe it to me to answer it truthfully.' His voice quietened. 'Do you still love me, Carly?'

Carly didn't speak, at least not straight away. It was as if she recognised that her world was going to change irrevocably, no matter what she answered. She became aware of the loudness of her heartbeat and, incongruously, the fact that her leather boots were sinking into the muddy grass. She could see the bare trees which surrounded them and in the sky a dark flock of birds who were heading somewhere. She wondered where. To their own warmer future? She saw Luis's expression: his eyes were narrowed and the lines etched along the sides of his unsmiling mouth were deeper than she remembered. The faint drizzle had settled on his black hair—so that it seemed to have covered the tangled tendrils like a fine mist of diamonds.

She thought about the tears she had shed since she'd left France. About the great, gaping hole where her heart used to be. She thought about how much she'd missed their sparring. His teasing. And a million things in between.

She thought about the practical difficulties which lay ahead if she told him what he really seemed to want to hear. Of how on earth they might be able to align two obviously incompatible lifestyles to any degree of satisfaction.

And then she remembered what he had just said.

Anything is possible. And with Luis, she honestly believed it was.

She nodded, her mouth working furiously as she tried to control the emotions which were building up inside her and threatening to spill out. *I am not going to cry,* she told herself fiercely. *Because I have an anatomy lecture to get to.*

'Yes, I love you, Luis Martinez,' she blurted out. 'I tried very hard not to, but in the end I couldn't help myself.'

'Couldn't you?' he questioned softly.

'No. You were like a fever to which there was no known antidote and once you'd got into my blood, I couldn't seem to get rid of you. I still can't.'

'That bad, huh?' Tenderly, he smiled. 'That's not the most romantic declaration I've ever heard, but it's certainly the most original. Just like you, my clever, sweet Carly.'

And that was when the tears came and there was nothing she could do to stop them. They spilled down her cheeks and dripped onto the collar of her jacket, like giant drops of rain.

But Luis was there to dry them and Luis was there to kiss her and once they started kissing, they couldn't seem to stop, and Carly's heart seemed to burst out of her chest as he gathered her in his arms and held her.

She touched his shoulders, his hair and his face, as if she couldn't quite believe he was there. But he was. Every vital, warm, living and breathing atom of him. *He was there. With her.* And if she was to believe what he was telling her, which against all the odds she did, he wasn't ever going to leave her again.

She made it to her anatomy class, with seconds to spare.

EPILOGUE

'ARE YOU AWAKE?'

Carly gave a slow and luxurious wriggle as her eye-lashes fluttered open to meet the soft question in Luis's black gaze. 'I am now.'

Dark brows arched upwards. 'Did I wake you?'

'Wasn't that your intention when you started playing with my breasts like that?'

He smiled. 'Do you want me to stop?'

She sighed and closed her eyes. 'What do you think?'

'I think you're endlessly fascinating, Dr Martinez, and I love you very much. And I want you to know that these last six years have been the best of my life.'

Her eyes fluttered open and she bit her lip with expectation, never tiring of hearing him say these words. 'Really?'

'You know they have, *querida*.'

Yes, she knew. Just as they had been for her.

It hadn't been easy to rearrange Luis's life to accommodate her demanding role as a medical student, but then she'd discovered that the best things in life always had to be fought for. And Luis wanted her to achieve her dream as much as she did. He told her how proud he was of what she'd done and what she'd achieved, in spite of all the odds being stacked against her.

These days, he travelled as little as possible and had made his main base in England. From their sprawling Hampshire estate with its easy proximity to the sea, he now masterminded his latest business success—three ocean-going cruise ships as well as a flourishing yacht business. As for the rest of his global concerns, somewhere along the way he had become—as Carly told him with some pride—a consummate delegator. He employed the best people who gave of their best—and consequently the Martinez foundation had evolved, and was flourishing.

And even though he never really grew to *love* the English climate, he made sure he took them on plenty of sunny and luxurious vacations to compensate. Which was why Carly could often be found reading a haematology textbook on the beach, beside the clear aqua waters of the Caribbean.

She sighed, feeling Luis's thumb tracing enticing little circles over her nipple. From the window a clear river of light flooded in, illuminating the large bed in which they lay. She loved their home. They had bought a house overlooking the water not far from the medical school, from where she had graduated last week with honours.

But before the graduation ceremony had come their wedding, a wedding which Carly had resolutely refused to consider while she'd been in the middle of her studies. It had driven Luis crazy. For someone who had shied away from matrimony all his adult life, it had become one of his fiercest ambitions to wed her. The trouble was that he'd fallen in love with a woman who seemed resistant to wearing his ring.

'But you don't believe that men can do fidelity, remember?' she had flung at him, only half teasingly.

'Wrong tense,' he had growled back. 'I didn't—until I met you!'

The more he tried to persuade her to change her mind, the firmer she stood, but in a funny kind of way that had only made him love her more.

She had finally agreed to become his wife just before she graduated, telling him that she wanted to bear his name and to be Dr Martinez. And that simple declaration had thrilled him in a way which had left him shaken.

They had married in a small grey chapel overlooking one of Hampshire's green valleys and Carly had worn white roses in her hair and a simple dress, which had whispered over the flaggedstoned floor as she had walked to the altar to greet him.

Bella had been there, her initial poorly disguised jealousy at Carly's fate suddenly eclipsed by the presence of Luis's jet-setting friends at the ceremony. The Sultan of Qurhah was in attendance, with his beautiful wife and their gorgeous new baby. Niccolo Da Conti and Alekto Sarantos were easily considered to be the best-looking men there and the fact that they both happened to be billionaires only added to their appeal as far as Bella was concerned.

'Good luck with that,' Luis commented drily to his bride as he watched her sister slink across the room towards Niccolo, in a dress so tight that he privately wondered how she was managing to walk.

Carly turned in the direction of his gaze. 'But he's single, isn't he?'

'Yes, he's single.' Luis laughed. 'But if you think *I* was a commitment-phobe, let me tell you that Niccolo Da Conti takes the concept into a whole new stratosphere!'

'And you turned out to be the least commitment phobic man on the planet!'

'Only because I met the only woman who could change my mind.'

'Oh, Luis.'

'Oh, Carly,' he murmured indulgently.

Her mother had been there, too; a mother amazed by Carly's 'luck' in finding herself such a rich husband. And if Carly was disappointed not to have been commended for working her way through med school—she kept it to herself. She'd learnt that there were some things you could never change and therefore it was a waste of time even trying.

She'd learnt so much, along with the demands of medical science.

That her love for Luis grew stronger with every day that passed and that she wanted to have his baby before too long.

That a man whose heart had been wounded only needed the constant love of a woman to repair it. And that love was boundless and limitless.

She'd learnt that sometimes things happened which you wouldn't have even dared to dream about. She was living that dream and so was Luis. He didn't want a life in the fast lane any more. His days as 'The Love Machine' were over. He told her that he'd never really believed that one woman could be everything for one man.

But now he did.

'Come here,' he growled softly. 'I have something I need you to hear.'

Carly smiled as she turned her face to his. 'What is it?'

'I love you,' he said, his arms tightening around her waist. And then he said it again in Spanish just before he kissed her.

* * * * *

LET'S TALK

Romance

For exclusive extracts, competitions
and special offers, find us online:

- facebook.com/millsandboon
- @MillsandBoon
- @MillsandBoonUK

Get in touch on 01413 063232

For all the latest titles coming soon, visit
millsandboon.co.uk/nextmonth